Books by Bill Ballantine

WILD TIGERS & TAME FLEAS

HORSES & THEIR BOSSES

NOBODY LOVES A COCKROACH

NOBODY LOVES A COCKROACH

by Bill Ballantine

BOSTON   TORONTO

NOBODY LOVES A COCKROACH

Rhymes by Charlotte Russell

Illustrated by Toby Ballantine

LITTLE, BROWN AND COMPANY

Published simultaneously in Canada
by Little, Brown & Company (Canada) Limited

PRINTED IN THE UNITED STATES OF AMERICA

INTRODUCTION

This is a book about the little monsters that pester our lives by
dirtying our cities and chewing on our homes, clothes, and furnish-
ings, our livestock, pets, and armed protectors. This is not another
educational tome — learned or coy — about the strange world of insects, birds, or mammals. Actually, this is more a book about people
— social history, rather than natural history. You might say it is
for people who step on spiders, squish ants, swat flies, loathe cockroaches, despise pigeons, are scared to death of bats and rats, and
wish that termites never had been created.

In gathering the material for this book, I went to those who have
made entomology their life's work and also to others who know even
less than I do about insects but who have had bizarre experiences
with the creatures similar to my own. I followed this procedure,
too, in dealing with rodents; arachnids; pestiferous birds; that
unique flying mammal, the bat; and all the other pests that vex

humans with what it pleased that great magazine editor the late Ted Patrick to call "all their charming villainy."

Much of what was gleaned in my rambling among the entomological elite and masters of mammalogy was new to me, because while growing up I'd not found it necessary to pay much attention to insects and small mammals (I was more interested in the big ones, such as tigers, elephants, and circus showgirls). I hope to bring some of that excitement of discovery to others who like myself may not have given much thought to the pests that beset us beyond the urge to make even shorter their brief lives.

In these reports direct from the battlefields in the war of mankind versus the little devils of nature, you'll not be burdened by an abundance of anatomical detail or physiology. If that's what you're looking for, there are at least a dozen excellent books that can provide it. I've included only those body parts and functions of my subjects that I've found especially intriguing.

One significant difference between the human mind and that of an animal lies in our insistence on naming things. We have names for every living creature and growing thing ever discovered by man. In many instances I use the scientific names of the protagonists gathered here. I do this not to pretend exceptional knowledge of entomology, zoology, or ornithology (which sometimes still slips off my tongue as "orthinology"), but simply because someone might find such identification useful. It is my contention that, to a man who steps on a spider, it doesn't really matter whether the poor creature is a *Pismidigridia* or a *Gratfundamere fistulina*. It certainly doesn't matter any more to the spider.

Until I got into this book I'd never been too sure of the science of classification of animals, called taxonomy — a correct order of precedence that is as rigidly adhered to as are the seating arrangements at a formal State Department dinner.

Perhaps the best way to set straight the descending scale is simply to memorize it, like a rat memorizes a path through a maze: Kingdom, PHYLUM, Class, Subclass, ORDER, Suborder, Superfamily, FAMILY, Subfamily, Tribe, GENUS, Subgenus, SPECIES, and Subspecies.

There were times in writing this book when I felt like a rat in one of those mazes, but then, each of us suffers his own labyrinth. Occasionally it was difficult to tell the people from the pests, and along the way a great gallery of curious characters was turned up.

We're dealing here, for instance, with a man who does brain surgery on flies, and with a small group of dedicated United States government entomologists whose fondest desire was to make an outer-space astronaut out of a cockroach. We have, on the inside, a man who liked to make ants drunk, and another who had grandiose plans for a "Playant Club" using as waitresses pinch-waisted girls costumed as ants with antennae instead of bunny ears. (This same fellow planned to turn his TV set into a formicarium.) There are people here who have made house pets of bats and rats, and circus performers of fleas; there are scientists who are gleefully feeding spiderwebs into computers. As you stroll past the exhibits of oddities and curiosities from all over America, you'll meet all sorts of whacky pigeon partisans, as well as sinister pigeonnapers and men who nab these filthy fowl officially in nets shot from crossbows, who shoot them with telescopic rifles or who spread sticky goo to give the birds a chastising hotfoot. On display inside this spreading tent of exotic wonders are professional exterminators from big cities and small, and learned chemical researchers from Switzerland who spend long years and plenty of long green in developing pesticides. There are victims of termites, of rats in New York City slums, and of the pests that inevitably are camp followers of military adventure.

So, now if you'll just step this way, ladies and gentlemen, the men in the ticket boxes to the left and right of the main entrance will be glad to accommodate you. Step right up. Your change, sir, don't forget your change.

There were times in writing this book when I felt like a rat in
one of those mazes, but then, each of us rations his own labyrinth.

CONTENTS

in memory of
my dear friend Norman Carroll
to honor his compassion for those who are deprived

NOBODY LOVES A COCKROACH

The Cockroach

She slips into the drawer
and rustles down the lining.
She streaks along the floor —
evades the plots designing
swat or capture. Scared,
at last she drops her case
of eggs; the tube is aired
and left behind the race.

We guess it's jettison
for getaway — a fling —
forgetful panic's run,
or else (depositing
in manic urge the only
thing she has to leave)
she sends an offering lonely
to chance by final heave.

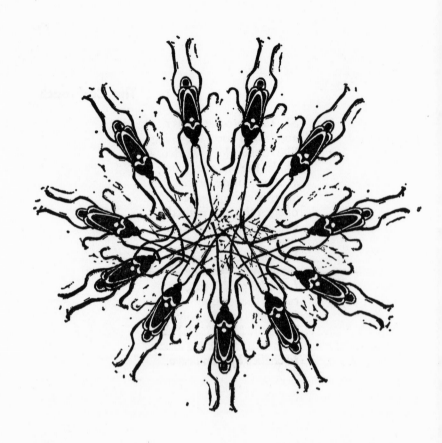

1

Hunted and Unloved: *The Cockroach* Of all the villainous pests here assembled the cockroach is my favorite. Cockroaches are hideous, loathsome little devils, but I respect them for tenacity and sociability, sensitivity to a menacing world, and for their seeming intelligence.

During bachelor days I got to know many cockroaches personally as they padded about the greasy stoves and leaky toilets of the Manhattan dumps I lived in. I especially remember one cockroach that used to come out on a shelf over the kitchen sink to watch my weekly ritual of washing the dishes. So assiduously did he (or she) keep his beady eyes on me, his radar-like antennae pointed quiveringly toward me, I'm convinced that he was waiting to tell the others when I'd finished my swabbing so that they could swoop in to banquet unmolested on my miserable garbage.

The poor cursed cockroach is one of the earth's oldest inhabitants and more remarkable than any creature confined to a zoo, yet hardly anybody loves him. Nobody even likes him, for the cockroach is terribly unappealing, odious, and saddled with a pitiable anatomy. The cockroach cannot hold up his head; the eyes must look constantly and humiliatingly toward the floor; mouth parts turn backward. He has none of the physical excitement of his jumping cousins the katydid, locust, cricket, and grasshopper, nor the aristocratic hauteur and spectacular grotesquerie of two of his more distant relations, the mantis (more preying than praying) and the Malaysian walking stick (at thirteen inches, the largest known insect). And the cockroach stinks worse than the worst of them. An oily liquid secreted by scent glands gives him that inimitable bitter-almondy odor familiar to all slum dwellers. To add to his repugnance, the cockroach has a habit of spitting fetid inklike juice around his home and making disgusting spittle trails leading to it, so that he can find his way there in the dark, aided by his remarkable antennae, his only truly heroic and graceful possession. In the polls of the National Pest Control Association, a nationwide organization of exterminators, the cockroach invariably is voted "Pest of the Year," well ahead of the next most unpopular household pests: the brown dog tick, carpenter ants, termites, earwigs, fleas, rats, and people who try to sell you something over the telephone.

Cockroaches thrive on garbage but will scavenge almost anything: wool, soap, paint, grain, leather (especially old shoes and rare-book bindings), cigar butts, orchid buds, coffee grounds, even their own eggs and cast-off skin, but especially anything that has been touched by glue or flour paste. Postage stamps are a rare cockroach delicacy, and he will rip wallpaper right off the walls to get at the dried sweet paste underneath. Brazilian cockroaches have been known to nibble eyelashes off sleeping infants; sailors at sea sometimes wear gloves to keep cockroaches from eating their fingernails during the night. One species of cockroach, the wood-eating Cryptocercus, has millions of microscopic protozoans living in its large intestine which, by releasing their special liquid, are able to convert the ingested bits of wood, already ground up by valves along the digestive tract, into sugar and other nutrients.

The cockroach lives largely off that segment of our populace which FDR called "one-third of a nation," the undernourished and ill-housed, the have-nots and almost-haves who live under a fearful strain of day-to-day grind and guilt, at the mercy of big business, politics, and the church — each inflicting its own hypocritical brand of morality. The poor tolerate these burdening social forces for the same reason that they do the cockroach — because they have neither the choice nor the energy to do otherwise. Tenement dwellers view cockroaches with an air of resigned desperation. A New York City fireman, engaged in the department's regular door-to-door fire prevention campaign in the slums, was surprised when one especially befuddled tenement dweller told him — after he'd made his routine pitch about the causes of fires — that she'd take one, thank you please. Poor thing, she thought he was peddling fires, and wanted one to drive out her cockroaches.

The middle class, who harbor cockroaches only occasionally, become righteously indignant over such visitations. They blame them on their dirty neighbors, the laundress (especially if she's colored), the delicatessen's delivery boy (especially if he's a Puerto Rican), the gas-meter reader, the new family that just moved in down the block, or a visiting cousin (especially if she lives in a tackier neighborhood). Or they say archly that *somebody* must have brought them in from *somewhere*: the office, the subway, the bus, the library, the movies, the bridge party, the bowling alley, the Legion meeting, the discothèque, the PTA smorgasbord — or perhaps they came in one of the boxes from the supermarket. But anyhow, goddammit! *Get rid of them!* And don't *any* of you kids dare breathe a word to anybody, and, no, you most certainly cannot take one to "show-and-tell."

The rich simply cannot afford cockroaches. However, members of the multimoneyed class do occasionally encounter the obnoxious six-legged freeloading pals of the poor (family Blattidae, of the order Orthoptera), for cockroaches sometimes turn up in swanky places. These accidental confrontations often have a traumatic effect on the human participants. One such — attested to by the socialite mother of a friend of mine — occurred in a chic Park

Avenue hotel. The hotel's social hostess, in an all-out effort to land a lucrative charity ball account for her establishment, was lunching with the chairlady of the committee, when to her horror a large languid cockroach appeared on a tulip in the luncheon table's centerpiece. Fortunately the headwaiter spotted the interloper before the distinguished lady guest did. He swooped in grandly, hissing a question that required no answer, "Madame does not *like* flowers?" and in one deft dive swept the centerpiece — offensive insect and all — right off the table, to be carried safely out of sight.

There is no record of a single cockroach ever found in a bank. A cockroach would perish in a bank, for in order to swallow its food it must have liquid. There is nothing for a cockroach to drink in a bank. No water fountain, no inviting puddles of stale beer, no bottle and shot glass hidden in desk drawers — not even in the deepest innermost sanctum. Bankers don't even drink cambric tea on the job. Nor is there anything to eat in a bank. What banker deigns to carry his lunch? You never see a banker sitting behind his polished mahogany desk taking 6 percent bites out of a peanut butter sandwich or a lettuce-tomato-and-mayonnaise on rye.

There are more cockroaches in churches than in banks, because churches are always having covered-dish suppers, box socials, and holy communions — and sometimes parishioners bring peanuts or potato chips to nibble on in the back pews. A minister or priest would not be shocked by a cockroach in vestry or confessional, but no banker would grant even a small loan should a cockroach suddenly march across the collar of a supplicant in financial conference.

Writers, artists, sculptors, professional dancers, circus troupers, theater people, and other gypsies have much in common with cockroaches. Persons who work with ideas, instead of merely playing the old shell game with money and real estate, are survivalists just like the cockroach, who is actually a living fossil, descended from the Palaeozoic Protoblattoidea and first recorded by man in the sixteenth century. The cockroach was here when dinosaurs emerged from the steaming muck, and he saw them fade out a hundred million years later. Cockroach fossils have been discovered in ancient rocks dating back to the Carboniferous period — about 280 million years ago. Of six orders of insects whose remnants of that period were found, all but the cockroach are extinct. The cockroach moved across the land bridge that once joined the Continent to the British Isles; his kind is older than Pike's Peak, the Alps, or the North Pole ice cap. They were old-timers when Texas oil and West Virginia coal were formed.

Cockroaches are so close to struggling artists that the children of one painter friend of mine call them "buddy bugs." Aspiring ballet dancers, who have it rougher than any other climbers to a creative career, number cockroaches among their more distracting adversaries. A couple of dancer acquaintances, who live in one of the scruffier parts of the Bronx, recently were guests — along with their five-year-old daughter — at an ostentatious dinner soirée in our part of the country, at which the guest of honor was a distinguished silver-maned big-nosed Italian poet-philosopher. When the soup course was served the child took one look in terror at the floating croutons and screamed, "Mamacita Papá! Las CUCARACHAS!" The hostess felt so humiliated that she almost resigned her chairladyship of the Social Affairs Committee of the local chapter of the Brush, Potter, and Plume Club.

My own experience with cockroaches also had been largely in the city, and so I was astonished to learn there were cockroaches in the country as well. This revelation came after I'd married and prepared to settle down with my wife in the Hudson Valley about forty-five minutes' drive from the George Washington Bridge, in a marvelously tumbledown, pre-Revolutionary house that hadn't been favored with a constructive lick in forty years. We both were dismayed to find cockroaches already in residence.

For weeks we couldn't discover the hiding holes of our rustic cockroaches. Nothing we sprayed, dusted, or painted on seemed to get to them. I even tried shooting a cap pistol, and routing them with Fourth of July sparklers, but the cuties never went into the same cracks twice; they were sneaky little creeps. Finally I rigged a flash camera with an ultrasensitive shutter trip, and the resultant pictures showed our unwanted residents excitedly exiting into the electric kitchen clock. Evidently they camped there to enjoy the constant warmth given off by the motor. (For the same reason cockroaches now live in TV sets and in the mechanisms of electric refrigerators.)

When I removed the back of the clock cockroaches by the hundreds streamed out in panic. What an Armageddon *that* was! We slaughtered them by the dozens with thumping thwacks of folded newspaper, an empty Flit can, a fly swatter, a Ping-Pong paddle, and an old tennis shoe. Our dachshund slinked out and didn't come back until morning, and we couldn't find our pair of Siamese cats all the next day. The best time of day to attack a cockroach, I learned later, is 4 P.M., for that is when this insect reaches its circadian crest of susceptibility according to Dr. William N. Sullivan of the USDA's Entomology Research Division, who arrived at this conclusion after spraying a total of four thousand roaches with pyrethrum.

We shouldn't have been surprised to find cockroaches in the country, for many of the thirty-five hundred known species live out of doors, especially in the tropics. Some of them have bodies two and a half inches long and wingspans of seven and a half inches; other cockroaches are as tiny as rice grains. The United States has little more than half a hundred different kinds of cockroaches. They include: the Oriental; smoky-brown; field cockroach; spotted Mediterranean; Australian; American; brown-banded (the TV cockroach); Cuban; Surinam; Pennsylvania woodroach; cinereous; Madeira; and the German. Our smaller roaches in this country (German, brown-banded, and female woodroach) are all under five-eighths of an inch and have short life cycles of from two to five months. The large roaches with which we are most familiar (Oriental, smoky-brown, American, Australian, and most male woodroaches) live from five months to over one year. The world's biggest cockroach is one called *Megaloblatta*, but the only monster we Americans are likely to see is labeled by scientists *Blaberus giganteus* (and by housewives *Ohmygawd!*). Some specimens of *B.g.* measure as long as two and three-eighths inches and are found mostly in Central and South America, where they are known commonly as "giant drummers" or "the divine face." A similar species inhabits southern Florida; real-estate men find nothing divine about them. They refer to them euphemistically as "palmetto beetles" and try their damnedest to keep them out of sight until the lease is signed.

Only about half a dozen cockroaches are really troublesome to us. The German (*Blattella germanica*) is the commonest here and the most obnoxious, for it is the only one resistant to chlordane, the insecticide that easily knocks off all the others. Britishers allude to the German cockroach as a "shiner" or "steam bug." Around New York it is known as the "Croton bug," because it first invaded the city along the pipes that brought water from the Croton Reservoir; to the cockroach the advent of that pipeline was like that of the railroad to our Western pioneers. The other real cockroach blackguards in this country are: the brown-banded (*Supella supellectilium*), which slyly lives all over a building and hides its eggs in furniture, closets, TV sets, and high places, and is a leaper; the woodroach (*Parcoblatta*), which lives outdoors under loose bark of dead trees, in logs, stumps, and firewood piles, and is the most accomplished flier of all roaches; the American (*Periplaneta americana*), dubbed by British dock workers the "Bombay canary," which indulges in Sybaritic living indoors year round in damp basements and sewers — foraging mostly on ground-floor level — and enjoys vacationing on dump and refuse piles in summer; the Oriental (*Blatta orientalis*), which likes dank dark places, especially coal bins, and is known in England as the "black clock" or "black beetle"; the smoky-brown (*Periplaneta fuliginosa*), common in our South; and the Australian (*Periplaneta australasiae*), largely a Florida roach.

The cockroach, an indefatigable traveler, at one time was a candidate to journey beyond his wildest dreams — that is, if cockroaches are subject to dreams, and I'm inclined to believe they are. In the early days of the National Aeronautics and Space Administration, when first serious thought was advanced toward sending living bodies into orbit, consideration was being given — before risking a human being — to the experimental use of large mammals such as dogs, bears, goats, and primates (a pair of chimpanzees, Ham and Enos, actually were rocketed off for short heavenly jaunts). The brilliant idea of dispatching a regiment of cockroaches into outer space came from the Entomology Research Division, Agricultural Research Service, Pesticide Chemicals Research Branch, U.S. Department of Agriculture at Beltsville, Maryland. (You simply cannot reduce that large mouthful to one of those cute initial designations that bureaucracy is so fond of; what could you possibly make out of ERDARSPCRBUSDA?) It wasn't that anyone envisioned a ticker-tape parade up Broadway for the first cockroach on the moon, but these fellows were in dead earnest — as I've found entomologists usually are. Although I broke up just thinking about it, none of those involved at Beltsville regarded the idea of a cockroach astronaut as being at all capricious.

The roaches were to be part of the projected biosatellite program then in its initial planning stages — a series of "high-priority biological experiments," thirty proposals chosen from a submission of 175 made by industry, schools, and government agencies in which fertilized frog eggs, wasps, bird mold, seedlings, fruit flies, rats, hamsters, primates, human tissue and cultures were to be carried in the nose of a Thor-Delta rocket, orbiting at a height of two hundred nautical miles, significantly below the Van Allen radiation belts.

Interest of these entomologists in this peculiar cockroach venture was an outgrowth of their department's disinsection program, conducted — as a leaflet describing it states — "with a view to expediting as much as possible the disinsection of aircraft as required under the International Sanitary Convention for Aerial Navigation." The term disinsection merely means spraying an airplane with insecticide to prevent insect pests and vectors of diseases of man from being accidentally carried from one country to another by air. Scientists have a way of making the simplest procedures sound importantly complicated.

Alas, eventually nothing came of the laudable scheme to orbit cockroaches, but the efforts made by the Beltsville entomologists, biologists, and chemists kept them happily rolling along for months. They'd been itching to dig into something like this. American biophysicists felt that they were being prevented by our space engineers from contributing valuable biological experiments to the satellite program. The first consideration seemed to be to get men into space unhampered by what was regarded as superfluous gear. Our biologists feared that other nations (Russia) were forging ahead of us in space biological research. For instance, in 1964, at a space symposium organized by the International Committee of Space Research (COSPAR) in Florence, Italy, it was learned that Soviet space biologists, by utilizing unoccupied corners of their large man-carrying spacecraft for biological research, had gained some valuable, though inconclusive, information about what happens to the reproductive ability of low forms of life such as fruit flies and plant spores during space flights. It was clearly shown, by the mating of fruit flies (*Drosophila*) in "biocartridges" carried on Russian space flights, that some freakish forms of life are brought about by exposure to vibration, acceleration, radiation, and weightlessness. Soviet satellites also had carried other types of insects, as well as bacterial cultures, seeds of wheat, onions, lettuce, carrots, and different strains of the single-celled pond scum (*Chlorella*), which biophysicists believe may eventually be used to regenerate the air of interplanetary spaceships and provide the crews with a renewable source of food.

At the Beltsville laboratories, the cockroach activities aimed at participation in the space program centered around the effects of extraterrestrial environment on biological rhythms. Biological clocks are mechanisms believed to be possessed by most living things. They permit plants and animals to behave as though they could tell time. The scientists wanted to know if those so-called clocks of the cockroach would be shifted in phase or damp out while in outer space, or if they are true circadian rhythms (from *circa*, "about," and *diem*, "day," indicating rhythms of about one day in length). It is feared that on man's eventual trip to the moon, his human clock — geared to the cycles of moon-sun seasons — may become reset in the new time zone and reduce his chemistry to chaos, which is not an ideal state for anybody's chemistry to be in — just observe what happens after too many martinis. There is some basis for this anxiety, as scientists of India have found that fruit flies exposed to cosmic radiation twenty miles above the earth are less likely to hatch than earthbound ones (reported by Dr. O. S. Reddi and M. Sanjeeva Rao in the British scientific journal Nature, January 1964). For America to have sterile astronauts would be an intolerable violation of all our accepted principles of heroic imagery.

Also, in this respect, a female English scientist, Dr. Janet E. Harker of Girton College, Cambridge University, has located at least one of the built-in clocks that keep a cockroach on its schedule by secreting a special hormone that marks the passage of time in periods of twenty-three hours and fifty-three minutes. The cockroach clock consists of four specialized cells in a large nerve ganglion just under the insect's esophagus, and it causes the cockroach to follow a twelve-hours-on, twelve-off routine of running around all night and sleeping by day. Dr. Harker reversed the day-night rhythms of certain specimens, resetting their clocks by keeping them in the dark daytimes and under lights in their cage at night. In that way the natural rhythm of those insects was made to be twelve hours out of phase with that of so-called normal cockroaches. Then she transplanted cells extracted from the mixed-up cockroaches into the bloodstreams of others that had normal cycles. All those invaded cockroaches, thus equipped with two clocks running out of time with each other, developed cancer. Dr. Harker, according to the British magazine Discovery, was baffled. What did she expect? You go fooling around with anybody's clock, you get into trouble. She thinks however that the abnormal concentration of the hormone secreted by the clock cells may have had something to do with the unexpected turn of her experiments. She concluded: "A great deal remains to be discovered in this field." Which puts it very nicely indeed while not holding much hope for the poor cockroach. But then, most people don't really care how many cockroaches get cancer as long as they don't go spreading it around. We don't want cockroaches personally, even if they do make valuable contributions to the advancement of medical science. Let biologists breed them in the labs; who needs them at home?

The cockroach is a valuable laboratory creature because of its frugal habits, tenacity, and modest space requirements. It adapts well to confined life, and its blood has a lower freezing point than water. A cockroach leaves no feeding rubble and very little excrement ("like a pinch of snuff," I've been told). Its oxygen requirement is only 1½ or 2 percent by volume, whereas man blanks out if his level falls below 10 percent.

I visited the laboratories of the Beltsville Entomology Research Division during its period of cockroach enchantment to see specifically what was being done to put the crawlers into orbit. The roaches being used were Madeiras (*Leucophaea maderae*), woodroaches about two inches long (with wings spread, they are almost as big as mice), pale brown with darker pronotum, native to Africa, but first described from the Portuguese island of Madeira. Also found in Haiti, Java, Brazil, and the Philippines, the Madeira is a ready breeder that began to invade New York City's Harlem, purportedly from Puerto Rico, about twelve years ago (although the John C. Pallister Collection of mounted cockroaches at the New York Museum of Natural History has a Madeira captured in Manhattan in 1940).

Of all cockroaches, the Madeira is the ideal laboratory subject. It needs no water other than that found in a diet of apples, carrots, and dog-food pellets. It can go for long periods without any food or water; the record drought for a Madeira was forty-three days, and most can go dry for fifteen days. The Madeira requires no anesthetic; it will keep perfectly quiet when placed between two sheets of tissue paper. It is resistant to infection, so that operating instruments need not be sterilized, and it lives as long as two and a half years. The Madeira never panics, experiences no psychosis, never gets sea, air, or morning sick, and can be hung upside down for as long as fifty-four days. It is big enough to accept electrode attachments pushed in at a loose leg joint (similar to that of the human knee) in order to measure its electrophysiological and locomotor activity. One disadvantage to the use of Madeira roaches in lab experimentation is their inordinate fondness for grapes, a gourmet item that is hard to justify to eagle-eyed government accountants.

In the Beltsville labs I found two of these repulsive giant cockroaches ensconced in a cylindrical sealed metal case about the size of a ten-gallon milk can (I learned later that originally it had been a lard can) and being subjected to forty-five-minute cycles of light (one foot-candle) and darkness similar to those experienced by astronauts holed up in a satellite; two other cockroaches were on a normal twelve-hour cycle — 6 A.M. to 6 P.M. light, followed by twelve hours of darkness. These conscriptees for science — not only nameless, as were all the other cockroaches present, but even numberless — were having their motions recorded through delicate sensing and charting devices. The insects emit electrical impulses of one hundred microvolts while at rest and as high as two million microvolts when active. As a man who has trouble deciding which wire goes to what terminal post in repairing electrical appliances, I don't pretend to fathom the intricacies of the recording of those cockroach twitterings and twitchings, but on the off chance that some readers are electronic wizards on the level of Thomas Alva Edison I repeat here what the erudite *Journal of Economic Entomology* had to say about the procedure: "The signals produced by the [capacity] sensing device [a Thermocap relay] were fed from the terminals of the milliammeter mounted in the instrument through an L-pad voltage-divider network into a standard 5-millivolt Varian recorder with a chart speed of one inch per hour." For those who need to know more than that I recommend the other eight long descriptive paragraphs contained in the December 1962 issue of that trade paper, pages 985 to 989. The point is, the government men had these cockroaches exquisitely bugged.

I was shown the biopack that was to carry cockroaches into space. I had expected it to be an elaborate, expensive creation by IBM or some such maker of electronic marvels. The biopack turned out to be a common beer can. Well, that's the way it is sometimes in the hallowed halls of science. When man finally lands on the moon he'll probably find that an old pair of sneakers makes for better walking in the craters than his specially designed hand-tooled space footgear that cost maybe $19,785.93 a pair — without laces. The can had been converted by the addition of electrodes soldered to terminals on a new metal lid, and a cloth lining (containing lithium hydroxide hydrate and activated charcoal) that was held against the inner wall by wire screening. The cockroach occupant of the space biopack, after being immobilized by a few whiffs of carbon dioxide, was sterilized by a dip in 0.5 percent sodium hypochlorite, and then mounted, on its back, with transparent plastic tape on a small rectangular plastic slide. Each biopack carried two cockroach slides back to back. While in the biopack the cockroaches were kept alive by automatic feedings of water and sugar, plus glycerol, a sweet, syrupy, trihydroxy alcohol (*ah-ha!*), colorless and odorless, a ready absorber and retainer of moisture. Thirty days would be the limit of cockroach confinement during a satellite journey; a cockroach can be kept alive on such a liquid diet for twenty-eight days. The earth's atmosphere — half nitrogen, half oxygen — was to be supplied artificially to the cockroach biopacks when in orbit. By means of a three-transistor amplifier and a voltage-doubling generator, electrophysiological signals could be telemetered back to earth from a cockroach in outer space. All I can say is we've certainly come a long way since when my folks used to sit around our expandable living room table back home in Millvale, Pa., listening to the A. & P. Gypsies and Billy Jones and Ernie Hare, the Interwoven Pair, coming in real good on a galena-crystal detector with cat's-whisker finder, through one earphone detached from my brother's expensive $12.85 headset and laid in an empty washstand bowl so that everybody could hear at the same time.

Besides having their circadian rhythms recorded, those Beltsville cockroaches were subjected to a monitoring of their electrophysiological responses. It was interesting to learn how a cockroach was prepared for that ordeal. According to a printed description which I have before me: "The electrodes are inserted into the membrane between the distal end of the coxa and the trochanter of each rear leg and extend inward to the proximal end of the coxa." That's all very well, but before you start reaching for your dictionary let me simply say that what they really mean is that after the usual anesthetization, sterilization, and mounting of the insect on its plastic slide, a sterilized 32-gauge silver wire is stuck into each of the long rear legs at their bending midpoint. The electrodes are held firmly in place by a tape wrapping, and also are secured by the same method to the slide. In wrapping the tape, care is taken to provide a pathway for discharge of fecal matter (big of them). Some contentious scientists, contending that "immobilization is a very serious psychological insult to any kind of animal," feel that cockroaches would react differently if monitored without attachments, left freely to roam in some sort of cloistered shed, such as a coil wound around a plastic cage that essentially formed the insect's housing. There is no question that restrained roaches are more subject to disturbance than those which have their freedom, but the rigid combination-mounting of roach and electrode is defended by its instigators because it allows the withstanding of considerable impact, vibration, and spin.

One of the ticklish problems faced by Agriculture Department probers, who primarily deal in entomological and chemical research, was in assimilating the mysteries of electronics in order to miniaturize and integrate with the satellite systems. To carry on their work more efficiently the entomologists felt that they needed more sophisticated equipment — especially a data-acquisition system that would cost in the neighborhood of $20,000 and be able to monitor and log data from twenty-five different cockroach channels every thirty seconds, studying the entire spectrum of all rhythms and accumulating information that then would be punched onto tapes to be fed into a computer for subsequent analysis by Ph.D.'s; in fifteen minutes this equipment could do fifteen days' work of a man. Despite all the high-flown rhetoric, impressive descriptions of experiments already made, and sincere proposals for more ambitious ones, it was most difficult to convince NASA of the need for such expensive gear, or for that matter of the overall importance of Project Cockroach. I was privileged to read some of the voluminous exchange of correspondence between its backers and NASA's Ames

Research Center at Moffett Field, California, and can say that the letters stand among the finest examples of literary bureaucratica — gems of lucid obfuscation. Among the required objects listed on the presentation to obtain funds for an enlarged cockroach-in-orbit effort was this touching item: "Biological material: 12 Roaches *Leucophaea maderae*: 5 × 20 × 50 mm each." It was by far the cheapest listing of the entire request even if the roaches did originate at Princeton University and would have to travel to Washington, D.C., by airmail special delivery in a specially outfitted mailing tube.

But, passionate enthusiasm and dedication of the Beltsville team notwithstanding, the grandiose plan to put cockroaches into space finally petered out. The cockroaches were grounded.

In mid-December of 1966 America's first biosatellite was put into orbit on the nose of a Delta rocket to close out that year's schedule at Cape Kennedy. It was the opening mission in our nation's $100 million program to test how weightlessness and space radiation affect the growth of plants and animals. The capsule, weighing 944 pounds, carried more than ten million items, including a thousand flour beetles, 560 thumbnail-sized parasitic wasps, ten thousand fruit flies — but alas, no cockroaches. It was scheduled to make forty-seven orbits in a circular path about 195 miles high, then parachute into the Pacific. After recovery, the specimens were to have been flown to Hawaii for analysis. On the mission's fourth day the capsule's retrorockets failed to fire and instead of descending by parachute into the atmosphere the capsule continued in an uncontrolled orbit — lost for all time. If and when it drifts back into the earth's atmosphere the capsule and its cargo will be burned to a crisp.

I never understood why it was necessary to send all the way to Princeton for some of the satellite-experiment cockroaches (was it because Dr. S. K. Roberts, the world's pioneer authority on cockroach rhythms, was then there in the biology department? Or perhaps the roaches at Princeton had higher IQ's). There certainly are enough cockroaches of all varieties available at Beltsville, in the USDA's department of cockroach rearing, to populate Venus,

Mars, and the moon several times over. A visit to their lair is like something out of Edgar Allan Poe. INSECT REARING it says in painted bronze letters on the glass panel of the door leading into a room about the size of an ordinary bedchamber. Lining the walls are cabinets containing galvanized-iron drawers (each eighteen inches by fourteen by four, with sixteen- or twenty-mesh bronze or copper tops). In the drawers are thousands of almost every known kind of cockroach. You've never seen so many cockroaches! And in each compartment is a cockroach hideaway made of a pint-size cardboard tubular ice-cream carton; water is supplied from a glass test tube with cotton stuffed in its mouth. The constant rustling of the creatures is semiterrifying; the characteristic cockroach stench overpowering.

"They won't bite you or sting you," said entomologist John Fales, the man in charge. "They just nibble."

But who wants to be nibbled — even by a distinguished potential astro-roach. Mr. Fales slid out box after box to show me all his favorites. "Quite a pretty little thing," he said of the Australian. "Such a nice yellow stripe down its sides." I thought it was about seven steps beyond disgusting.

There were some odd names: the death's-head, with mask on pronotum more like an owl's or cat's face than a skull; the Florida skunk roach; the lobster roach that is used by Washington's National Zoo as reptile food; the Madagascar roach which hisses air from a sac when alarmed — a real terrorist, scientific name *Gromphadorhina portentosa*. The largest United States roach species is one grandly called *Blaberus cranifer burmeister*; sounds like a rich Munich brewer.

I was shown two species fairly new to this country: the spotted Mediterranean cockroach (*Ectobius pallidus*), which appeared in Massachusetts in 1948 — originally at Falmouth, then at Woods Hole and Plymouth; and *Nauphoeta cinerea*, a feed-mills denizen that has been widely distributed by commerce. Cockroaches are amazing travelers, but they don't spread about as rapidly as people seem to think they do. The brown-banded cockroach (*Supella su-*

pellectilium) first noted in this country at Key West, Florida, in 1903, had become common only as far west as Nebraska by 1929.

The two new species brought the United States total to fifty-five; all except a few in the Southwestern states are well known to entomologists. The spotted Mediterranean roach seems to have roused them the most. The first specimens were found in the summer cottage of a Mrs. S. P. Graeff on the Cape Cod coast twenty miles north of Falmouth and submitted to a Dr. Ellsworth H. Wheeler of the University of Massachusetts. This particular roach, then unknown here, is widely distributed in Western Europe: Germany, the Netherlands, Belgium, France, Switzerland, Italy, southern England, Spain, and Portugal. Since a lot of Portuguese live around Falmouth, naturally they were blamed for the invasion.

Mr. Fales was kind enough to stop admiring his cockroaches long enough to explain to me the life cycle of his favorite insect. I learned that for most cockroaches the metamorphosis is simple — three stages: egg, nymph, and adult. Several species, notably the delicate green tropical roach, *Panchlorae*, and the Madeira, are ovoviviparous — that is, produced from eggs that have a well-developed shell, but which hatch within the mother's body. Cockroach eggs are not laid singly, but are assembled in a leathery, bean-shaped capsule called the oötheca, often seen protruding partially from the tip of the female's abdomen. It is carried either until just before hatching or until released to undergo further incubation at some quiet spot selected by the mother — pasted, by a mouth secretion, to some convenient surface, or arbitrarily abandoned at large. When a pregnant cockroach is threatened by a human pursuer invariably it drops its egg sac and runs. Some students of cockroachiana attribute this action as one of the instinctive preservation of the young for survival of the race. But more likely the mother roach is merely jettisoning the sac selfishly to allow for her quicker getaway. It is the conclusion of all but the most sentimental entomologists that in the cockroach world mother love appears to be nonexistent. Mother's Day to a cockroach is just like any other.

The number of eggs and egg sacs produced differs with each species. Here are the figures for maximum capsules and number of eggs in one capsule of the four leading brands of United States cockroach: American, 58 and 16; German, 5 and 40; brown-banded, 20 and 17; Oriental, 50 and 8. Nymphal molts range from 5 days to 13. Maximum adult life of the American and Oriental is 730 days; the German, 232; the brown-banded, 206. Nymphs emerge at varying periods of time dependent upon temperature and humidity. On hatching, the nymph's skin is cast off, and other molts occur at intervals of several weeks until maturity is reached. With each molt the cockroach increases in size, and on the last molt wings are acquired, which are used for flying only by a very few species. With what seemed to me like a great deal of reverence, Mr. Fales informed me, "Every time they molt, they're all white — like little angels."

The Beltsville cockroaches thrive on a diet of dog-chow pellets. A list of their ingredients make them seem almost good enough to eat: meat bonemeal, wheat germ, ground groats, yellow corn and wheat, soybean meal, cereal food crumbs, dried whole whey, animal fat, supplements of vitamins B–12, A, and E, activated vitamin D, thiamin, niacin, iodized salt, manganese sulphate, and cobalt carbonate.

The San Diego Zoo in Southern California maintains large breeding colonies of cockroaches. They are used to supply live insect food for its collection of birds, the world's most extensive. Feeding roaches to birds stimulates their breeding. Some of the groups being thus encouraged toward an expanded family life are gulls, storks, ibis, pheasants, turkeys, guinea fowl, cranes, kookaburras, motmots, magpie-larks, thrushes, starlings, and tanagers. In all, about three hundred bird species are being fed natural insect food at the zoo, but not all of them rate cockroaches. Live insects are a rich source of nutrients, particularly proteins and fats, essential to the normal growth and nourishment of birds, and they provide the B-complex vitamins required for many metabolic functions of the animal body. Birds cannot be "in song" unless all nutritional requirements are met.

At the zoo, the roaches — German, American, Oriental, and brown-banded — are reared by the hundreds of thousands. The German and brown-banded are housed in wide-mouthed gallon jars, their residence inside being a loose roll of corrugated cardboard surrounding a jar of water (equipped with cotton wick) and an open packet of dog-chow pellets. The American and Oriental roaches are handled in twenty-gallon galvanized garbage cans, and their corrugated cardboard roll is made from a strip fourteen inches wide by ten feet long; food and water containers are proportionally bigger as well. Removal of batches of the cockroaches for feeding to the birds is facilitated by squirting a whiff of carbon dioxide through the escapeproof wire-mesh lids of the containers; the gas immobilizes the roaches temporarily, but neither harms them nor makes them less palatable.

In cockroach mating, the female attracts her lover by opening her wings and dragging them, vibrating, along the ground. The courting male raises his wings straight up to get them out of the way, sticks out his abdomen proudly, and scampers stiff-legged *backward* toward the end of his ladylove's abdomen, grabs her with his hooked phallomere (which resembles a Boy Scout jackknife), and accurately rams his genitalia into her. The pair copulate, posterior to posterior — oddly facing in opposite directions — for about half an hour, although lovemaking among certain hardy breeds has been observed to go on for as long as twenty-four hours. Andy Warhol would love it.

Now, about the language of cockroach love — here is one entomological description that I've come across: "A low squeaking sound is consistently obtained in either sex by delicately running the border of the pronotum upon the mesonotum or upon the strongly denticulate base of the costal vein or of the tegmen. Both surfaces are heavily scleroted, turned opposite to each other, non-pubescent, and are finely rugose so as to make stridulation possible." Sort of takes all the romance out of it.

Just beyond the cockroach nursery at Beltsville sexual attractants were being extracted from female cockroaches. Agricultural Secretary Orville Freeman's attempt to touch tactfully on this project once broke up a White House Cabinet meeting during a discussion of substitutes for chemical pesticides. Mr. Freeman began: "If you want to see how a cockroach acts when there's some sex around —" only to be drowned out by a wave of laughter, followed by a laconic remark by UN Ambassador Adlai Stevenson, "Orville, I've been wondering about that for a long time."

High-placed dignitaries may snigger and josh about the subject of cockroach sex-attractant extraction, yet one day it may lead to the elimination of all cockroaches. An entomologist named Robert T. Yamamoto was in charge of Beltsville's sex-starved maiden cockroaches (Periplaneta americana). Once female cockroaches are mated they lose their scented appeal forever and go on producing egg sacs for the rest of their lives. At about fourteen eggs a week, American cockroaches can bring forth more than eighteen hundred eggs in their two-and-a-half-year life span. The male takes no further notice of a sullied female; he goes strictly for virgins.

At Beltsville the cockroach femmes fatales are kept for four-month periods in eight ten-gallon milk cans — about a thousand to a can — fitted with mesh galvanized screening on which the insects rest. By means of a glass tube air enters the can, is circulated (two cubic feet per minute), then leaves through another tube and goes to a flask (cooled by dry ice) where condensing vapor deposits the sex attractant. Cockroaches in the cans are subject to extraction of their sex attractant for twenty hours each day; the remaining four hours are given over to feeding, watering, and resting.

After milking ten thousand virgin female cockroaches continuously over a nine-month period, Dr. Yamamoto saved, by an elaborate purification process, as much as 12.2 milligrams (four ten-thousandths of an ounce) of pure attractant, enough to excite millions of males. It just goes to show how desperate females can be without males around to relieve the tension. To human nostrils the attractant has only a slightly oily smell, but just a little bit more than one-third of a thousandth of a billionth of a billionth of an ounce of attractant wafted into the cage of torpid male cockroaches is enough to set them scampering frantically about, furiously vibrating their wings and acting like a bunch of sex-starved whalers in an orgy of *malamarorking*. It is hoped that the attractant can be used to lure male cockroaches into lethal traps, or to induce them to crawl across chemicals that will render them sterile, but not otherwise harmed; they then will mate normally, but produce no offspring.

I think we'll all be sorry when cockroaches are gone forever. We'll miss them. They're not really that bad. Despite its scurrilous reputation, the cockroach is not a filthy animal — it just lives off filth. It is more fastidious about washing its feet, legs, and antennae than is a cat; it constantly, diligently polishes its sleek, brown shell. Although known to be a carrier of pathogens of polio, typhoid, gastroenteritis, and other diseases, the cockroach has never been securely linked with the spread of any of them — in the sense that flies spread intestinal diseases, mosquitoes malaria, and lice typhus.

Cockroaches have been experimentally infected with Coxsackie virus, and the viruses of mouse encephalomyelitis, and yellow fever. Hepatitis definitely has been related to the cockroach through a study made of a cockroach eradication program in a low-rent housing project at Carmelitos, California, in Los Angeles County near Long Beach. Before the eradication Carmelitos had almost 40 percent of all the hepatitis cases in the area, although the project covered only one-tenth of a square mile of the fifty-square-mile Bellflower Health District in which it was situated. At the end of the cockroach-killing in 1960, the incidence had dropped to 6.6 percent (Carmelitos then had nine cases while the Bellflower area had a total of 135). In 1962 there was no more hepatitis at Carmelitos, although there still were thirty-five cases elsewhere in the area.

Cockroaches had infected 95 percent of the apartments. It was believed they were the vector and had picked up the disease-carrying microorganisms from broken sewage lines, unsanitary toilets, uncovered garbage, or, most likely, dirty-diaper pails. It is true that babies and infants can be fecal carriers of the hepatitis virus for months, and experiments have proven that man can be infected with hepatitis from human feces administered orally. Soldiers in the field frequently contract the disease from flies carrying human excreta from latrines in camps where sanitation is carelessly administered.

There were plenty of fecal suppliers at the Carmelitos Project — roughly 1,400 of the 1,800 children were under fifteen, and more than half were babies and infants whose mothers no doubt were much too harassed to bother about efficient sanitary housekeeping. In the project's 712 housing units in 124 buildings (582 of them pre-World War II vintage) women residents well outnumbered the men — 700 to 300 — and an average of thirty families moved in and out of the project every month making one-half the population new each year. With so large a turnover immunity to hepatitis reasonably could not develop, and there was not much possibility of subclinical cases of the disease. So it was concluded that the dramatic drop in cases of hepatitis, which coincided with the great decrease in cockroach infestation, indicated that the successful cockroach extermination campaign had a lot to do with the rout of the disease. The chemical used was an industrial silica aerogel, SG 67, commercially called Dri-Die 67. At the onset of the roach-elimination program there had been no thought of using it to control hepatitis. The favorable results were an unexpected happy side benefit.

Cockroaches have been valuable in cancer, heart disease, and nutritional research because of this insect's hardiness and excellent reproduction rate. (A cockroach is born so nearly complete that in only half an hour it becomes a perfect miniature of an adult.) Inquiry into the possible nervous factors in cancer of human beings has been suggested by the recent discovery that the cutting of a certain nerve — the recurrent — induces tumors in cockroaches. Radiation, hormones, and chemicals have all produced cancers in experimental animals, but the nervous system had never before been clearly implicated as a cause of such disorders without being linked to other factors. The lowly cockroach, by showing scientists that tumors can be instigated in an animal by injury to its nervous system, unexpectedly has made a major contribution to cancer research.

Cockroaches have always been an aid to the medical profession, but in less sophisticated periods of mankind their contributions have been rather crude. Jamaica Indians used a mixture containing ashes of cockroaches to eliminate worms in children; a mash of cockroaches and sugar was applied to ulcers and cancers. Certain tribes of North American Indians once believed that their children could be cured of whooping cough if cockroaches, each one named for an afflicted child, were imprisoned, each in a tightly stoppered bottle, and given to its namesake. When the roach expired from lack of air, food, and water, the sickness was supposed to disappear, and frequently it did — if the child also had been dosed with herb cathartics. In Russia, a cockroach powder known as Tarakane was popular for the treatment of dropsy. Some natives of Iquitos, Peru, still treat influenza with internal applications of cockroach powder mixed in pisco (the local white mule). In the 1880's, Mississippi and Alabama rednecks drank cockroach tea for tetanus and supplemented this with a poultice of boiled cockroaches over the wound; they also ate cockroaches fried in oil with garlic to relieve indigestion. In Cairo, Egypt, it is believed that estranged lovers can be reunited if one of the parties to the separation places a charmed, deceased cockroach under his or her pillow before bedding down for the night. Recently in that ancient city a sixty-year-old "purveyor of charms," one Victoria Barsoum (according to a Reuters dispatch), was deposited in a jail cell, charged with fraud and embezzlement, after a police plainclothesman had caught her crediting one of her stable of dead cockroaches with such extraordinary powers for reconciliation. Mme Barsoum stoutly denied that the selling of defunct cockroaches was a crime, except maybe under the Pure Food and Drug Act, adding that she regularly paid all the required taxes on her income, which police say was about fifty pounds Egyptian ($120) a day. The cockroach fakir further proudly proclaimed that her clients were all gilt-edge, upper-social-register and included distinguished business executives, bankers, and political poobahs. That seems reasonable. It is inconceivable that any lower-class types would ever remotely consider the stinking cockroach — dead or alive — as an endearing cupid.

And now we come to the question that concerns everyone who is forced, in the battle for human dignity, to turn live cockroaches into dead ones. What on earth is the best way to get rid of them? In certain sections of Massachusetts you can do this by folding one — live preferred — in a piece of paper with a small amount of money and slipping it into the home of someone whom you'd like to infest with the creatures. In exactly nine days, according to legend, your six-legged guests will desert your home for the other one. But, for those of us who are not denizens of that state, there are more reliable ways of disposing of cockroaches. The U.S. Department of Agriculture, in its Leaflet No. 430 (*Cockroaches and How to Control Them*), recommends filling all cracks passing through floors, and walls, and those leading to spaces behind baseboards and door and window frames, with special attention paid to places where steam and water pipes enter rooms. Cleanliness is strongly stressed. All baskets, bags, boxes of food, and laundry brought into the home should be carefully examined for cockroaches. Infestations can be controlled by application of sprays and dusts, but it is wise to remember that most cockroach insecticides are poisonous to humans, pet animals, and songbirds.

The following chemicals are commonly used against cockroaches in oil solution, water emulsion, or dust mixture: chlordane; diazinon; dieldrin; DDT; lindane; malathion; pyrethrum; sodium fluoride; and DDT-pyrethrum aerosol — the only one that does not leave a cockroach-killing residue on the treated surface. Dust and water sprays are preferred when there is danger of fire from oil-based sprays. Chlorthion also may be used, but not in places where milk is being processed or stored. Diptere should be used only by professional pest-control operators — in a 1 percent spray. Finely powdered boric acid and borax also kill cockroaches, acting much slower than the aforementioned insecticides, but with the advantage of being able to be molded into bait tablets for use in places where it is not feasible to spray or dust, or as food temptation where there is nothing much edible available, as in office buildings. Fumigation is very effective against cockroaches, but should only be attempted by professionals. Phosphorous paste, if spread on small pieces of lightweight cardboard and rolled into rubber-banded cylinders with the paste inside, can be used in places where messy sprays and dusts are not welcome, such as libraries and clothes closets, and in the framework of upholstered furniture. Also, they can be tacked easily to the backs of cabinet drawers. However, this stuff is terribly lethal and must be distributed with great caution in relation to children and pets.

If the foregoing mediums of cockroach elimination are unsuitable in your situation you can always try the ages-old British method of trapping cockroaches in an empty marmalade jar — that is, if you have limitless patience and feel that you can afford the suggested baits: beer, peeled bananas, and a solution made of anise seed. The record United Kingdom cockroach catch — for a period of three months in twelve traps — stands at 8,430. Sometimes I wonder about the British. As well as cockroach traps, a pamphlet published by the British Museum (Natural History) also recommends fumigation, using sulphur dioxide "generated by burning brimstone." A warning is given that "this gas may tarnish and corrode metal articles, bleach coloured fabrics, discolour wallpaper, and harden rubber, such as one finds sometimes in a player-piano." Room temperature of 130 degrees also is suggested to flush out cockroaches, but the average American development dwelling should not be subjected to such inordinate heat except during Fire Prevention Week, when firemen are likely to be sleeping with their boots on.

Besides mankind, the chief enemies of the cockroach are toads, tarantulas, centipedes, and the red mite (*Pimeliaphilus podapolipophagus tragardh* — wouldn't you think they could have made up a shorter name for such a teeny little thing?). There also is one kind of tropical wasp that works out on huge jungle cockroaches by inflicting a sting that does not paralyze but merely destroys the will, so that the cockroach moves only when it is led. The wasp leads the giant insect by holding onto one of its antennae, and the victim walks obediently to the wasp's lair, where an egg is laid on him; when it hatches he serves as living sustenance for the young wasp.

Insects are supposed to teach humans such virtues as industry, thrift, prudence, loyalty, and the joy of living. The only bit of wisdom that the cockroach seems to impart is this: mind your own business, and try not to get stung by brainwashers, or led around by the nose — and you'll survive.

The Fly

In your eye
as you fly
rides your coming feast in shattered image.
Frames hexagon
have led you on.
Your fellows buzz already in the scrimmage.

Now your wings,
light-shot things,
batter by (two flimsy bits of crisp) —
thin veils you wear
to lift you there.
Your feathered tongue unrolls in glistening wisp.

On your feet
you stop to eat.
Each hairy ankle's loaded with the gleam
of dusty crop
you shake and drop
to shape a fate unfigured in your dream.

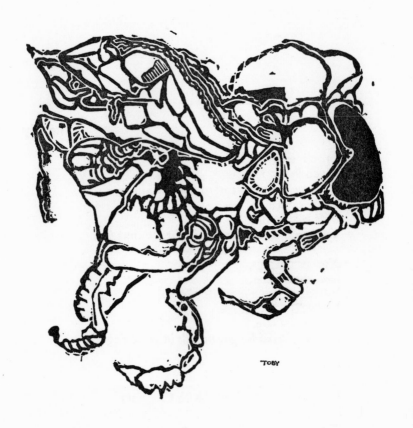

2

Ubiquitous Ubiquitous: *The Fly* The cockroach generally is regarded as a detestable, frightful creature, yet the fly, considerably more dangerous (as a killer of man it ranks high), is regarded with a great deal of amiability.

Because of its small size we are inclined to overlook the fly's inherent obnoxiousness, and to regard it as no more than a minor nuisance. But the main reason for our bland acceptance of the fly is its ubiquity. The fly is everywhere, familiar to everybody. Ranging the world are more than 87,000 species. Rich, poor, or middle class — no one escapes the delicate filthy touch of the fly. It doesn't discriminate between pink skin, brown, black, tan, terra-cotta, yellow, or red-white-and-blue. Perhaps the most important contributing factor to the fly's widespread acceptance is its one superior talent — it can fly. It is a small, graceful monoplane that soars effortlessly through space, swooping in beautifully for accurate six-point landings and blithely taking off again — far better than any man-made aircraft — in any direction: forward, backward, sideways. And who wouldn't like to be able to walk up walls and across the ceiling upside down as the fly does?

People take the fly too much for granted, and not many bother to learn about this fascinating insect, man's constant and most filthy companion throughout history. About all that I knew about flies before I started compiling material for this book was what little I'd picked up when I was a sixth-grade student at the Millvale Second Ward School (C. C. "Gooseneck" Williamson, Principal). When lazy springtime afternoons began to drag and sweet zephyrs mixed with the smell of chalk dust, some of the scholars (myself among them), when we became bored with the interminable, enervating droning on of Miss Pauline Mohn (who had one glass eye and wore her hair in the style of a decrepit bird's nest), would create a minor diversion by snatching up a large fly and sticking it to the desk top by the wings with spit — or, if we were lucky, library paste; then, by placing a paper spitball or a gum-eraser crumb on its upturned legs, we transformed the hapless helpless creature into a foot-juggler. My interest in the circus probably was sparked then and there.

Some of the meaner kids (transfers from the tough First Ward, which was down near the river by the railroad tracks) used to pull the wings and maybe a leg or two off their flies and let them stagger stupidly around until they fell or were pushed into the inkwell, but in my set such cruelty was considered beyond the pale.

About the only other encounters we kids had with flies back then was when we practiced jumping in the horse manure pit that was out behind the jail, where the daily generous droppings of the fire engine horses were deposited. We met a lot of flies that way, and it's a wonder that we survived such intimate fraternity. But we never considered for a moment the unsanitary aspects of such recreation; I can't remember my parents ever once admonishing me because of dung-hung shoes or stained clothing. I don't believe my parents were especially tolerant. It's just that life in those days was more relaxed; people hadn't yet been made conscious of the vital importance of hygiene.

Nobody then ever blamed flies for spreading diseases. Illnesses simply were God-given, and if you didn't toe the line one might descend on you. There was no such thing as a professional exterminator for flies or any other household insect pests — such as silverfish, roaches, rats, ants, or bedbugs. If any of them ever turned up, your mother just sent one of the neighbors' kids down to the corner drugstore for some kind of powder to squirt around (never her own kids, for that would have incriminated her), or for some poison junk that had a death's-head on the box and would be spread on little pieces of bread that then were placed carefully around in the cellar high enough so that the dog couldn't get at them.

In those times people didn't regard insects too seriously; there were more worrisome things to be taken care of — like gallstones, kidney pains, warts, piles, and ill-conceived babies. Why, we still had medicine men peddling their nostrums at curbside. I remember, as a very small boy, standing fascinated on Hyde's Corner (Johnny Hyde ran the town's biggest, fanciest drugstore there where Grant Avenue made a right-angle turn and became North) to watch a bearded itinerant healer — complete with plug hat, feathered Indian aide-de-camp, and tall five-gallon jars of alcohol in which tapeworms languidly floated — as he pitched his phoney patent-medicine concoctions to the assembled populace off the tailgate of a wagon under the flickering light of kerosene flares.

Even after I'd become a teen-ager and worked behind the counter in Hyde's Drugstore, there wasn't too much call for fly sprays. Every spring we'd put in tremendous insecticide window displays — one devoted to Flit, the other to Black Flag — but the customers mostly bought the rat, roach, and bedbug eradicators, pretty much ignoring the antifly liquids and dusts. Flies were considered more or less domesticated — like the cat, dog, and canary bird — and why waste good hard-earned money trying to kill them? Just put up some window screens to keep them outside where they belong.

Since I grew up with such limited knowledge of the workings of the fly, naturally I was intrigued one morning to find in the *New York Times* a news story datelined Cleveland, and headlined, "Tests Indicate That Even the Fly May Love, Hate, Fear and Suffer." The two-column story, by-lined by Walter Sullivan, the *Times* science editor, was a report of the annual meeting of the American Association for the Advancement of Science in that city. It told about a Dr. Vincent G. Dethier, professor of zoology and psychology at the University of Pennsylvania, Philadelphia, who was involved in extensive study of the brain of the fly, conducting experiments in memory and learning with that insect, and also subjecting the fly to brain surgery. The idea of a fly-brain surgeon was fascinating. I was able to reach Dr. Dethier by phone, and after first cautioning me that "those newspaper fellows always exaggerate," he invited me down to Philadelphia to have a look at his fly research operations.

Dr. Dethier received me in his small, modestly furnished office, Room 323, in the Joseph Leidy Laboratory of Biology, the last building along Hamilton Walk on the university grounds. In juxtaposition on one wall were a dignified certificate proclaiming the doctor a *Fellow in the American Academy of Science 1961 Massachusetts* and a colored anthropomorphized cartoon portrait of a fly, much enlarged, signed by Vernon Grant, whom I remembered as a famous children's book illustrator of the Forties. Atop a bookcase stood a heroic-sized wire sculpture of a fly that had an Alexander Calderish look, but turned out to be the work of an entomology student at the university.

Dr. Dethier treated me to a modest luncheon in the university's flyless cafeteria, and there I began my probe into the intricacies of fly-brain surgery. When I asked Dr. Dethier (he pronounces it Deeteer) about the love, hate, fear, and suffering business, he smiled indulgently and said, "Newspaper writers consider our work so dull that they always try to jazz it up. How can anyone say that a fly experiences love, hate, fear, and suffering? Among humans, it's 'love' because we say it is; to a fly such an action — I don't say emotion, because I'm not at all certain that a fly ever experiences emotion as we know it — may be designated by another term, some word in fly language, whatever *that* may be. I've never heard any, have you?" I sensed that Dr. Dethier was going to be a baffling subject to interview.

He continued, "However, if you put a fly in a fly situation calculated to have the same effect on it that a so-called stressful situation — one involving fear, anger, or neurosis — has on a human being, there will be frustration from the insect's point of view and you find that certain changes take place — heart rate changes, for example. Flies *do* show psychological changes similar to those which occur in humans and to which we tag a name."

Dr. Dethier went on, putting into terms understandable to me as a nonscientist his contradiction of the widely held notion that there is a fundamental distinction between the higher animal that thinks — i.e., one that has perception — and the lower animal, such as an insect, that "is just a little machine." The typical housewife, for instance, shows little compunction about swatting a fly, but hesitates to kill a chicken, mouse, or kitten. Actually, according to Dr. Dethier, there is a continuous gradation from small brains to large ones, not only in size but also in function. He believes that behavioral studies of insects have shown them to have primitive forms of emotion, even though their brains are infinitesimal.

Research into the functions of the insect brain was begun recently — in 1959. In Germany, electrodes have been placed in the brains of crickets, and in Great Britain portions of ant brains have been destroyed to find out what areas control various functions. If it is not known what the Russians and the Chinese are doing in this respect, I think we should find out. Such work has shown that a large part of the insect's microscopic brain is concerned with seeing. The British have stated humorlessly that ants being studied by them have indicated that they can learn the way through a maze only if a certain area of the brain is undamaged. Dr. Dethier's own interest in this phase of entomological biology dates from childhood when he was inordinately fond of caterpillars. He was curious then about why his pets hungrily devoured leaves from certain plant species, but left others strictly alone. He wondered what process within the insect led to this preference.

"Nobody knows whether low-form animals have the same behavior patterns as higher animals," he said. "We ask experimentally, can a fly learn? Do flies show equivalent emotional behavior to that of higher animals?"

That superb satirist of our folkways, James Thurber, took a dim view of fly intelligence. In his Fables for Our Time, he tells of a fly who was much too clever to be fooled by a spider's web ("I never light where I don't see other flies and I don't see any other flies in your house"), but who subsequently was trapped by flypaper even though a friendly bee warned him about it by saying, "Hold it, stupid, that's flypaper." But the foolish fly just said, "Don't be silly, they're dancing," settled down, and got stuck along with all the other flies. Thurber's moral was that there is no safety in numbers, or in anything else.

When I asked Dr. Dethier to what use the results of his fly-brain surgery research would be put, he said he hadn't the slightest idea. As a pure scientist, he was obtaining the knowledge for its own sake and not for specific application to human problems. The Norwegian explorer Fridtjof Nansen puts this sort of thing rather well: "The history of the human race is a continuous struggle from darkness toward light. It is therefore of no purpose to discuss the use of knowledge — man wants to know and when he ceases to do so he is no longer man."

Because insect brains are so simple, their study may shed light on mental processes that are difficult to observe in more highly developed animals. Fly brain cells are in many ways similar to those of higher animals, but whereas man has many millions of brain cells, the fly, like all other insects, has but one hundred thousand. A fly's brain, I learned, is about the size of a pinhead, and is translucent — white to pearly opalescent. Oddly, it has a tunnel through its middle, front to back, to allow the esophagus to get to the stomach. This is because a fly's nervous system is located on its underside, and its digestive operations topside — just the reverse of man's. The fly's recurrent nerve, coming from the front of the brain, also goes through this tunnel to the alimentary canal so that it can carry messages from there to the brain.

Dr. Dethier's flies are being examined in an attempt to understand behavior in terms of the nervous system. While a fly's behavior is complicated, its nervous system is relatively simple, and it is felt that a thorough study of such a simple system might give clues to the problems of more complicated systems. Sounds logical enough.

The fly's main conductor of nervous impulses is a double-stranded affair which runs the length of the insect's body on its underside. Situated along this dual cord are lumpy masses of nerve tissue called ganglia. The first three of these, fused together, form the fly's brain; the next three pairs, also in the head and also fused, control the workings of the animal's complex mouth parts. Ganglia within the thorax operate wings and legs; other pairs of ganglia within the abdomen control that part of the body. Thus, each of the insect's three body divisions is semiautonomous and able to carry out reflex actions on its own, without first having to go through the switchboard of the brain itself. Therefore a fly's behavior is the result of immediate reactions to messages received from the world around it. The fly responds to heat, humidity, odors, and vibrations, but it does not think about what to do in a given situation; all actions are instinctive.

One of Dr. Dethier's least successful experiments with the fly occurred while studying its short-term memory. It was found that the fly cannot under any circumstances be induced to press a tiny lever with a foot in order to get its food, a trick that most laboratory animals learn with ease. But in other areas Dr. Dethier has been spectacularly successful. For instance, largely because of his work with the fly, more now is known about hunger and thirst in this insect than in any other animal, including the human being.

"In a fly," Dr. Dethier told me, "we know exactly what hunger and thirst are — reflex phenomena. They operate on a feedback message system something like a thermostat. A certain kind of chemical on the taste buds will send electrical messages and a fly will feed automatically as long as this information goes into the brain — until the reflex system in the digestive tract says shut it off. You can manipulate a fly, play it like a push-button machine."

By cutting one certain nerve from a special region of a fly's stomach, it then is unable to relay information back to the brain whenever the stomach becomes full, and the fly simply goes on eating and eating and eating. It cannot stop. I know some people whose similar nerve, if not severed, must at least be a little threadbare. One of Dr. Dethier's flies, so altered, became so enormously fat that its belly was stretched into transparency. Nothing yet has been discovered that will keep a fly from being hungry — the fly is always hungry.

The flies chosen by Dr. Dethier for his surgical and motivational experiments are a special strain of large garbage flies, in culture since 1947, members of a varied assortment of compost and dung flies known scientifically as Muscaria, so-called "higher flies" that comprise about thirty thousand species, or roughly two-fifths of all known flies, and resemble the common housefly *Musca domestica*, the one that most Americans are referring to when they speak of the fly. Muscaria thrive on compostlike vegetable debris, including rotting wood, leaf mold, and peaty soil; on dung, carrion, and similar materials of higher protein content, leading on to carnivorous larvae; on the tissues of living plants, stems, roots, living fruit, and berries, including leaf-mining and gall-forming larvae; and on the products of fermenting, rotting fruit, and the fermenting sap from wounded trees. This fly species besides being among the largest of flies has other advantages for use as a laboratory animal. First of all, of course, is the fact that it's dirt cheap, readily available, and easily bred — all you need is some old garbage. Secondly, lifetime studies can be made, for a fly's life at best is very short — sixty days' average, much less than that of termite or cockroach, the insects customarily used for lab experimentation.

Dr. Dethier's initial methods and equipment in working with flies were rather primitive, but now are extremely sophisticated. The electronic monitoring setup alone cost about $25,000 to install. All of the optical and manipulating equipment came from

Germany; the electronic gear is American-made. (Incidentally, German scientists find our electronic equipment superior to their own, and prefer it.)

Dr. Dethier breezily conducted me on a brief tour of his fly laboratory. In the main room a lone fly was pitiably suspended in the center of a glass-walled case about the size of a small-town business executive's office desk. The fly was mounted on a matchstick by a wax blob to which its wings had been adhered — just like the flies that used to foot-juggle on our school desks. This particular specimen was being monitored for its taste reactions to various sugars, acids, and proteins — foods that almost always are accepted, although salts, saccharin, and other artificial sweeteners are not. One of the fly's six feet was dangling in a test tube which contained the particular solution then being monitored. Flies taste through their feet. Readings on how much the fly eats while under observation are made from a hypodermic syringe arrangement. (The fly has the choice of accepting or rejecting whatever food is offered, but is not able to select any particular food.) Electrodes inserted into the fly's brain are connected to a frighteningly efficient-looking mess of wires, coils, rheostats, switches, dials, and what I call thingamajigs. The voltage of the fly's electrodes — less than one-thousandth of a volt — has to be greatly amplified so that it will record the fly's impulses on two oscilloscopes — one a "slave," duplicating the work of the other, and making a permanent record photographically of the graph thus created. Everything is battery-operated due to local line-current fluctuation so large as to be unreliable for scientific experiments of this nature. The great glass cage rests on a massive table whose legs are mounted on floaters to eliminate vibration; it is insulated against picking up local television, radio waves, and the rumble of street traffic. The total effect is completely Kafkaesque.

I asked Dr. Dethier if this impressive rigmarole wasn't inhibiting to the fly.

"Not at all," he replied. "He can do everything but fly. He'll live just as long as one foot can dangle in the water. There's no feeling in the wings, so holding him that way doesn't hurt a bit."

I was told that flies even can mate while thus confined, but who would want to, all trussed up like that, and so public — like in Macy's window. But then, enduring such isolation maybe is not too hard on the fly, for in one important respect it differs from man. The fly basically is a solitary animal, brought together with others only by circumstance. There is no group interaction of any sort among flies. The fly remains a loner.

The monitoring system was so grandiose that I would have completely overlooked the fly operating theater had it not been pointed out to me by Dr. Dethier. It was simply a glass furniture caster filled with wax and sunk into a small table-top pit which was perforated to allow the circulation of carbon dioxide, used as an anesthetic. America's foremost fly-brain surgeon proudly showed me his array of surgical instruments. They included: homemade adaptations of razor blades; drawn-glass needles; insect pins; jewelers' forceps of Swiss steel; and various surgical scalpels and iridectomy scissors used for operating on human eyes. Brain surgery on flies is done under a forty-power dissecting microscope. I await the momentous day when it is announced that a successful kidney transplant has been performed on a fly. But then, I guess flies don't have kidneys. Come to think of it, I've never heard of a fly peeing on anything.

"You have to behave yourself to do this kind of work," commented Dr. Dethier. "You need steady hands." Of that, I'm sure. I could never do it. I'd probably snip off the fly's head, make the wrong incision, or accidentally emasculate the poor creature. When I asked Dr. Dethier for the best advice he could give an aspiring fly-brain surgeon, he said, without hesitation, "Think small."

A recent revolutionary advance in microscopy now allows biologists to examine insects under 4,500-times magnification. I have seen photos made with the aid of this advanced technology, in which the sensory hairs of the fly's remarkable feeding device, its tongue, look like desert cacti. The microscope used is a scanning-electron one recently developed by the Westinghouse Electric Corporation, primarily to be used for the inspection of tiny electronic circuits. Biologists are delighted by this development of the electron microscope, which was conceived originally in the Thirties, able to magnify up to a million times, but registering only a silhouette image because it shoots electrons through the object under scrutiny, much as an X-ray machine does. An ordinary light-microscope always had the limitation of not being able to see clearly objects much smaller than a wavelength of light (a ten-thousandth of a millimeter or so) and was able to magnify only two thousand times maximum. This new scope, however, registers a three-dimensional image by shooting its electrons with such force that other electrons are dislodged from the target's surface. These minute particles, literally fragments of the subject, are gathered up, amplified, and projected onto a television screen with great clarity, and the image can be readily photographed.

Before leaving the fascinating realm of Dr. Dethier, I asked his professional advice on the best way to swat a fly. An aging Hindu — a greasy, potbellied fake-fakir named Massa Kuta Singalee ("The Fireproof Man") — a fixture in the Sideshow of the Ringling Bros and Barnum & Bailey Circus when I trouped with that great tented show back in the late forties, always advocated hypnotizing a fly before swatting it. "You spread fingers," he used to advise me, "wiggle, wiggle, waggle — you never miss a once. The fly is *hypnotize!* No move." Massa Kuta used to keep score religiously, and if you could believe his figures, he also could have been billed as "The Maharajah of Swat." At the end of one season he bragged on "seven thous', sixteen hun'red, eighty and six" — killed while traveling across twenty-seven states and the District of Columbia. Dr. Dethier said he'd never heard of that method. "I always just aim directly for the front," he said. Me, I'm just the opposite; I find that I chalk up more kills by crashing down on a spot well *behind* the fly, and the bigger the spread of newspaper the better. Don't roll up the paper into a club, but use it as flat as possible — gives the fly less chance to get out from under.

In regard to fly swatting it is well to remember that the fly escapes because of its ultrasensitive hairs — on its antennae, legs, mouth parts, body, and even wings. These hairs, protruding through the insect's skeleton and connected to the skin underneath by a sort of ball-and-socket arrangement, warn the fly of air being displaced by the advance of an approaching weapon. The fly's escape is automatic — as is most of this insect's behavior — and is believed to be activated by its ganglia, those lumpy masses of nerve tissue situated along the insect's main nerve cord, of which we spoke earlier.

A fly can't survive much of a whack, for its body is fragile and has a thin, soft covering protected only by a plethora of hairs and bristles, which are no defense against the first section of the Sunday *Times*. Antennae are mostly inconspicuous and variable in shape. Mouth parts are for piercing and sucking, lapping, sponging, but never for biting — and may be reduced and functionless. The common housefly's tongue is something like an elephant's trunk. When not in use sucking up food, it folds back under the head.

A human oculist would have difficulty applying his specialized knowledge to the eyes of a fly, for they are completely different from our eyes. The housefly's eye is made up of four thousand six-sided facets, each a miniature visual system which consists of a tiny lens, a light-transmitting system, and sensitive retinal cells. Each facet is isolated from its neighbor and no two point exactly in the same direction. A single facet registers a single impression, a fragment of the total scene. Of course, no one except a fly knows for sure what sort of a picture such a composite eye delivers to the brain, but it is believed that eyes of this type are less efficient than those of higher animals, and that all facets together combine — like tiles of a mosaic — to form a complete image. The effect is much like that of the enlargement of a newspaper halftone reproduction, in which dots of varying density combine to produce a complete picture. If the fly's eyes can detect color, the effect might be rather hallucinogenic. Compound eyes are great for detecting movement, as an object in motion registers impressions on different facets, one after the other. A fly's vision is poor on detail, and flies cannot read signs at a distance of more than three feet. They sleep with their eyes open, but do not snore.

Flies do not swarm in the true meaning of that word. Bees

swarm — as a corporate body amassed around their queen, maintaining their integrity while moving about or static. We cannot say the same about these inherent loners, the flies. In German *der Schwarm* means a true swarm, but for a mere massing of individuals the term is *der Haufen,* and *das Gewimmel* for a milling throng. Germans seem more to understand the fine distinctions of mob action. When flies swarm there is no sense of community; the assembly simply is made up of a number of individuals, each intent on the same thing at the same time. Most fly swarms are predominantly male; many scientific observers of them conclude that, contrary to popular belief, the swarms are not simply for mating purposes (it is known that females visit swarms to choose mates), but simply are a habitual hangover from some past, less practical use. Swarms of flies often look like clouds of smoke; around church steeples they sometimes cause fire alarms to be turned in. Masses of flies found hibernating in a house in wintertime have not come there in a swarm, but as individuals. Such hibernation is easily broken by a mild spell. Often in churches hibernating flies revived by warmth will fall on the heads and hymnbooks of shocked parishioners, or drown in baptismal and holy-water fonts, and on occasion drop into the wide-open mouth of a choir singer.

A fly really lives two separate lives in succession: first as a larva, and then as an adult. Larva and adult of a fly differ more from each other than many orders of insects do. In some flies the larval period is the more insignificant; in others, just the opposite. For instance, the larva of the tsetse fly, nurtured within the mother's body, has hardly any separate existence, but adult life of this insect is all important. Crane and blow flies, however, gain ascendancy over their rivals while in the larval stage. And adult warble flies of cattle and deer live for a short time only, and solely for mating purposes.

Flies are eager copulators. Mating often takes place when females are hardly free of their pupal skins and still in a soft state. Anxious males frequently wait patiently alongside pupae for female flies to appear. Mating swarms are common, with males rising and falling, as individual females fly in, find a mate, and take off with him to surrounding vegetation. One male fly, the small black

Hilara, courts with a darting, dancing flight close to the surface of still or slow-moving water, and by offering his ladylove a tiny ball of silk spun from special glands. She uses it for insect trapping. Other flies offer their female quarries tidbits of food, sometimes wrapped in a frothy balloon of an anal or oral secretion. In some species the balloon is empty, and eaten by the female. Misogynous scientists suggest that the custom is to divert the female from eating the male, but others more romantic believe that it is to put the female in a receptive frame of mind for mating.

Flies have four stages in their life history: egg, larva, pupa, and adult. *Larva* is the Latin word for mask, and *pupa* means baby, or doll. Larva and pupa have no wings. Every winged insect is a full-grown one; small insects are not the young of larger ones but are distinctive species. The little flies of spring do not turn into the big flies of summer.

Eggs of flies generally are oval and white or pale yellow. To the naked eye they are featureless, but the microscope reveals horns, discs, stalks, and raised networks of surface ridges. The eggs under strong magnification look somewhat like the snapshots we've been getting back from the moon satellite. Dull and tiresome. The surface irregularities hold a thin film of air which acts as an auxiliary lung — a respiratory plastron, such as that which provides many aquatic bugs and beetles with a temporary supply of oxygen, and which is replenished by diffusion of oxygen from the water. This natural device prevents the fly egg from drowning after a rain shower, and also increases surface tension so that the egg is able to float, as in the case of mosquito eggs. The average female fly produces from one to 250 eggs at one time, and the maximum for most flies is a thousand during a lifetime. The housefly may lay twenty-one batches of eggs, live five months, and complete a generation every two weeks. An especially ambitious bee fly, however, can lay from eight hundred to one thousand eggs at one time, and the blow fly might total nearly two thousand per laying. A pound of meat exposed to blow flies for half a day in bright sunshine can turn up with as many as 165,000 eggs on it.

Fly larvae usually are maggots with pointed heads; some have mouth hooks. Dipterous larvae are deposited in every conceivable medium: in all kinds of water from brackish to hot mineral springs, even in running streams and waterfalls; in every type of dry medium from mud to sand; in all sorts of decomposing material and excrements; in wounds of plants and animals; as scavengers in nests of birds and insects, and in dens of mammals; and as parasites in plants and on live animals. Some larvae grow to varying stages of development within the mother's uterus, leaving it in some cases only just before pupation. Few fly larvae can live exposed to light and air, but must be buried in something that is more or less humid. Dung is attractive to fly maggots because of its high nitrogen content.

One of the best fly-breeding grounds is a compost heap; it conceals and protects from light, heat, frost, sudden deluge, drying wind and predator enemies. Larvae of the black fly, unlike those of any other fly, are entirely aquatic and make no use of rot or decay. Certain female midges of the genus *Pontomyia* lead such brief, frenetic, and insecure lives that they go slightly mad over egg laying by indulging in parthenogenesis, the development of eggs from virgin females without benefit of fertilization by spermatozoa; all the hatchings are female. These avid Lesbian layers find males so unnecessary that among some species males are completely unknown. Certain of these self-sufficient nonconformist flies lay eggs even before breaking out of the pupal state. As a male non-fly I consider such panicky action preposterous.

It seldom happens that a fly is able to live out its expected life span. Losses are great due to starvation, drought, drowning, cold, heat, asphyxiation, and swatting. It is a favorite conceit of entomologists that if all the descendants of one pair of flies born in only one summer survived they would cover the entire earth to a depth of forty-seven feet. Harold Oldroyd, a Yorkshireman who is one of the world's most eminent authorities on the fly, seriously disagreed with that assumption, recalculated, and decided that there would be only enough fly offspring to spread a layer that thick over an area the size of Germany — but still that's more flies than anyone would care to wade through on a sunny August day. One authority (Professor C. F. Hodge) claims that one pair of flies could produce

191,010,000,000,000,000,000 adults "if all lived" from April to August, forming a layer three stories high, if the space per fly is figured at one-eighth of a cubic inch.

The poet Gertrude Stein once said that a rose is a rose is a rose. But a fly is not always a fly. Many of the insects whose names are compounded with the word fly are not accepted by entomologists as true flies. Among the nonfly flies are the dragonfly (order Odonata); mayflies (Ephemeroptera); stone flies (Plecoptera); fireflies (Coleoptera — actually a beetle); ichneumons (Hymenoptera — a wasp); scorpionflies (Mecoptera); caddis flies (Trichoptera); and butterflies (Lepidoptera). On the other hand, land midges, gnats (water midges), bots, and warbles are true flies. And there are moth flies, bee flies, and louse flies.

The true fly differs from most other insects in having but a single pair of wings. The name of the fly's order, Diptera, derives from that fact: di, meaning twice, and pteron, feather. The wings are membranous and, in most species, unpigmented; they are located on the second, or middle, segment of the thorax. To confuse matters, there are some wingless flies, who live as parasites on bats and sheep.

The wing beat of the ordinary housefly is 345 beats per second; fastest wing beat of any insect is that of the tiny fly known as the midge, 950 beats per second. (In experiments with truncated wings at a temperature of 98.6 degrees Fahrenheit the midge's wing-beat rate rose to 133,080 beats per minute, and the muscular contraction-expansion cycle then was the fastest muscle movement ever measured — 0.00045 or one-2,218th of a second.) The housefly is able to travel at least thirteen miles, except in arid desert country where excessive dehydration forces it to make much shorter jaunts.

The common housefly, a nearly middle-sized fly, is very close to the average size for the entire animal kingdom — from the tiniest one-celled species (Protozoa) to the largest whale. The biggest known fly, the Australian robber, has a wing expanse of three inches. The tiniest flies, hardly visible to the naked eye, likely are the midges that do their piercing mostly at night, and are called "punkies" or "no-see-ums" by exasperated hunters and fishermen.

The range of size between the largest and smallest flies, while only one-tenth of that which separates elephant and mouse, nevertheless is a trial for the flies at either extreme. Very small ones are at the mercy of the breeze; convection currents carry them high and strong winds move them horizontally. This buffeting is hazardous to individual flies, but beneficial to the group, for thus it is taken to fresh productive environments. Monster flies seem to be approaching the end of an evolutionary line. Bound to go the way of the dinosaur, they are trapped by their outsize. Conspicuous to predators, low in fecundity, and slow in development, big flies are finding it more and more difficult even to maintain themselves, let alone to venture forth on new trails.

Diptera is one of the four largest orders of insects, with many species yet to be named. Flies are distributed in astronomical numbers throughout the countryside. Hessian flies, wheat-nibblers of the family Cecidomyiidae, have been estimated at two hundred thousand per acre, and puparia of a fly known to everyone but me as *Ephydra gracilis*, washed up on the beach of Utah's Great Salt Lake, have numbered as many as 370 million per mile of shore. At Khartoum, on the Nile River in Egypt, it is said that a thousand million Chironomids emerge at night. Countless millions of *Chaoborus edulis* are caught at Lake Nyasa, southeast Africa, and pressed into sticky masses called Kungu cakes, each as big as a man's head. The natives relish them as we do fruit cake or plum pudding.

After reading everything about flies that I could lay my eyes on, I'd say the world's most discriminating flies are the Asilids *Andrenosoma albopilosum*, thus far found only on one single beach of Corsica, and in several small Italian villages. The most repulsive undoubtedly are the *Scatophaga stercoraria*, the furry yellow flies that cluster over horse or cow dung. The dung is their world, their bag. They mate in it; their eggs are laid on it; the larvae feed on it and pupate in the soil beneath. As adults, these flies never are far from dung-sweet-home, be it ever so humble. The *Scatophaga* is one of the most relentless of murderer flies. Highly developed prestomal teeth are used to rasp the skin of an insect victim and to chew a hole in its neck membrane, then to sever the nerve cord.

With the victim thus crippled, its body fluids are sucked out of head and thorax by the attacker, the abdomen being handled separately — a grimly efficient fly, and the species is worldwide.

Possibly the most macabre family of flies is the Phoridae, which embraces the coffin fly (*Conicera tibialis*). This fly family is so strange that scientists have been unable to agree on its classification (Brachycera or Cyclorrhapha), but feel that it definitely has gotten itself well out on a limb of the evolutionary tree, as well as on the morticians' list edged in black that is headed by Jessica Mitford. The coffin fly likes secretive, dark, damp, and moldy places, and is able to maintain itself through many successive generations on dead bodies in coffins beneath the ground. These flies live a complete life cycle in the dark, as enough air for breathing comes from natural cavities in the soil. They retain access to the surface, coming and going at will from six-feet-under. Phorid flies also like mushroom beds and love dead snails. (I do too if they're cooked in garlic sauce.) Phorid larvae live as scavengers in the nests of ants, termites, wasps, and bees. These flies have great resistance to asphyxiation and chemical action. In tropical countries they sometimes are ingested by mistake (no white, Anglo-Saxon Protestant ever eats a fly on purpose), and in one well-documented instance of such a case in Burma, a European living there passed in his stools for over a period of a year larvae, puparia, and adult Phorids, indicating that a colony of the flies had set up light housekeeping in his intestine.

Various genera of flies have developed the elongate, tubular proboscis well suited for extracting nectar from deep tubular flowers. Most primitive of them is the crane, of the family Tipulidae — that granddaddy of flies we affectionately call daddy-longlegs, a gangling, elongated thing with narrow wings, absurdly skinny long legs, and slow flight; to flies it is what a biplane of the Wright brothers era is to modern streamlined jets.

The most tranquil and content of the flies that feed on flowers is the family Syrphidae, the hover fly, most important pollinator of all flies. The hovers are known to everyone and loved by all, even though they sometimes seem rather stupid. Harold Oldroyd, in his definitive work on the fly *The Natural History of Flies*, tells of an instance when hover flies pollinated cucumber flowers in a greenhouse, thereby causing the resulting vegetables to be of such poor quality they could not be marketed. But I'm sure they meant well. The adult hovers, having abandoned their carnivorous diets for one of sweet nectar, live arcadian lives, quite different from the frenetic, preying, bloodthirsty existence of the robber fly.

There are flies that live in seaweed along the shore, kelp flies of the family Coelopidae, the largest being known as *Coelopa frigida*. Seaweed makes a warm, compost-like environment for them and provides a nourishing slime for feeding the larvae. These flies have evolved into flattened, leathery, greasy insects that are able to rise to the surface and take off from the water. Normally, they stay on the seaweed for life, but occasionally the *Coelopa frigidae*, overwhelmed by their love of the smell of cleaning fluid, will congregate in a drycleaning establishment or a garage and become a temporary nuisance. In the Pacific there is a truly oceanic fly, of the genus *Pontomyia*, that runs about on top of the water, supported by surface tension at the tips of its middle and hind feet. By using the tips of its wings as paddles, it can swim beneath the surface in a sort of penguin fashion.

Despite all the exotic terrorists abroad, entomologists agree that, all in all, the common housefly, *Musca domestica*, is man's most notorious enemy fly, for this fly frequents cesspools, dung heaps, and garbage cans, and after tramping around in those hideous places thinks nothing of dropping into our households to wipe its dirty feet on our food, dishes, and cooking utensils, stick its dirty proboscis into our children, and drool on our wives. The fly's foot is one of the greatest carriers of disease organisms known to man. But we shouldn't castigate the housefly too much as a cause of infectious disease, for bad hygiene really is the main reason behind an outbreak of a contagious disease, or of one that enters the body through mouth, nose, or throat. Flies multiply only if there is ample waste material for them to breed in.

Our little enemy, *Musca*, has one other dirty habit. It likes to vomit wherever it goes. Even on so small a scale that can become unpleasant. Those little specks left behind by flies are vomit spots, not excrement. In order to liquify solids so that they can be sucked up by its hollow tubular tongue, the fly regurgitates upon them. Too, while the housefly is not noted for feeding off carrion, its larvae will infest open wounds and wound dressings. They also will set up shop in birds' nests, dead and live snails, and in egg pods or locusts. But unless you are an active ornithologist or a gourmet specializing in French and Chinese food, you need not be especially concerned about this matter.

Musca's chief danger to man lies in its great adaptability; it can suit its behavior to local conditions as it finds them. It also has been able to develop immunity to certain powerful insecticides. The housefly in developing this sort of resistance is demonstrating the evolutionary vitality that has enabled it, of all flies, to develop along with mankind by learning to exploit the great variety of breeding materials found in his waste.

Flies seem always to have been a plague of mankind. The Bible (Psalms 78:45) indicates that flies were one of the special great wraths sent by God against the incredulous and disobedient: "He sent divers sorts of flies among them, which devoured them; and frogs which destroyed them." The wrathful Lord also sent "frost, locusts, caterpillars, evil angels, and hot thunderbolts" and He "smote all the first-born in Egypt" and "turned their rivers into blood, that they could not drink" (sounds just about like President Johnson's escalated war in Vietnam).

The fly is a major cause of debilitation in mankind. Malaria, yellow fever, dengue, Bancroftian and Malayan filariasis, elephantiasis, certain types of encephalitis, and occasional cases of tularemia and anthrax, all are caused by the mosquito — which many of us nonscientists may be surprised to learn actually is a fly (the word is Spanish, meaning a diminutive mosea, or fly). In war zones the mosquito often has been a worse enemy than entire armies of fellow men.

But we needn't go to war zones of the South Pacific and the Orient or to tropical jungles to find villainous and lethal flies. The ordinary housefly in a first-class urban slum area can carry as many as thirty-three million microorganisms of bacteria in its gut and have half a billion more swarming over its body and legs. The most accomplished opera singer couldn't recite, in one lyrical outburst, all the diseases that can be caused by organisms found on the body of our own *Musca domestica*: typhoid, tapeworm, hookworm, whipworm, bubonic plague, diarrhea, yaws, amoebic dysentery, tuberculosis, anthrax, leprosy, opthalmia, trachoma, erysipelas, septicemia, gangrene, gonorrhea, and Lord only knows what else. The fly, at one time or another, has been blamed for almost every ailment of man except stuffed nose, backache, astigmatism, hypertension, acquisitiveness and excess ego. Outdoorsmen in North America are familiar with the painful bite of that great pest the deer fly, which loves to zero in on the back of the neck, forehead, and eyebrows — possibly because perspiration tends to collect more in those areas. The deer fly is capable of transmitting tularemia, the so-called rabbit fever.

It is surprising, considering how long man has been tormented by flies, to learn that all the significant medical discoveries implicating bloodsucking flies with human disease have come about only since 1869, when a fellow named Raimbert showed by experiment that the bacillus of anthrax could be disseminated by flies. The malaria parasite was discovered in 1880, but the facts that anopheline mosquitoes could become infested with malaria parasites by biting a malaria patient, and that development of the parasite took place within the mosquito, weren't discovered until seventeen years later.

Flies have been pretty rough on man's livestock also by spreading and perpetuating many of their diseases. The chief vectors of the principal arthropod-borne diseases of livestock are bloodsucking species of flies; the diseases transmitted are essentially blood infections. Those vectors ordinarily carry on their disease-spreading and propagation in two ways: mechanical transmission, the direct transfer of infective blood from diseased to healthy animals; and biological transmission, a specialized and complex relationship between vector, organism, and host, characterized by reproduction and structural change of the disease-causing organism within the body of the vector.

The tsetse fly of the African veldt likely is the most-feared vector pest of domestic animals, not only because it kills so many of them by bringing nagana, tsetse fly disease, or African animal trypano-somiasis, but also due to the fact that this fly carries as well the trypanosomes responsible for human sleeping sickness. Unlike mosquitoes, both male and female tsetse flies are bloodsuckers.

Today, for all of man's ingenuity, the tsetse still ranges over an area of four million square miles — Africa south of the Sahara, plus a tiny part of the Aden Peninsula. In the five years between 1901 and 1906, sleeping sickness induced by the tsetse fly killed two hundred thousand natives of Uganda, Africa, then a British protectorate, lying north of Lake Victoria. The epidemic became so vicious that eventually the entire area had to be evacuated.

Many other diseases are transmitted to farm livestock by flies. These infections, generally acquired while the animals are grazing, include anthrax, equine infectious anemia and encephalomyelitis, African horse sickness, and Japanese B encephalitis. The last name is not a disease of domestic animals but a fatal virus infection of man, which is carried principally by the horse after transmission by mosquitoes. From flies, sheep pick up the louping ill, Nairobi sheep disease, and blue tongue. Biting flies spread swine erysipelas from pig to pig, and also bring swine pox. Flies also infect cats (with enteritis), rabbits (myxomatosis), and such small wild animals as squirrels, mice, woodchucks, opossums, and grouse (tularemia). Even chickens are not safe from fly infection. Flies present barnyard fowl with the potent toxin of *Clostridium botu-linum*, which causes botulism, a disease that results ordinarily from eating contaminated canned goods. Obviously chickens can't afford such luxuries in their diet; they get botulism from ingesting blow fly maggots that have developed in contaminated meats.

United States farm animals are infected mostly by horseflies. They are sinisterly silent, biting before the animal really knows they've arrived. Their garishly colored eyes — iridescent and shot with zigzag bands of gold, red, orange, and poisonous green — are like something out of one of Dr. Timothy Leary's celebrated Psychedelic Celebrations. The scientific name for the horsefly is *Haematopota*, but this fly is known to beef breeders and dairymen by other names in various locales: cleg, stout, breeze, dun, whame, burrel, and certain other terms that only sound proper out on the wild plains of Texas or our other cowboy states.

The horsefly is large, measuring from three-quarters of an inch to more than an inch and a quarter. In color it is ash-gray or brown with speckled wings, which in repose are held inclined together like a barn roof. Mouth parts of a horsefly are strong enough to pierce leather, and a bite leaves a respectable hole. A single grazing animal can lose as much as 100 cc. of blood to a horsefly on a good summer day.

Horses and a few other mammals are greatly disturbed by a fly called the stomach bot (Celtic for swollen), a furry, yellow, beelike creature. The common adult bot fly lays its eggs on an animal by cleverly glueing them onto its hairs, usually on the front legs. The horse then licks them to relieve the irritation and thereby causes the eggs to hatch; the tiny larvae adhere to the horse's tongue, burrowing into its mucous membrane. Slowly, they work their way back along the tongue, arriving at its base in about three weeks — four, if the tongue is especially long — where they cast loose for an exhilarating drop to the stomach. They attach themselves to its lining and in nine or ten months the larvae, grown into tough maggots, are ready to pupate and be passed with the horse's excrement.

Some flies merely attack farm animals without giving them any disease organisms. Among them the horn flies are especially irritating. They are small — only half the size of the average housefly and more slender but real nasty, as most undersized creatures are, especially circus midgets. These flies get their name from their habit of resting about the base of the animal's horn when not biting, which is most of the time. They breed in cow dung, but cannot do so if it contains the slightest trace of a chemical called phenothiazine. Some cattlemen get that deterrent into the dung by feeding it to their herds.

The screw-worm fly was our Western cattle- and sheepmen's

worst enemy until the United States government in 1962 stepped in with a $6 million eradication program that really worked. The cost of the experiment, which embraced the entire state of Texas and part of New Mexico, was shared on a fifty-fifty basis by the state and federal governments and individual livestock producers (paying ten cents per head for sheep, fifty cents apiece for cattle, and a dollar each for horses). The method was fairly simple. Larvae of screw-worm hybrid flies, produced in an old airplane hangar at Mission, Texas, just west of Brownsville, at the rate of 100 million a week, both males and females (because no one could tell the sexes apart) were sterilized by gamma rays, and then placed in six-inch-square paper boxes (440 pupae per box), where they hatched. The boxes subsequently were dropped scattershot from airplanes to the grazing grounds of cattle, where virgin female flies already in the fields mated with the sterilized immigrants to produce no eggs. Since each female is capable of only one mating, such sterile matings meant the end of the line for those particular females as far as furthering the race of screw worms was concerned.

A similar eradication program was instituted against the Mexican fruit fly (Anastrepha ludens), principally to protect the citrus groves of the rich Imperial Valley of California and save millions of dollars annually. From 180,000 to 200,000 of this species of fruit fly, sterilized by a chemical treatment called chemosterilant, were distributed weekly in the Tijuana area in an attempt to eliminate this orchard pest which wreaks its havoc by burrowing under the skins of fruit to lay its eggs.

One species of fruit fly, the Mediterranean (Ceratitis capitata), is one of the most destructive insect pests in the world. Some maggots of this scurrilous fruit-blighting fly were found in a grapefruit at Orlando, Florida, back in the spring of 1929, and that great citrus-growing state got the scare of its lifetime. The Mediterranean fruit fly, native to Africa, came to Spain in 1842, and since then has spread all over the tropical and subtropical world. In Hawaii it had wiped out the growing of all fruits except pineapples, bananas, and coconuts. But it had been successfully kept out of the United States by strict quarantine. In less than a month after those first-time-in-America Mediterranean fruit fly maggots were discovered in Florida, the state was under quarantine, with an eradication area of fifteen thousand square miles established, stretching across the state's citrus-growing middle from the Atlantic to the Gulf of Mexico, and guarded by inspection stations along its north and south borders. Congress had appropriated $4,250,000 with which to fight the dread insect that could destroy the state's entire citrus industry in one swell foop — as Woody Allen likes to say. This quarantined area included 120,000 acres of citrus, producing 73 percent of the state's crop; 248 of the state's 318 citrus-packing houses were located there. The total investment in Florida citrus at that time was $300 million, earning an annual gross of about $30 million. So a great deal stood at stake. If the fly escaped the state and got into the country at large even greater financial loss would have resulted — something in the neighborhood of an almost $2 billion investment, producing an annual income of about $240 million — very big money in those days. All the fruit of over a thousand groves was destroyed, plus all host fruits and vegetables within a mile of those places. Spraying covered everything within ten miles of each infested area. All fruit was carefully watched by inspectors from tree through packing plant to shipment. All shipments out of the area were sterilized by temperatures just below freezing or by heat to kill all stages of whatever flies might have been overlooked. Trucks and trains carrying fruit had to be screened; all highway traffic was thoroughly inspected. From May through December of that year 2,670,994 vehicles were stopped for searching (28,850 contained fruit and vegetables hosting the terrible fly); 1,773,446 pieces of tourists' baggage were looked into. There was some irresponsible smuggling, but on the whole the citizenry behaved honorably. Before the campaign was over, inspectors had cast their eyes on almost fifty million trees (and incidentally killed more than two thousand rattlesnakes in the process), destroyed about two hundred thousand boxes of citrus fruit, and sprayed about two million acres.

In April 1930, the anniversary of the popularly called Medfly's first appearance in Florida, Congress made another appropriation

of a bit more than $3 million, and appointed a three-man Federal
Fruit Fly Board composed of distinguished entomologists to be in
charge of what further work had to be done. Only a few more
scattered infestations came to light, and the entomologists turned
their attention (and the money) to wilder sections of the state, to
make sure that the insect hadn't just gone off to breed on wild
fruits to develop and then return strong for another attack on the
citrus belt. They combed the whole of southern Florida, including
the swampy Everglades and remote islands that could only be
reached by canoes paddled by Seminole Indians. Six hundred inspectors searched everywhere, and sent to the laboratory at Orlando 140,579 specimens of larvae that seemed suspicious — but
not a single one was a Mediterranean fruit fly larva. The last two
living pupae of the fly were found under an orange in St. Augustine
on July 26, 1930. And that was the end of the great Florida Mediterranean fruit fly panic of 1929, which set off this country's first
great eradication program and is still remembered as one of the
most spectacular.

The fruit fly (family Drosophila) is not all bad. On the positive
side it has been used extensively in genetics research to help un-
ravel many baffling mysteries of heredity. It is an exceptionally fine
research insect because thousands can be reared in a small space
and require a minimum of laboratory care. The fruit fly completes
a generation in ten days, whereas with other lab animals, having
much longer life cycles, there is a limit to the number of generations that one scientist is physically able to study. This little fly,
also known as the wine-and-vinegar fly, is much admired by wine-
makers for spreading spores of yeast in grapes and making fermen-
tation possible.

Many flies provide food for other animal life, and the self-
sacrifice of some helps to maintain our fresh-water fish population.
Certain flies prey on harmful insects, feed on chiggers and other
persistent pests, and help to get rid of decaying animal carcasses by
devouring them.

By human standards the fly has been evolving for quite a long
time, but alongside such veterans as the cockroach and the croco-

dile it is a neophyte, hardly dry yet behind the ears. Harold Ol-droyd has pointed out to us that up until 1850 man was only one of the ecological factors that determined the slow evolution of the Diptera, and he states further: "Zoologists at the present time are keenly aware that we have discovered organic evolution just at the time when our own activities are putting a stop to it in many directions, or at least violently altering its course. Some have said that future evolution lies in the mind." In the last century during which man, with great and often misguided vigor, has been altering the face of the earth, no fly family has escaped the wrath of his powerful insecticides. In the future they no doubt will reduce and possibly eliminate most bloodsucking flies, although it is possible that eradication of one species will only help to create another.

The wanton destruction of wildlife now going on all over the world (so few gunners are really sportsmen) likely will hasten the end of the horrible horseflies; drainage will contribute to their demise, for they breed in mud and damp soil. If the newly-independent African nations are able to stand firmly on their own feet politically and industrially, then the tsetse fly soon will be permanently on its way out. Advanced hygiene will help defeat the housefly, but as common modern man is such a wasteful creature and a hopelessly careless and inconsiderate slob, it is likely that there always will be plenty of breeding material for these flies. And certainly the tough little fruit fly will not go down easily to defeat by man.

Insecticides and chemical sterilants will get stronger, more lethal, and perhaps radiation will be turned more extensively on flies, but who is to say how selective these advanced methods of insect murder will be? Will they confine themselves to the harmful creatures they are meant to control or will they — as small confining wars sometimes do — get out of hand and strike down our vegetation, our birds and harmless insects, as well as man himself? It's something that upset author Rachel Carson very much, and in turn her book *Silent Spring* stung the authorities so sharply that the United States Congress House Appropriations Subcommittee on Agriculture felt it necessary to release a reassuring report in rebuttal to Miss Carson's warnings that pesticides were being applied so indiscriminately that they endangered human beings, animals, and plant life. Yet, for all the official disagreement with Miss Carson's thesis, only a month following her death in 1964, President Johnson signed legislation strengthening federal controls over the sale of poisonous pesticides widely used on ranches, farms, and in homes.

No doubt in spite of insecticides the fly will outlast man. There will be flies feasting on our remains as the last human organism disintegrates. The carrion may be lethally radiated, but still the fly will enjoy at least a half hour more of life on earth than man. Perhaps flies deep in a tropical jungle will not be affected when the Great Society's big-daddy bomb falls, will never know or care what happened to man, and simply go on living in the steam and ooze blissfully as before, to be on tap to greet whatever new, mutated, grotesque forms of life survive the atomic holocaust or develop from its stinking rubble.

The Ant

Puritan files
march without levity
bumpy millennia,
stepping in brevity —
gravely scramble
time-pocked miles.

On straight-faced ride
athwart toward squash
hard vessels guard
their souls, awash.
Each wet inside:
sweet serious slosh.

3

Busy, but Mostly Dizzy: *The Ant* A cockroach seems handsome only to another cockroach, and, while most of us tolerate flies and envy their aeronautical skills, they are not usually regarded as the most beautiful creatures in the world. I don't find ants overly attractive either, yet whenever entomologists begin talking about the ant, they usually make glowing reference to its voluptuousness, dwelling particularly on its "petite neck and trim little waist." From the way they run on you'd think every ant is a Sophia Loren, or at least a Mae West or Lillian Russell. I don't get that impression at all. To me, the average female ant looks like a sack tied in the middle.

Mark Twain called ants "the dumbest of all animals," and I'm inclined to agree. I'm fed up with hearing about the honest virtues, industry, and nobility of the ant. To me, he's a slob pure and simple — unregenerate, ignoble, inefficient, immoral, and mediocre. I stand ready to strike back, but except for Twain and the professional exterminators, I guess I stand practically alone.

Any self-conscious modern corporation would envy the kind of public relations enjoyed by the family of ant, Formicidae of the order Hymenoptera, which has more members than any other insect group (there are some fifteen thousand known species of ants, with several hundred being discovered and identified each year).

While other insects — many of them much less harmful and hateful — scurry about in fear of life and limb, the ant leads a charmed existence, protected by its beatific patina and safeguarded by deeply rooted superstitions. (Doesn't everyone know that stepping on an ant brings on rain, arthritis, and belly cramps — not necessarily in that order or all at the same time — or breaks your mother's back?)

To most householders some insects are as fearful as a plague, and all types are revolting to some degree. The ant alone escapes general opprobrium and is universally respected as a paragon of propriety and nobility. About the only time people get annoyed with ants is at picnics. When ants try to hustle the deviled eggs, potato chips, and bologna sandwiches, when they get to sliding down the dill pickles and wading through the mayonnaise, then the most devout ant lover turns on them.

However, discounting picnics, ant enthusiasts are fierce in their allegiance. A man who will sweep a spider from its laboriously constructed web, or who will take up rolled newspaper to stalk a fly for ten intense minutes around a living room, will walk tippy-toe about an anthill to avoid inconveniencing a single one of its occupants. Kids who think nothing of sticking pins in butterflies or their mothers wouldn't dream of impaling an ant, decapitating it, or splitting one in two. A housewife who screams bloodymurder at the first threatening tremor of a cockroach's antennae will contentedly watch ants trundle cake crumbs across her pantry for hours on end, and will successfully stave off all attacks on the safari by her annoyed husband. ("Let them alone, dear; they're so cute, and they probably have hungry little mouths to feed.")

Once out in Montana I was surprised in a rude roadside hash house when a rangy, lank-jawed cowboy, upon casually brushing an ant from the lunch counter, was admonished by a burly truck driver seated on the next stool. "Don't you know, mister," he said with an aggrieved expression, "that if you so much as even *tetch* any part of an ant you cripple him for life?" The cowboy said he was sorry, but I think this was only because the trucker was bigger than he was. I kept quiet, because I was wearing a straw hat and sunglasses. After the complainant had left, the cowboy explained, "I wasn't a'tall sorry for that sunabitchin' ant. She was a'goin' for my pecan pie."

As an indication of how some people can get carried away by the comparison of ants to humans, I cite an excerpt from *Walden*, by the poet-naturalist Henry David Thoreau (first published in 1854), concerning a battle between ants that he witnessed: "I should not have wondered by this time to find that they'd had their respective musical bands stationed on some eminent chip, and playing their national airs the while, to excite the slow and cheer the dying combatants. I was myself excited somewhat even as if they had been men. The more you think of it, the less the difference. And certainly there is not the fight recorded in Concord history, at least, if in the history of America, that will bear a moment's comparison with this, whether for the numbers engaged in it, or for the patriotism and heroism displayed. For numbers and for carnage it was an Austerlitz or Dresden. Concord Fight! Two killed on the patriots' side, and Luther Blanchard wounded! Why here every ant was a Buttrick — 'Fire! for God's sake fire!' — and thousands share the fate of Davis and Hosmer. There was not one hireling there. I have no doubt that it was a principle they fought for, as much as our ancestors, and not to avoid a three-penny tax on their tea; and the results of this battle will be as important and memorable to those whom it concerns as those of the battle of Bunker Hill, at least." Amen. That's the kind of jolly bloodthirsty prose that gets people to march willingly into foolish battle against each other.

Approval of the ant is not something dreamed up for kicks by the fantasy chasers of the pop-op generation. Since ancient times the ant has been acclaimed for its wisdom and cradled indulgently as the possessor of pristine character. Solomon in Proverbs (30: 24–28) mentions the ant as one of four things "which are little upon the earth, but they are exceeding wise." (The others: conies, "a feeble folk, yet they make their houses in the rocks"; locusts, who "have no king, yet they go forth all of them by bands"; and the spider, who "taketh hold with her hands, and is in kings' palaces.")

Some old-time advocates of the ants bald-facedly claimed astronomical knowledge for these insects and insisted that they observed holidays; Pliny went even further, crediting them with regular market days. He also lauded ants for honoring their dead with funeral rites similar to those of humans (including coffins fashioned of empty husks or follicles of certain seeds). Others among these early chroniclers claimed that ants had labor unions and told of having witnessed bargaining sessions among ants in which segments of earthworms and various seeds were used for barter.

If you can believe those keepers of myrmecological records, ants' morality was blameless, for did they not have a sense of shame that required yielding to passion only in darkness and never on days set aside for labor? And was not idleness punished severely, sometimes by sentence of death? And did not ants hate cicadas because they spent summers singing? And were not dormice despised for slumbering all the winter?

Back in 1634, an English physician named Thomas Muffet, in the second book of a two-volume work entitled *Insectorum sive Minimorum Animalum Theatrum* (more commonly known as *Theater of Small Animals*), wrote a paean to the ant that makes the Boy Scout credo sound like the Pledge of Allegiance to the Mafia: "Since, therefore (to wind up all in a few words) they the Ants are so exemplary for their great piety, prudence, justice, valour, temperance, modesty, charity, friendship, frugality, perseverance, industry, and art; it is no wonder that Plato, in Phaedone, hath determined that they who without the help of philosophy have led a civill life by custom or from their own diligence, they had their souls from Ants, and when they die they are turned to Ants again."

The most familiar ancient reference to the sagacity of the ant is the admonition of Solomon, son of David and King of Israel, in Proverbs 6:6–8: "Go to the ant, thou sluggard; consider her ways, and be wise: which having no guide, overseer, or ruler, provideth her meat in the summer, and gathereth her food in the harvest."

The truth is, ant intelligence is highly overrated. Measured by mankind's standards, very little ant action can be classified as intelligent. Ant communities are said to be the insect world's nearest approach to human civilization, and there are undeniable resemblances — notably in the methods of garnering food and in the nurturing and protection of the young — yet the highly complex community activities of ants are carried on blindly. Logical, reasoned behavior as we know it scarcely exists in insect life, and the ant is no exception to the norm. In the realm of the ant, there are no foreglimpses, in the human context, of events to come.

Nor do ants have the marvelous mystical ability so often accredited to them by antophiles. Seemingly astonishing ant feats usually are found to have prosaic explanations. Much of an ant's mystifying behavior is merely the result of unreasoning, inflexible response to stimuli.

It is true that ants are able to learn and remember (they've been known to negotiate a maze with as many as ten false turns), and to correct mistakes to a degree, but even these dim glimmers of a lurking intellect usually are thwarted by monstrous hidebound behavior patterns that emphasize this insect's inherent stupidity. They are often trapped by their narrow inflexible outlook. Much as I hate to disillusion starry-eyed anthropomorphists, the soul, as humans understand the term, simply is not present in the social colonies of the ant.

The ant, however, does have a remarkable nervous system that differs drastically from that of most other insects. Instead of having two distinct masses of fused nerve ganglia in the head (front mass acting as brain; second mass controlling mouth parts), the ant is blessed by one large union of the two masses — a single organ that possibly increases the ant's capacity to learn. One factor that certainly benefits the ant considerably is its ability to live long enough to learn from experience (workers sometimes live up to seven years and queens for fifteen).

Our concept of freedom is one of which ants are unaware. Ants passively accept their lowly station in the animal kingdom and never try to escape their bondage. When handled by humans, they may bite at first, but soon cease struggling.

Ants are ignorant of faith, hope, and especially charity. One ant seldom will help another in peril; tenderness to those in distress is not the general rule. The sick and dying are summarily booted out of the community. Sometimes the dead are served up as ungarnished cold cuts.

Ants practice segregation by classes — and even by body odors. In fact, recognition of one's fellow workers is reduced to a matter of physical contact or smell. Conversation, as ants know it, consists of mutual pecking of abdomen or thorax, and of batting each other with antennae, forelegs, or skull.

In some cases, among the more highly developed ants, scent trails to aid searchers for newly located food caches are laid down by scout ants pressing their abdomens momentarily to the ground to leave a scent that lingers only for a few moments. But such perspicacious behavior is unusual. Mostly ants return to the nest not, as many ant observers believe, to proclaim specifically to the stay-at-homes news of food finds but simply to act so utterly goofy — running about like mad, pecking and slapping antennae about, sometimes even swinging into a jaws-agape ant version of the Watusi — that the mob finally gets the idea that something must be up, God knows what. So they all hop to and jump into their particular chores — nest repairing, feeding the brood, kissing the queen, sweeping out, washing dishes . . . who knows? They scurry crazily, bumping, tripping, falling all over themselves. Some of the more nutty ants spurt out of the nest in panic and scatter in all directions, and a few of these deserters inevitably stumble by accident upon the food source that excited the scout. After a hundred million years that's how ants go about getting in their provisions. You call that smart?

Yet everyone thinks that they're such energetic little devils, and why can't a man be more like an ant? In an unpublished manuscript, *Historia des Fourmis* written about 1742 and now in the archives of the Academy of Sciences of Paris, France, René Antoine Ferchault de Réaumur hits this virtuous nail on the head: "Although we may not always have occasion to praise the ants, we are as a rule well-disposed towards them — we have for them none of those aversions that are rather frequently entertained to so many other insects. One of the virtues most useful to a society is the love of labor; we love men who toil and we incline to love small animals that toil to a degree which we should like to see shown by all men."

Why the hurry? Where has all that fuss and fume gotten ants in the past one hundred million years? Really, they've not advanced one iota. Mammoths, mastodons, and dinosaurs reached heights of glory before they took their inevitable nosedive; ants, however, just went on being ants — prosaically from morn to midnight, day by day, year after year. Dullsville. According to myrmecologists, an ant today looks and acts just about like an ant did back when birds had teeth and horses were no bigger than foxes.

The ant somehow managed, through the most severe and violent earth changes, to continue placidly nurturing its young and avoiding annihilation by its enemies. Okay — so ants survived. I say it's not enough. Why reward zero progress?

Ants aren't really the energetic producers they seem to be. To my knowledge, no ant colony has ever been subjected to a modern time-motion study. I'm surprised that no one has applied for a large juicy grant to undertake this. I'm sure the results would prove revealing. Around our house alone from time to time, I've noted dozens of lazy ants.

Casual observers who claim that ants post sentinels to guard their homes and surrounding territories are wrong. The supposed watchers at outposts really are just ants that have managed to slip away from the slavery of the nest to indulge themselves in rest. The reason they remain motionless for hours is not because of vigilance.

They're asleep. Their only value to the community when thus disposed is that some invader might possibly stumble over them and thereby set up an alarm.

Whatever successful completion there is of ant projects is due in large measure to the peculiar sexy system ants have of working together. It is called trophallaxis, meaning "exchange of nourishment." Ants dart about constantly licking one another in order to trade food particles and glandular excretions. Ants from the same nest, upon meeting, exchange licks and loving antennae strokes, and often pass, from mouth to mouth, droplets of fluid dredged up from a social stomach known as the crop. The queen of a colony is forever being groomed by licking, though she never goes anywhere. Her eggs and nesting larvae receive even more careful attention from the workers' tongues.

All this promiscuous tongue-lapping seems to establish a common bond among the colony's diverse, scatterbrained inhabitants, and generates a lot of interest between the worker ants, their queen, her brood, and each other. It is believed by some ant authorities that a sort of social hormone thus is circulated through the colony, and that somehow it regulates the proportion of worker and soldier ants, and quite possibly that of males and females. But I fail to see how this would work what with everybody kissing everybody else so indiscriminately. It's probably just some sort of lubrication system, because it must be pretty gritty and dusty down in an ant nest.

Leadership certainly is required for such harum-scarum creatures to get their work divided and tasks distributed among themselves, and for them to be able to act in concert as they do. But these leaders are not the dictator types commonly attributed to ants. They do not go about barking orders and circulating authoritarian memos. Work is instituted by the example of a few veteran ants who, even after a winter's hibernation, hold onto certain memories of foraging grounds and trails. These ants act as work starters or excitement centers. By doing their jobs better and quicker than the other ants, they act as stimuli to them. By the same token is work concluded: when the work starter tires, the others cease to get a charge from him and drift off from the task at hand. It is begun again only when the stimulator ant decides to get back to it.

I'm not really surprised that such an enticing system of sensual reward had to be devised in order to keep ants on the job, for ant labor is the worst kind of drudgery and the communal social life of an ant colony is dreary indeed. Fun and games are alien to ants. Toil lasts from sunup until well after dark and an ant seldom enjoys a moment of solitude. Seven days a week it's nothing but work, work, work — dismal grubbing, exhausting and back-torturing, in stuffy subterranean chambers and crude narrow galleries. And don't forget that to an ant the smallest chip of wood looms as a heavy beam does to us; a grain of sand becomes a boulder. To an ant the hairs on a man's arm must look like a forest of one-inch twisted steel cables. And always there is that fat queen to be catered to with tongue-licking and stuffing with hard-to-get goodies. And her myriad of freshly laid eggs (some inconsiderate queens turn out a fresh batch every few minutes) must be taken care of — stacked and constantly moved around to take advantage of whatever warmth becomes available as the sun moves from dawn to dusk. Lo, the poor ant.

It's a singularly dull life, and nowhere is it better demonstrated than among the clodhoppers of antdom, the farmers, those ants called leafcutters that cultivate special sorts of fungus from temperate Argentina north to as far as New Jersey in the States. Leafcutter ants endlessly strip trees of leaves and carry them, whole or in segments, back to the immense underground nesting chambers, by holding the bits overhead as though they were banners of a picket line. In a single night these ants can defoliate quite a large tree; they are one of the most serious of tropical pests. Leafcutters do not feed upon the leaves but chew them into a spongy mulch (also occasionally made with rose petals, sliced grapefruit, and rotting oranges), on which fungus strands grow. When their ends are bitten off by the ants, knobby lumps having myriads of tiny nodules are produced which are used as food by the adult ants and also as nutriment for the developing ant broods. The more brazen of ant idolators have the nerve to refer to these cauliflower-like heads as mushrooms, but I certainly wouldn't want them broiled up and served to me on a steak.

Constant action by worker ants is necessary for the continuing success of the fungus crop, as the garden's growth seems to depend upon the ants' saliva, believed to contain an antibiotic that inhibits undesirable weed fungi and also encourages the proper kind. Without the aid of its ant crop-workers, the fungus gardens perish. Every young prospective queen, upon setting forth on her nuptial flight to establish a new colony, carries in a pouch beneath her mouth a tiny pellet of the authentic fungus to be used in starting fresh cultures at the new location which she will select after her mating.

The two genera of leafcutters containing the largest individuals are *Acromyrmex* and *Atta* (popularly called the parasol ant). Leafcutter ants all are characterized by long spindly legs, each terminating in a pair of hooks which are used for tree climbing and for anchoring while harvesting operations are being conducted.

A good-sized leafcutter colony might be populated by several million ants. Multiple nest entrances — often each as large as a man's fist — for such a sizable congregation may be spread over an area of more than a hundred square yards. A really active nest about three years old could boast nearly a thousand entrances, with passages often descending as much as twenty feet and terminating in chambers the size of a footlocker. Since there is little competition for the raw material of their fungus gardens, leafcutter ants comprise one of the most peaceable segments of the largely bellicose world's ant population.

People really don't notice how savage ants are. Because they are so small and cute and have such slim waists, they can get away with most anything. However, no other insect is as aggressive as the ant; no creature in all the animal kingdom is more pugnacious, ruthless, or ferocious. Ants do terrible things to each other.

Decapitation is their favorite form of annihilation and ants are well equipped for it with powerful saw-toothed jaws that operate laterally. The word "ant" literally means "the cutter-off"; it traces back through Middle English *ante*, which derived from Old English *aemete*, akin to Old High German *ameiza* (a for off, *mezian*, to cut — i.e., to cut off).

Ants seem always girded for warfare — ready to take on any marauding ants that dare invade their nests or foraging territories, and just as eager to head out on plundering expeditions of their own. In battle, besides chomping off heads, they blind opponents with acid sprays; bite, and then squirt poison into the wounds; and pierce enemies' brains, thus paralyzing the nervous systems. Mostly, ant grapples with ant, mandible to mandible, though sometimes the fighting expands to interlocked groups of six, eight, or ten warriors. The odd thing about most ant skirmishes is that the battling stops at nightfall; the warriors return to their respective homes, to begin afresh the following day at dawn.

Ants indulge in other crimes besides war. There are those that steal food from other varieties of ants and kidnap their larvae and pupae — either for eating or enslavement. So-called robber ants (*Solenopsis fugas*) live in the walls of other larger ants' galleries — much as mice live in peoples' houses — and conduct raids on their hosts' nurseries, carrying off helpless larvae for food. A noted British entomologist wrote charmingly of them: "It is as if we had small dwarfs harbouring behind the wainscoting of our homes and every now and again carrying off some of our children into their horrid dens."

The sanguinary ants (*Formica sanguinea*) are slave raiders. They invade territories of peaceful ants to rob them of pupae which they carry off to be reared as enslaved workers.

The Amazon ants of Europe and the Americas (*Polyergus kufescens*) were forced to become ant kidnapers because while their peculiar jaws, shaped like scimitars, make a wonderful fighting weapon they are utterly useless for doing domestic work, breaking up food, or feeding the young. The Amazons therefore must depend upon captured gray ants to do this necessary work for them.

An especially vicious predator is the pregnant queen of the North African executioner ants. When ready to produce her brood, she sweeps grandly into the throne room of a colony of

Nigerian ants, mounts the back of their queen, and proceeds to spend the weekend sawing away on the royal cranium. When the attacked queen finally succumbs, her reign is considered terminated, and the intruder then is acclaimed the new and rightful ruler. The workers now fall all over themselves to pay licking homage and begin attending to her burgeoning babies. The queens of Argentine ants (Iridomyrmex humilis), in order to usurp the thrones of their rivals, the fire ants, gang up on them for a veritable orgy of head severing.

The most horrifying of all ants are the bulldogs (Odontomachus, subfamily Ponerinae) of Australia and the Solomon Islands. They are monsters, with interlocking jaws that look like matched claws of a pair of hammers. Because they are loners, the bulldogs are not dreaded nearly as much as the army ants of Central and South America (Eciton vastator and E. erratica) which travel in great swarms, ruthlessly through jungle forests — engulfing, overwhelming, dismembering, and devouring every living thing in their onrushing path. Even more formidable are the driver ants (Anomma arcene, or Dorylus) of India and tropical Africa, the males of which customarily measure more than an inch, head to tail. These voracious ants have no permanent homes, but live off the land.

Army and driver ant columns, often a foot broad and three hundred feet in length, containing hundreds of thousands of individuals, advance about 150 yards every eight hours, a murderous carpet laying waste the forest floor, spreading terror in its aisles, in thicket tangles, across swamps, up and down steep ravines, and along the tenuous bridges of vines. Only those arboreal denizens that can take to the air or scurry far enough above the sweeping attack are safe from it.

Even such forest fiends as tarantulas, rats, claw-pinched scorpions, and wolf spiders are caught up in the onslaught, to be suffocated and torn limb from socket. Serpents as long as four feet have been killed by driver ants; they can cripple a good-sized python if that reptile giant becomes entrapped just after a feeding when it is sluggish. There is no escape from these ant belligerents; they fear nothing. Although nearly blind, their senses of touch and smell are so acute that they can perceive the slightest movement. Unattended babies are not safe from the voracious raiders; rivers are no barrier to them. To cross streams, they either make pontoon-like bridges of their bodies or form themselves into a huge living ball, with queen and larvae at center, which floats until solid ground is reached. The Japanese have probably never set eye on these vicious ants. Their ideogram representing the ant is made up of the character for insect combined with those signifying unselfishness, justice, and courtesy. So solly.

Just as with armies devised by human beings, these armies of ants have their camp followers who profit from the spoils. Always close to the advancing horde are such freeloaders as the anole lizard, the ant bird, the parasitic fly, the stink bug, and the velvet ant, which actually is a wasp.

In bivouac the army and driver ants hang in a seething cluster nest of bodies protected within a hollow tree or simply dangling from a tree limb. The queen is ensconced in this ball's center and access to her is through tunnels walled by the inert bodies of common soldier ants.

The queen is *raison d'être* for the whole business; if anything happens to her, the colony perishes, for with her gone the colonists lose their purpose in life, which is to keep her royal highness stuffed with food, well groomed, protected, and to tend to the feeding of her ever hungry larvae. The queen lays all the colony's eggs in enormous batches upwards of twenty-five thousand a week at intervals of about a month, producing ten broods annually. It is this reproductive cycle that determines the rhythm of the colony —a pattern consisting of a nomadic raiding phase of about two weeks, during which the army stays each night in a different place, and a dormant period, lasting about three weeks, when the campsite remains fixed. At that time the larvae which the army has been transporting and feeding begin to spin their cocoons. Ant larvae never eat while pupating; the pupa stage is one long sleep. So now, while waiting for the queen to push out more eggs, there is no one to feed but the adult ants, and the raiding diminishes. As the batch of new recruits starts being born, emerging from mummylike wrappings, the young exude some delectable secretion that greatly stimulates the older ants and sets them off on another stretch of marching and serious pillaging which lasts until the new, most recently born larvae are ready to enter the cocoon phase of their lives. This brings on another static period which lasts until the exudations of these latest emerging marauders stimulate the depredating colony again to be on the move.

Army ants are given more credit for intelligence than they deserve, just as army humans are. What appears to be brilliant insect generalship really is the result of an undisciplined mob of ants muddling through. On the face of it, the marshaling of an ant troop seems to parallel the orderly assemblage of human warriors: the largest huge-jawed ants in the fore and on the flanks (the killers); behind them, the medium-sized worker ants (the administrators and quartermaster corps); and, in the center, the smallest workers transporting the brood (the big brass and homefronters). But studious observation has indicated that the more murderous members of this ant mob have not been placed deliberately at the front and sides of the mass, nor have they come there of their own volition — they've been pushed there simply because of their inability to find footing among the overwhelming numbers of the bustling surge of lesser ants.

Nor are the army ants' flanking movements, so much admired by human militarists, the result of astute generalship. The ants in the foreground (often called "skirmishers" by those who still view war romantically or cynically as a source of financial gain) make brief sallies — never more than a few inches — into the scent-free territory ahead, which has not yet been affected by the chemical trail laid down by anal excretions of the advancing horde as it lumbers on. Now, when the pressure behind becomes too great, these forefront explorers are pushed to one side or the other, thus inadvertently forming flank movements. The continual branching and rebranching of the forces, if appraised in human terms, therefore is due not to ferocity, but actually to timidity.

This system of the so-called skirmishers, of dashing out and scurrying back, subsequently to be pushed to left or right, sometimes results in a milling swarm as much as fifty feet across, which has the advantage of being able to surround prey completely, allowing it to be overcome by the ants following and to be utilized for the common good. In the irregular terrain of a tropical forest it is unlikely that the ant army's advance units would ever make full circle and join up with its own column's rear, but this happens sometimes in unobstructed territory. Then the ants, slavishly following the circular trail, continue to march and march and march, their pace becoming slower and slower, dizzier and dizzier, until finally they all succumb to weakness and die.

In the United States, we have army ants called American legionaries. They differ from true army ants of the tropics inasmuch as they do not move about in masses but run swiftly in single file, and remain in their bivouacs for much longer times. They too live by knocking off their fellow insects, but the cadavers to be used as food are put into storage and are carried along on moves, which usually are made at night under the protection of leaves borne aloft like flags. Like their foreign counterparts, these domestic warmongers also are almost blind.

One of the worst ant pests en masse in North America is the imported fire ant (*Solenopsis geminata* from South America), an especial nuisance of our southern states. Its abode is an earthen mound about one foot high and two across the base; an infested acre often holds from twenty to sixty of these hillocks, with approximately 100,000 ants occupying each one. The mounds make the harvesting of hay and grain very difficult by causing damage to farm machinery. The ants themselves add their own inimitable misery by giving field workers and livestock venomous double-barreled bites that are, according to one victim, "like getting stuck with a red-hot needle."

Fire ants first turned up in 1918 at Mobile, Alabama, but until 1957, although they had spread to 170 counties in nine Southern states, no one seemed particularly concerned about them as a menace to crops, livestock, or people. Then in that year the United States Department of Agriculture surprisingly selected the fire ant as a prime villain and launched a massive campaign of calumny against it, which resulted in the announcement of an eradication program that ultimately would treat some twenty million Southern states' acres with a blanket spray of the chemicals dieldrin and heptachlor, both relatively new and untried at that time. The overall cost was to be about $7 billion.

The results of the spraying were not all that everyone had hoped they would be. One Alabama official characterized the spray program as "a glaring example of riding roughshod over the responsibilities of other public and private agencies." Miss Rachel Carson became so aroused that in her startling book *Silent Spring* she locked horns with the federal government in an unmerciful attack on the fire ant program. She charged it with being ill conceived, lacking in elementary preliminary investigation of the lethal effects of the chemicals on wildlife and livestock, and excessively expensive ($3.50 per acre, as opposed to 23 cents per acre, the reputed cost of a 95 percent control method advocated by the state of Mississippi's Agricultural Experiment Station). She also claimed that the central government agency had deceived the public by diminishing the damaging effects on agriculture by the fire ant and by exaggerating its menace to human life and livestock health. She questioned whether the dangers of the fire ant merited the outlay of such a huge expenditure of federal funds since the insect hadn't even been mentioned in the USDA's 1957 bulletin of recommendations for the control of insects attacking crops and livestock, nor had it rated more than a brief paragraph in the official encyclopedic yearbook for 1952 (still the agency's bible on insects), which features a color-plated section of seventy-two insects entitled, "Some Important Insects."

Miss Carson's brouhaha eventually accomplished reforms, for today there is no more indiscriminate mass spraying of fire ants, and the principal chemical weapon used against them is a delayed-toxic-action concoction called Mirex bait, which worker ants imbibe and then carry into their colonies for fatal distribution to the queen and her larvae. This new chemical is not harmful to humans, animals, birds, fish or bees, and it leaves no deleterious residue in milk, meat, or crops.

The worst household damagers among ants in this country are the carpenter ants (*Camponotus herculeanus pennsylvanicus* — a ridiculous name). They are audacious, shiny black demons that slyly chew their way into timbers of houses and barns, pergolas, garage doors, fence posts, wooden shingle roofs, garden benches, porch swings, logs, dead trees, chair and table legs, conversation pits, newel posts, pianos, telephone poles, bridge supports, bass fiddles, tennis rackets, Ping-Pong paddles, beached boats, and, for all I know, the wooden legs of retired New England whaling captains. Many a verandah railing, pillar, and supporting beam has been converted into a hollow shell of its former stalwart self by this ant's partiality for apartments gnawed out of wood.

As a small boy, luckily I was present on the morning when the floor of our backyard outhouse gave way to inroads made by carpenter ants. The borough's tax assessor — named, I happen to remember, August Heinrich Breitenbacher, a big fat fellow — happened to be occupying it at the time, attending to what my parents used to refer to as "a hurry call." My Scottish grandfather, who occupied a little cottage behind our home, also was an interested observer of the disaster; its memory brightened his declining days considerably, and my father considered the tax rise he had to suffer well worth it.

These unprincipled wretches (carpenter ants, not tax assessors) actually are more evil than termites, which once mistakenly were called "white ants" (they are not members of the ant-wasp-bee order, but belong to the order Isoptera). Carpenter ants do not consume the excavated wood as termites do, but simply spit out the shreds after carrying them from the chambers under construction.

Another annoying ant pest of city and town is the pavement ant, which also has a tongue-twister entomological name all out of proportion to its tiny size — *Acanthomyops tetramorium caespitum*. It undermines sidewalks, concrete steps, garage and basement cement floors, and spends its finest hours demoralizing the cement slabs of that twentieth century blight of our countryside, the suburban development house. These ants lay off wood, but do considerable damage to gardens by attacking seeds, roots, stems of vegetables and root crops. Once dug in, these slab-sappers are the very devil to evict.

Not all ants are such tough customers. Some are rather gentle souls. Among the nicer ants is an innocuous acrobat ant who flips into a headstand whenever danger threatens.

Another meek ant (*Myrmecina larreillii*) never attacks anything and scarcely defends itself even when its nest is invaded, but just rolls into a little ball and pretends it isn't there. There are small bullying ants, delightfully called *Crematogasters*, that threaten other ants with the poisonous tips of their abdomens but seldom follow through with the kayo jab. These wood ants live in hollowed trees and employ a doorman who keeps the door opening closed by filling it with the top of his head; to be recognized for admission, residents must make prearranged signal taps on the pate. There are South American rain-forest ants that build tree-hung mudball nests which bloom with flowers. There are weaver ants (the tree ant, *Oecophylla smaragdina* of India) that make their homes of leaves that have been stitched together by silken strands ordinarily used by their larvae for spinning their cocoons. During sewing the thread is squeezed from the larvae by the jaws of adult ants; this action is often heralded as the only use of a tool by an insect. Rather farfetched, I'd say. Ant fanciers will go pretty far to make their insect pet look good. They even call one particular ant, the European red wood ant, a forester, just because it is an especially aggressive insect eater. More than ten thousand colonies of that ant were implanted in almost one hundred test acres of the forests of the German Federal Republic. That government, recognizing the value of these ants to forests, enacted a federal law protecting them as long ago as 1880. The Chinese were the first to use ants for this purpose by protecting orange trees in this manner way back in the thirteenth century.

Among myths and misconceptions in circulation concerning ants is the brash tale that certain ants are dairy farmers, that they herd ant cows. Some ants do tend aphids, which are plant lice and do not look at all like cows — no horns, teats, switching tails, or moos. Aphids are small, soft-bodied, and weak; they are the most defenseless of all insects. But they have one quality that has contributed immeasurably to their survival for millions of years. They suck from plants a fluid, called honeydew, that is compellingly attractive to ants. Aphids always pull up more honeydew than they need and the surplus oozes out at the slightest gentle stroke of an ant's antennae. To protect this source of honeydew, ants have evolved into bodyguards of the aphids and keep them virtual prisoners.

Aphid-tending ants' capacities for animal husbandry have been much exaggerated. They do not herd aphids like cattle. Ants merely discover and exploit the aphid's own propensity for herding. And generally aphids are not put out to pasture by ants. Any ant observed carrying an aphid usually is bringing it back to the nest to be cut up for meat. Nor are the corrals of mud or fiber that ants build to surround their aphid "herds" exclusive to them. Such enclosures are used to protect any ant food morsel. The main purpose of these barricades is to shield the ants themselves against excessive light or heat as they swill the lovely honeydew. Our own bars and cafés are cool and dark for pretty much the same reason. Also, ants do not treat aphids any differently than they treat each other as food sources — extracting droplets of food by tapping and caressing. And aphids are maintained exactly the same as are the ants' own broods.

Regarding aphid honeydew, Pliny, the Roman naturalist, believed nearly two thousand years ago that its summertime showers from trees was either: liquid resulting from air purification; sweat from the toiling of the heavenly gods; or star spit. In those days scientists could get away with anything. Pliny also contended that a giant ant, the size of an Egyptian wolf, was a goldminer in the mountains north of India.

If you are inordinately fond of ants, I suppose even today you could say that there are brewers among them, since some ants, the so-called honeypot ants (*Myrmecocystus*), store sugary liquids obtained from aphids, other insects, and oak galls inside the bodies of fellow ants as reserves against seasonal droughts.

In a honeypot colony the choices of storage tanks are made by accident; any young worker can be selected by any returning forager with its social stomach loaded with nectar. These tank ants, known as repletes or rotunds, are able to distend their tiny abdomens to the size of a small pea, as load after load is poured into them. In Mexican markets repletes are sold by the gallon to be pounded in a mortar, strained, and fermented into a mead that carries a real wallop.

Another ant misconception concerns the harvesters (*Pheidole*, *Messor*, and *Pogonomyrmex*) that depend primarily on seeds as a source of nourishment. Harvester ants do not plant crops, as some ant partisans claim. The rings of plants surrounding some of their lairs result from sprouting seeds which the ants toss out as being unfit to eat. Seeds may be harvested from these plants but that crop is purely accidental. The Texas harvester is the largest, greediest, and most painful biter of them all. The workers of some harvester ants are huge and have powerful jaws, which are not used in fighting but for threshing the gathered seeds.

We are told that men have watched ants more than ants have watched men — told, of course, by men. At one time no proper Anglo-Saxon home was complete without its formicarium. In England, during Victoria's time, the price of "The Lubbock Formicarium; The Nest of the Ambercoloured Meadow Ant," in polished oaken frame, with tripod magnifier included, was sixteen shillings ninepence. The listing of contents makes it seem cheap at twice the price: 1. Apterous Queen with Attendants . . . 2. Princes and Princesses . . . 3. Workers, Major and Minor . . . 4. Drones . . . 5. Eggs, appearing in May . . . 6. Larvae in Various Sizes . . . 7. Cocoons, appearing in July . . . 8. Cow Aphides (Bred, Pastured, and Milked by Dairy Workers) . . . 9. Domestic Pets, including the Blind *Platyarthrus hoffmannsseggii*, the Clavigerid and Lomechusa Beetles, etc. . . . 10. Clearly observable Interior Passages, Chambers, Sanctums, Throne room, Queen's Boudoir, Workers' Dormitories, Lavatory, Kitchens, Pantry, Servants' Quarters, Water Closet, Etc.

It's my theory that people bought formicariums for prurient reasons back in those days, because society then was infinitely more inhibited. Everyone hoped to catch the ants at something salacious or sadomasochistic. But, as a sex spectacle, the formicarium was a dud. An ant's sex life is of the duration and explosive quality of a Fourth of July skyrocket.

Sexually, ants are nothing that could be banned in Boston, although they do make love while airborne, which at least is something. One must be judicious in bruiting about so astonishing a fact. At a dinner party attended recently by folks who've never had to be familiar with ants, an elderly pillar of our community, her hearing-aid batteries running low, thought I'd meant aunts (a-u-n-t-s) and envisioned a sort of Mary Poppins orgy. For a few dreadful moments the good name of my family teetered above the abyss of neighborly ostracism. We could have been drummed out of the PTA or asked to surrender our library card — it was that close.

Ant (a-n-t) copulation is very interesting. On what is called "swarming day" the young winged males and females leave the nest and take to the air, where each encounters a mate and consummates the mating without returning to the ground. On this auspicious day the wingless ants, which are in a vast majority, suffer extreme frustration. Terribly excited, the poor things run along the ground as fast as they can, beating their antennae furiously as they try futilely to become airborne. Many climb to the tops of high grass stems and jump off, hoping against hope that some miracle will occur. It never does. Only the chosen winged few ever make it as Wright brothers.

It is no credit to ant morality that a colony's sex life ends after this one marvelous foray, because once the potential queens are impregnated the males responsible for the deflowering lose their wings and die. During these so-called "nuptial flights" (suicide flights, really, for the unsuspecting males) ants are prey to insectiverous birds, such as martins and swallows, and when the happy couples return to earth their short honeymoons often are cut shorter by the greedy snap of toad or lizard.

After her all-too-brief husband has passed on, as we say (she hardly got to know the bum), the queen settles down to rule over a veritable matriarchy. All the worker ants are sterile females, but there are born into the nest from time to time a few winged females and males, known as drones, the royalty of the nest, who have nothing to do but lounge about, awaiting that momentous day when they will be grown up enough to have their one glorious explosive moment in outer space.

After a queen has had this brush with love, she too loses her wings, and although she may live for over a decade, once she digs in to found a colony she never again ventures aboveground. Truly she is a queen of the underground. But unlike the promiscuous queens of the human underground, she never again consorts sexually with a male (or female either, as long as we insist on comparing ants with humanity). That one mating suffices for life; from then on she just lies back and takes life easy, producing one egg batch after another.

A queen ant must be extremely patient, for sometimes she has to wait eight or nine months before her first eggs grow into useful ants. The initial eggs are small; the queen has to eat some of them in order to stay alive, although some of her food comes from the now useless muscles in her thorax that operated the wings. The first larvae are fed with saliva juices from the queen's mouth. When the callows finally are born they are small, weak, and may live only for a short time. But they're strong enough to dig out of the chamber to forage food for their mistress. Once she gets insect meat and honeydew from the outside world inside her, the queen blossoms and begins laying eggs in earnest. Soon the colony is overrun with healthy adult ants, digging tunnels, carving new rooms, laying floors, hanging wallpaper, and whatever else it is that ants do down there. I wouldn't know. I've never been hooked as an ant watcher.

My favorite practitioner of that futilitarian sport is Lord Avebury, who published a book in 1881, *Ants, Bees, and Wasps.*

The topper of all his experiments was one headed "Behavior to Intoxicated Friends." (I liked it so much better than "Behavior to Chloroformed Friends.") Lord Avebury considered his inebriate experiment extremely difficult.

"It is not in all cases easy," he wrote, "to hit off the requisite degree of intoxication."

A total of ninety-three ants were made drunk by His Lordship. Eventually all of them were tossed by their apparently thoroughly disgusted fellow ants into a bowl of water that thoughtfully had been provided by Lord Avebury.

"The sober ants," noted the distinguished scientist, "seemed somewhat puzzled at finding their inebriated fellow creatures in such a disgraceful condition, took them up and carried them about for a time in a somewhat aimless manner."

To give you some idea of the deadpan style of Lord Avebury's research, I quote from the book part of his carefully kept tables:

November 20 — I experimented with six friends and six strangers beginning at 11.

At 11.30 a friend was carried to the nest
    11.50 a stranger was dropped into the water
    12.30 a stranger was dropped into the water
    12.31 a friend was dropped into the water
     1.10 a stranger was dropped into the water
     1.18 a stranger was dropped into the water
     1.27 a stranger was dropped into the water
     1.30 a friend (partly recovered) was taken to the nest
     2.30 a friend was taken up and carried about until
     2.55 when she was taken to the nest, but at the door the bearer met two other ants, which seized the intoxicated one, carried her off, and eventually dropped her into the water.
     3.35 a friend was carried to the nest.

Out of these 12, five strangers and two friends were dropped into the water; none of the strangers, but three friends, were taken to the nest. None of the friends were brought out of the nest again.

Lord Avebury concluded, "It seems clear, therefore, that even in a condition of insensibility these ants were recognised by their friends."

Many peoples have gone to the ant in the hope of gaining knowledge or special powers. Arabs have a notion that an ant placed in the palm of a newborn baby will make it clever and skillful. The Arawak Indians of northwestern South America put biting ants on their babies to coax them into taking their first steps. In our own Ozarks, a mixture of powdered carpenter ants and lard is rubbed on the legs of infants who are backward in learning to walk. Primitive huntsmen often subject themselves to punitive biting in order to be successful in the chase. Arawak young people cannot take a wife or a husband until they undergo an ordeal in which biting ants imprisoned in a frame between strips of reed matting are placed upon the completely naked body. By enduring this torture stoically, boys are said to become skillful, clever, and industrious; girls acquire strength and willingness to work hard.

Our ancestors used formic acid to treat leprosy and rheumatics; an application of ant eggs (pupae actually) was supposed to prevent beards on women and children, but seldom did. A soaking in horseant oil once was reputed to be good for gout and palsy. To prevent scurvy, woodcutters in Maine used to gulp down alive large black ants found in pine trees (full of vitamin C, no doubt, from chewing on pine needles).

Early medical history contains many references — some dating back to Hindi writings as early as 1000 B.C. — to the use of ants in closing incisions and for suturing. In making a suture the jaws of ants are directed so as to clamp shut the open edges of a wound; then the bodies are snipped off leaving the saw-toothed jaws firmly attached until the wound heals. This simple clamp-stitching still is used by primitive peoples who are far from clinic or hospital.

"The ants' most dangerous enemies are other ants," wrote Auguste Forel, a psychiatrist and pioneer observer of ant behavior, "just as man's most dangerous enemies are other men."

But aside from the perils posed by their own kind, ants are troubled by many other creatures. In Britain there is the green woodpecker, or yaffle, whose long sticky darting tongue has spelled doom for scads of ants. In the tropics there are the toothless mammals called edentates — ant bear, tamandua, and scaly pangolin — waiting to spike ants with their sticky, snakelike tongues. In Africa, the piggish, sharp-clawed aardvark aadores aants. Australia has the echidna, a spiny ant epicure that looks like a hedgehog. A host of other beasts, birds, amphibia, and reptiles dine largely, if not exclusively on ants.

As scavengers, sneak thieves, or honored guests, more than a thousand different kinds of myrmecophilous interlopers infest ant nests — spiders, mites, such insects as tiny cockroaches and silverfish, crustacea, and other arthropods.

But, Auguste Forel to the contrary, people remain the ants' most formidable enemy. We have such big feet, plus the advantage of access to chemical insecticides. If ants interfere in the slightest with man's living comfort, they are in danger of being poisoned out of existence. Still, despite man's exquisitely devised methods of ant murder, the ant goes on surviving.

Even the august United States Department of Agriculture admits that, in spite of the effectiveness of chemical sprays and powders, it is not easy to rid premises of ants. The very first sentence of its Home and Garden Bulletin No. 28, *Ants in the Home and Garden — How to Control Them*, says this: "Find the ants if possible." A little farther on in the text comes this bit of advice: "Next apply an insecticide to the nests, if you can reach them." And later: "Finding a nest inside the house is often difficult. It may even be impossible without removing a wall or floor."

I've never heard of it, but perhaps ant dowsing is called for. Instead of the traditional willow fork a pair of ant antennae possibly could be utilized.

Against ants, besides patience, the USDA recommends chlordane in either an oil or water base. I think the most foolproof way to shake free of pesky ants is to call in a reputable exterminator, preferably one who despises Communists. Just tell him all about the kind of godless lives ants lead underground, never bathing, letting their hair grow long, licking each other all the time and slob-

bering over some big fat queen — and watch him go to work with
enthusiasm.

The least attractive way to be rid of ants is to eat them. Not
many people do. Headhunter Jivaro Indians of Peru guzzle parasol
ants raw; the Jicaques of Central America prefer theirs to be
stewed. Amazon River and Honduran natives pull off legs, heads,
and wings and eat only the bodies — toasted. The most common
method of dealing with ants is simple, if not too efficient. True ant
haters squish them singly, underfoot, though not many people will
own up to such dastardly business. No one wants to be thought of
as a transgressor. Those who do admit it generally consider the act
as an impersonal one, to be regarded in about the same light as that
of an Air Force bombardier triggering a lethal payload onto a populated area: the element of life is too far beneath to be embraced
conscientiously in the killer's ken.

The obliteration of an ant by summary squish is not bloody by
human standards. In fact, most nonscientists believe that ants have
no blood — but they do. The puddle of clear liquid resulting from
an ant squish is not sugar water, gin, or vodka. Although colorless,
it is genuine life's blood. Ants have neither veins nor arteries. The
blood just sloshes about at random. It is not so important to an ant
as to a vertebrate animal, because insects have no lungs, and therefore blood does not serve to oxygenize their tissues, but merely
nourishes and cleanses them.

According to naturalists, who have made countless careful studies under all conditions, nothing that is done physically to an ant
gives it any pain. Apparently, like all other insects, ants suffer only
inconvenience, not agony, from blows or the loss of important organs, and are immune to physical discomfort. Yet, can we be sure
of that? The learned ones have been wrong before and they could
be wrong again. A little-remembered American naturalist, Dr. William B. Long, who used to quarrel with Teddy Roosevelt on nature
problems, once wrote in relation to animal behavior: "All thought
except my own is strange to me; I am never sure of it but can only
infer and then estimate it from the actions of the animal under
observation."

Recently a neighbor of mine who is an ant watcher, but otherwise a rather enlightened fellow, suggested to me that ants are on their way out. There will be no place, he contended, for such foolish energy in the automated, Sybaritic existence into which man is joyfully plunging. Besides, he added, ants set a bad example for our young people because they are socialistic. No ant has private property, everything belongs to every ant, and all work together for the common good.

Soon, continued this churlish fellow, poll takers will decide that ants are a threat to democracy. Then Congress, the Supreme Court, IBM, LBJ, Miss Mekertish of the Telephone Company, the FBI or someone else with sky-limit power and authority — all properly legal, you understand — to alter our pleasant lives, will outlaw ants, and there will follow a super-dusting from the air that will curl your hair, along with the toes of each and every ant in our land, including those mushroom growers twenty feet down. Or maybe, instead, some big-time biologist on a big-time grant will rig up a foolproof wizard way to sterilize queen ants by sending small guided missiles against them during mating time — and that, gentlemen, will be it. No more ants.

"Before that happens," grumbled this crabbed citizen, "I'll turn my TV set into a formicarium; the picture tube is just right for ant viewing. And I'll run a kind of speakeasy Playant Club — only the ants themselves will have to work. Might have to make a few payoffs high up, but I think it could be done okay. Smuggle the ants in from Canada, if necessary. Or Mexico maybe'd be better — livelier ants. Issue membership cards and all, maybe even have pinch-waisted girl waitresses dressed up like ants — if they could pull themselves in with corsets like them Floradora girls. Ant nuts, and people who by then have forgotten what manual labor looks like, and kids who never got to learn what it is could come and watch my ants at work and drink beer. I'd coin a fortune and be on Easy Street in no time at all."

My friend was only half kidding. At the recent World's Fair in New York City an outfit calling itself "The Hall of Free Enterprise" actually set up an exhibition that promoted capitalism by exhibiting two large ant colonies as the horrible example of how not to live. *Socialism!* Even ant antagonists realize that kind of nonsense has got to be unmasked.

True intelligent socialism needn't be like the harsh, plodding, unrewarding life of the ants. With the right guidance, it can help humanity enormously. The great danger in any collective effort is that the strugglers lose their souls. But, if ever ants should be abolished, the powers no doubt will credit this insect's disappearance to its failure at cooperative social living. And soon we'll find ourselves, not obliterated as the ants were, but entrapped as the aphids are — plugged up behind a mud wall, with our precious hard-earned nectars being sapped away by those who have bigger mouths and stronger arms than we have. Step by quiet step, with band-blaring and flag-flapping masking the stealthy maneuvers, we'll be led into entrapment, where our inherent rights of freedom of communication and movement gradually will be eroded. Already, any American faces having his passport revoked if, not fitting into the categories designated as "appropriate" by our State Department (professional journalists, doctors, scientists, scholars traveling to obtain information for public dissemination, Red Cross representatives, and others whose visits "might benefit" the United States, according to one departmental spokesman, Robert J. McCloskey, in a *New York Times* statement) disobediently he travels to some far forbidden corner of this scarey spinning globe to see with his own eyes, to hear and evaluate for himself what's going on, to communicate with brother humans—of possibly some differing skin color or inner credo — in order to learn how they're making out as living beings in their own precious spans of time, possessing loving hearts and minds, families, feelings, and hungry bellies to fill.

Already, some people who dared enter the church of another faction against its unexpressed wishes have been arrested for unlawful entry, unlawful assembly, causing a public nuisance, and conspiring to commit a crime.

Already we have the McCarran Act, a federal law that provides concentration camps in the Southwest deserts for those whom our government thinks are merely *thinking* of conspiracy during a national emergency, a state which can be declared on order of the President alone.

In closing, then, let us all stand and sing one stanza of that venerable hymn, Number 26 in the gray book: "God Bless the Ant, Long May He Abide with Us." We may not approve of his ways, but he has a right to them. Besides, the ant could improve. Survival is fine as far as it goes. I still say it's not enough, but how can anything improve without it? The ant yet may find his soul.

The Pigeon

Who's kept for egg and squab?
You birds are beggared here
and ragged run the gutter —
go legging through the grass.

You blooming puffy bags
of psittacosis!
You gently throbbing nags
crammed with neurosis!

Campfollowers left
by troops in retreat —
abandoned like Jukes —
you chicks of the street!

4

Coos and Boos: *The Pigeon* If you like pigeons — and many otherwise sensible people do — they are reasonably charming, pleasingly
plump feathered things, sleek, with lovely pewter-gray coats and
snowy rumps, an exotic iridescence about neck and head, and eyes
glinting ruby-red. If you dislike pigeons, they are scruffy, ill-
mannered, stinking, voracious scavengers — winged moochers of
the city streets, handout hustlers greedily gobbling curbside leavings or whatever fresh fodder is scattered among them by sentimental misanthropes.

I don't particularly hate pigeons, but I seldom pass one without
wanting to kick its nasty little smug behind. I like even less the
misguided energumens who feed pigeons, for without food they'd
be much less of a public nuisance.

These contemptible birds have a total lack of awareness about
what constitutes proper social behavior. In hideous, cooing, undu-

latory mobs, they waddle stupidly about, fearlessly, even arrogantly; with superb contempt they spatter the pavement with their gooey, filthy, whitish droppings and make park benches uninviting. They flutter aimlessly, shamelessly streaking monuments, the statues of heroes and statesmen, the façades and embellishments of public buildings. Capriciously, they spot motor vehicles and such passing unfortunates as horses, dogs, cats, policemen, and pedestrians. Pigeon droppings even are a minor hazard to aviation — when they unbalance helicopter rotor blades and cause undue motor vibration.

Pigeons have gone so far as to be banned by the New York State Athletic Commission from attending boxing matches in New York City. (This came about because friends of a boxer named Eddie Lynch, who was a pigeon fancier, used to smuggle pigeons into his fights and release them; they wreaked havoc in the cheaper seats near the rafters.)

Musicians at the outdoor symphony concerts at Lewisohn Stadium in New York complained to the city that pigeons were disrupting their morning rehearsals and demanded either a license to trap them or a supply of umbrellas to raise over their music stands.

The pigeon is Urban Pest number one, and cries of outrage against the cosmetic effects of its befoulment eventually reach City Hall, which is where the action starts on pigeon persecution.

The crudest method of assaulting pigeons is by shotgun blast into roosting flocks; it has not been spectacularly successful — although stonemasons and glaziers usually find it stimulating. The most noteworthy of such shotgun forays that I've heard of involved three stalwarts of the Princeton, West Virginia, police force (Sergeant Crotty and patrolmen Belcer and Fralick) using a 410-gauge shotgun, and resulted in an accumulation of 223 pigeon corpses in one weekend — as many as fourteen killed with one burst according to a story in the *Bluefield Daily Telegraph*. Over 50 percent of those Princeton casualties were cut down from the roof of the First Methodist Church, which evidently the pigeons trustingly believed to be out of bounds.

The use of rifles to pick off pigeons one by one has proven a more efficient method of altering pigeon ecology. Buffalo, New York, leads in this more refined *modus operandi*. For the past fifteen years, each morning between 8 and 9:30 A.M. seven sharpshooters, attached to that city's Department of Small Animal and Vermin Control, have gone armed with .22-caliber rifles and an ample supply of lead-ball projectiles, to bring down pigeons taking postprandial naps on building cornices in the business district, which is close to the lakefront where spillage of flour and grain mills greatly attracts the birds.

Boston, Massachusetts, where the first blood of the American Revolution was spilled, undertook eradication of its estimated twenty-five thousand pigeons rather unobtrusively — in a week-long crash program — by scattering corn kernels soaked in a by-product of arsenic. (Powdered strychnine alkaloid mixed with laundry starch also is an excellent pigeon stiffener.) In only three days, from the skies over the baited areas, the Boston & Maine and the New York Central Railroad freight yards and the Port Authority's two grain elevators, six thousand mortally afflicted pigeons plummeted like aircraft shot down in battle. Word was slow getting around, but eventually the rest of Boston's pigeon population got the message and went on a corn-free diet. (Dayton, Ohio, also has used poisoned corn against pigeons.)

Before resorting to poisoning, Boston had tried scaring its pigeons with stuffed owls. Those hard-boiled Scollay Square types didn't bat an eye — they'd seen worse sights at the Old Howard. Doggedly, in relays, they dive-bombed the fake owls, reducing them to feathers and tatters. The Museum of Modern Art in New York City once tried papier-mâché owls as pigeon chasers; the avant-garde thought them divinely chic, and apparently so did the pigeons, who added their own distinguishing pop-art touches. A similarly futile experiment with phoney owls once was made by the city of Indianapolis before it was decided that riflemen were more effective.

Other notable pigeon purges have been carried out in Baltimore, Cleveland, Columbus, Chicago, St. Paul, Denver, San Francisco, and Athens, Georgia. In Mitchell, South Dakota, the problem is

aggravated by that city's famous Corn Palace, an exhibition building whose exterior, completely covered with real corn, barley, and
oats formed into decorative panels, offers a sumptuous banquet for
visiting pigeons and other birds.

Besides being tormented by methods already mentioned, pigeons
have been subjected to supersonic screeches, fireworks, steel snap-
traps, chemical irritants, wire-cage traps, and elementary school
brass bands. There is a not implausible story that authorities of
Philadelphia addressed that city's pigeon pests directly with signs
in Rittenhouse Square emphatically stating: PIGEONS NOT ALLOWED.

Application of sticky or slippery repellents is one of the oldest
and still most widely used methods of protection against pigeons.
Commonly called entanglants by pigeon eradicators, these sticky
materials are jellies composed of mineral oils made tacky by the
addition of rosin, certain rosin derivatives, lecithins, synthetic poly-
mers, lubricating greases, soap, or chicle gum (widely used as a base
for chewing gum). The purpose of an entanglant is more to annoy
than to hold birds in its grip. An old-fashioned bird repellent of
this type is birdlime. An ancient recipe for it, culled from a moldering pre-Revolutionary formulary, Culpepper's Oaths, Prayers, and
Pharmacopoeia, published in 1762, calls for placing tenderly boiled
holly mistletoe berries, or the bark of the wayfaring tree, into an
underground pit with layers of fern and surrounded by stones, until
it ferments into a sort of mucilage.

Pigeons in many large cities are subjected to electric shock treatment. In Washington, D.C., the Capitol, the Supreme Court
Building, and other notable edifices have been elaborately rigged to
give pigeons a tingling hotfoot to discourage their roosting on the
cornices, ledges, and windowsills. Similar electronic bird-proofing
was installed by the government's General Services Administration
at the main Post Office Building in New York City. Post office
officials there were gravely concerned because pigeon habitués of
Pennsylvania Station, adjacent to the post office, were being forced
from their old haunts by demolition of that venerable railroad terminal to make way for the new Madison Square Garden sports
arena. Bids ranging from $28,190 to $96,300 were received to pro-

vide installation of wires to carry a constant, nonkilling, electric current of 15,000 volts and .0006 amperes about the post office's fancy stonework, the roof parapet, pilaster caps, bronze grillwork and pediments over the building's twenty-one entrances, and at any other likely pigeon perches. Pigeons landing on the shockers get enough of a charge — equivalent to that received by touching an automobile sparkplug — to send them into the pigeon version of the frug, which sometimes I think they originated.

Several notable deterrents to pigeon population explosion have been gratuitously offered by various interested citizens. Madame V.K. Wellington Koo, wife of the renowned retired Chinese diplomat, once proposed that the city build pigeon lofts, collect the eggs and sell them to Chinese restaurants. Mme Koo (what an inspired name for a pigeon patroness!) said that such a system had proven profitable in China. A Gramercy Park ornithologist advocated feeding pigeons grain impregnated with chemicals that would make the birds "sterile and infertile" (might ultimately work, but it probably would be more practical to feed the birds something to induce constipation). A woman from the Bronx sent a snapshot of pigeon nesting towers erected in the South American city of Brasilia. (Karlsruhe, Germany, has similar housing for its parks' pigeons; there, all the nest eggs are pinpricked to prevent hatching. Vienna and Salzburg, Austria, feed their pigeons hormones to keep the eggs infertile.) The owner of a French bistro on Third Avenue suggested a method used in his home village: distribute bread crusts soaked in wine to get the birds tipsy so that they can be bagged more easily and painlessly.

Such private enterprises in New York City as Rockefeller Center, the Saks Fifth Avenue department store, the General Electric Company, and St. Patrick's Cathedral have employed pigeon trappers (from the Twin City Pigeon Eliminating Company of Downers Grove, Illinois). Certain individuals in the big city, the poachers who supply a thriving bootleg pigeon market, make their own contribution to the reduction of the pigeon population by clubbing the birds with baseball bats, croquet mallets, and golf clubs. Pigeon poaching of a more refined nature is done by the falconer. To pursue the sport of falconry a hawk is absolutely essential, and procuring a hawk is almost impossible without a pair of live pigeons — one to bait the bow net, used in trapping the wild bird, and the other to be flown from the tip of a high pole as a lure. And since hawk bait seldom is salvageable, it is wise to provide replacement pigeons. These ambushed pigeons augment the perfectly legal pigeon marketing engaged in at municipal poultry terminals, where thousands of the birds are sold to retailers. The New York City figure is six thousand birds annually — excluding the black market. The meat is peddled mostly in poverty-prone neighborhoods for soup meat, as a substitute for more expensive chicken, or as a vast improvement over such things as hog maws and chittlin's. In tropical Africa, India, the Malay Archipelago, and Australia, however, pigeons are regarded as an epicurean delight.

Pigeonnaping calls for saintly self-control and some stealth if a pigeonnaper is to avoid meeting disaster head-on in the persons of vicious septuagenarians — turtle-chinned ladies with pointy-toed high-button shoes (equipped with concealed hatpins, I'm sure) and choleric gentlemen armed with tightly furled umbrellas and brittle invective — who regard pigeons in the way ordinary folk do snowy egrets and whooping cranes. Also there is the ASPCA to worry about, as well as suspicious policemen. The capture of a pigeonnaper adds spice to their blue-coated lives, and gives the humorists on newspaper city desks a field day, especially if the hawk-bait procurer is a college professor (which a falconer frequently is). Then the headline over the story is sure to say: POLICE NET PIGEON POACHING PROF.

New York City's Department of Health has never taken any official decisive action regarding its pigeon menaces beyond requesting the Parks Department (which lays out about $150,000 a year to clean its 652 statues, monuments, fountains, flagpoles, etc., designated officially as "pieces of art") to remove its "Pigeon Feeding Area" signs and to put up ones ordering, "Don't Feed the Pigeons." (Because they don't say "please," pigeon feeders are furious.) Also, a formal appeal was made to the populace to cease and desist nourishing the pesky things. After bringing forth those mountainous molehills (in the autumn of 1963), the guardians of public health considered the pigeon affair closed and went on to more stimulating endeavors.

When an all-out offensive against New York City's pigeon pests was suggested, it was found that a conservation law protects the birds throughout New York State. Legislation to permit the killing of pigeons by anyone by any method, without the requirement of a special permit, was slipped quietly through the Senate in February 1964, but the bill was killed in committee in the Assembly when humanitarian organizations got wind of it. The staid *New York Times*, in an editorial taking the side of the embattled birds, wondered just how pigeons of New Jersey, Long Island, and Westchester would be kept out of a pigeon-pure metropolis, and intimated tongue-in-cheek that New York, in emulation of Berlin, should erect a mile-high, pigeon-proof wall around Manhattan, or better yet, shelter clumps of skyscrapers under gigantic plastic domes. It was also noted in the press that 8,095 structures had been demolished in New York City during the previous year (1962) and that twelve thousand new ones ($900 million worth) offered very few toeholds for pigeons. Missing from the new steel-and-glass monstrosities are such traditional architectural adornments as gargoyles; sculptured heads; nude stone figures; deep recesses; ledges; and other fancy appurtenances. Some of the newer buildings even have sharply pitched windowsills of slick metal, and there is a noticeable dearth of Corinthian columns.

The American Society for the Prevention of Cruelty to Animals came out in favor of humane treatment of the beleaguered pigeons by suggesting that it might be better to trap the birds and release them outside the city. Dean Amadon, curator of the Museum of Natural History, then pointed out that at least a two-hundred-mile distance would be required to overcome the built-in "return instinct" of the birds.

At the height of New York's pigeon fuss, an Israeli Arab of Haifa (Jabbour Khouri, 16 Sakyoun Street) applied by cablegram to City Hall for the job of pigeon pied piper. Nobody took him seriously, but perhaps they should have. He may have had the low-down on pigeons, for they've been around the Orient a good long time. Pigeon-post systems were popular in that part of the world as early as A.D. 1146, when Sultan Nurredin, the Caliph of Bagdad, allegedly established the first pigeon messenger service, flying to all parts of his realm and even to and from Egypt and Syria. From the end of the twelfth to mid-thirteenth century unbelievable sums of money — as much as a thousand dinars apiece — were paid for proven carrier pigeons. According to Xenephon, Ctesias, Lucian, and other ancient wisemen, pigeons were held sacred by the Syrians and Assyrians, who believed that the soul of their Queen Semiramis, founder of Babylon, had flown to the Celestial Hereafter in the form of a pigeon. A pigeon is said to have whispered advice from Allah to Mohammed (of course, he helped things along by putting seeds in his ears for the pigeon to nibble on — an old trick of animal trainers).

In Persia and India white pigeons accompany funeral processions to signify a winged link with Heaven. City laws of Istanbul, Turkey, forbid the removal of pigeon nests or molesting of the birds within the vicinity of holy buildings.

Life might be less harrowing for the pigeon in America if it were known by its true name. Our city fathers and businessmen, who have no compunction whatsoever in lowering the boom on a pigeon, might hesitate — if only in the name of public relations — to clobber a dove, which is what our pigeon actually is — a feral development of the European domestic rock dove, *Columbia livia*. The word pigeon is from medieval French, *pijon*, which derived from late Latin *pipionem*, the accusative case of *pipto*, from *pipire*, meaning "to whimper." Before it was domesticated in Europe, the rock dove bred in caves along cliffs, in holes, or under overhanging rocks. It was most common along the seashore where caves had been hollowed out by the pounding sea. In our country only a small number of descendants of the foreign rock dove have found suitable nesting places completely divorced from man. Most have taken up habitation around our homes, city and farm buildings, grain elevators, and other structures where food is available.

Unlike most birds, pigeons need a flat surface on which to stand.

They cannot roost on wires, despite Ludwig Bemelmans's story of the New York pigeons who regularly made a pilgrimage to Hartford, Connecticut, so that they could perch on a powerline there that had special qualities for curing arthritis, with which, according to Bemelmans, all big city pigeons are afflicted.

The doves we know as pigeons make a simple frail nest in which to lay their one or two eggs, which are normally immaculately white and hatch in seventeen to nineteen days. The young are almost naked at first and quite helpless. During the period of incubation a milky-white substance begins to form in the parent birds' crops. It is known as pigeon milk and is the only food of the young squab during its first five days on earth. After the fifth day the parent birds dilute this so-called milk with more and more water and grain; it is fed to the young after shorter and shorter periods of predigestion until at the end of about ten days the squabs are being given essentially whole grain and water from their parents. The babies obtain all their food by jabbing their bills into the mouth of either one of their progenitors, who with considerable effort bring previously swallowed food up into their mouths for the young to drink in. Even though there is an abundance of provender on the ground, the squab will starve unless the parent birds are around to feed them. The adult pigeons begin nesting again while still feeding their newly born. Both male and female share also in incubating the eggs, and normally the birds remain paired for life. If anything happens to either one, the other continues to incubate the eggs and feed the young, and remates in a rather short time apparently without giving the matter much thought.

Domestic pigeons were classified by Darwin in four groups. The first is that of the pouters, having a great-sized gullet barely separated from the crop and capable of inflation. The second group has three races: carriers, runts, and barbs. In the third there are five races: fantails, turbits, tumblers (they tumble backwards during flight), frillbacks (the feathers are reversed), and Jacobins (neck feathers form a hood). The fourth group contains the trumpeters and pigeons that scarcely differ from the wild root stock.

In general, the pigeon overseas fares far better than his American cousin. Londoners especially are profoundly shocked by pigeon slaughterings in the United States. Britishers live amicably with their pigeons. "Exterminate pigeons?" an official exclaimed. "My dear chap, there'd be no more certain way of bringing down the government." The situation in London's Trafalgar Square is characteristic of Britain's spirit of compromise with its pigeons: the square's concessionaries that sell pigeon food to visitors and bird lovers are licensed by the Ministry of Works, which also maintains a pigeon-repellent installation on the huge National Gallery, occupying the north side of the square.

It is against the law to feed pigeons in Paris, but typical Gallic ingenuity successfully skirts the unpopular regulation. A *depigeonisation* campaign involving poisoned grain failed utterly because organized pigeon fanciers lavished an abundance of uncontaminated food on the pigeons at dawn hours before the lethal grain was distributed. When it appeared, the birds were satiated. For a while the hottest-selling record in Paris was that of a hilarious scatological satire by French mimic, Henri Tisot, about President de Gaulle denouncing the winged threat to the Republic at a *depigeonisation* press conference.

Even so great a citizen of Paris as Pablo Picasso champions the pigeon. In the book *Life with Picasso* by Françoise Gilot and Carlton Lake there appears this note regarding Picasso's former residence, an apartment at Number 23, Rue La Boetie, near the Champs-Elysées: " 'One summer when I went on vacation and left one window half-open,' Pablo said, 'when I returned, I found that a whole family of pigeons had established residence in the *atelier*. I never wanted to chase them away. Of course they left droppings everywhere, and it would have been too much to expect that the paintings should have been spared.' I saw several paintings of the period that had been decorated by the pigeons. Pablo had never seen any point to removing their droppings. 'It makes an interesting unpremeditated effect,' he said."

Parisian officials no longer try to poison pigeons, but now woo them with food to lofts in two wards north of the Arc de Triomphe and around Montmartre so that their eggs can be destroyed.

France does not wish to eliminate the birds entirely but simply to reduce their numbers. Citizens are allowed to shoot pigeons with air rifles and slingshots, provided they are not used in public streets where "the sight would be likely to arouse public indignation." After various methods of trapping the birds failed, a former French parachutist invented a successful crossbow device which fires a huge net, weighing less than one pound, by means of arrows tipped with rubber balls to avoid wounding the birds; the net travels about thirty feet and the birds are lured into the netting area by special grain-distributing teams working under police control, so that they will not be molested by pigeon fanciers. In one year the contraption captured almost two-thirds of the city's estimated four hundred thousand pigeons. The captives are transported in baskets by truck to the southwestern coast (nearest Spain and Mallorca) and the northeastern (nearest England), and then released. Each bird is tagged so that authorities are able to recognize any that manage to beat their way back to Paree; those that do frequently end up as *coq au vin*. Pigeons have been soiling Parisian buildings, boulevards, and monuments for centuries. By 1960 the pigeon fouling had become so acute that the government launched an extensive clean-up campaign which was terribly expensive. Just to clean the Hôtel de Ville (City Hall) cost the city 810,000 francs ($162,000) and took seven months' work.

Italy, of course, adores pigeons. Just let anyone dare touch one feather of those flocks of the Piazza San Marco in Venice. Milan, Naples, Verona, Turin, and Rome all have scads of pigeons, and Italians would no more think of chasing them away than of chasing tourists away, or of ordering signorinas to wear larger bikinis.

The Germans, who first tried poisoning their excess pigeons (they didn't resort to gas chambers), now have evolved what seems like the best solution yet to the problem. They are evacuating pigeons and relocating them in the country to help farmers by eating grubs and other pests. Munich, Hamburg, Cologne, and West Berlin are involved in this resettlement drive, embracing a total of about 340,000 birds. East Berlin also has its problem with pigeons. Even the infamous wall cannot keep them at home. Hordes of pigeons live along Bernauerstrasse in deserted houses on the border between East Berlin and the French sector, but they find the pickings much better on the French side. Despite the government's praiseworthy attempt to relocate pigeons in rural areas, many Berliners on both sides of the dividing wall still cater to the winged pests. When poison food is spread for pigeons there always are residents waiting in the streets to sweep it up before the birds can eat it. One landlord of West Berlin has set aside a four-room apartment in his five-story house as a palace for three hundred pigeons, where they are fed generously and protected from official harassment.

Moscow once loved pigeons, now despises them. Near Red Square, in the park beneath the walls of the Kremlin, and at other favorite Muscovite strolling places there used to be pigeon-food stands. Side streets once belonged almost exclusively to pigeons and pedestrians — there were so few automobiles. Some traffic signs gave pigeons the right of way; any driver who jeopardized the life of a pigeon was fined two and a half rubles. But times change. The stands have vanished and the pigeon-favoring traffic signs too. The number of automobiles has increased enormously and drivers now think nothing of plowing full speed ahead into a flock of pigeons. Most ominously, squads of skulking men bearing nets have begun systematically to round up pigeons and to cart them off in closed vans. All questions asked of these net-wielders by bewildered and bothered citizens are answered, naturally, with a "Nyet."

Many United States cities have ordinances prohibiting the public feeding of pigeons. Miscreants in Cincinnati, Ohio, can be fined fifty dollars for each offense; in Syracuse, New York, the penalty is a hundred dollars. During that city's total war on pigeons in 1964 police checked feed stores to learn of customers buying small quantities of corn and other grains suitable for bird feeding.

"The police will keep such people under surveillance," stated the antipigeon brigades' field marshal, Mr. Robert Halloran, chief complaint clerk of the city of Syracuse, who'd been drafted into the job because most of the complaints received concerned either pigeons or starlings. Syracuse citizens, alarmed by the police-state tone of Mr. Halloran's statement, which had been reported by the newspapers, asked if they were to be shadowed like common criminals or Cosa Nostra chieftains.

"Well," hastily amended Mr. Halloran, referring to the police, "they'll check up on them, anyway."

Zealous as most bird lovers are, pigeon infatuates are worse. In San Francisco, an elderly window washer for the YMCA named John Sepp used to spend one week's pay each month on feed — about 450 pounds of grain weekly — for four hundred pigeons of that city's famous Alamo Square. He did this in memorial gratitude to the carrier pigeons that he claims kept him alive during the First World War by bringing him bouillon cubes for eighteen days after he'd been shot down while flying a plane in combat over the Austorvi Forest on the German-Polish frontier. I say "used to" in regard to Mr. Sepp's good work advisedly, for recently the authorities of San Francisco cracked down on all pigeon feeders and I imagine that Mr. Sepp was no exception.

In late 1964 the city-county supervisors got together and decided to do something about San Francisco's menacing pigeon problem. There were just too damned many defecating pigeons. A plan was drafted calling for "humane disposition" of some pigeons and a limitation on the places where the survivors could legally be fed. Pigeon partisans screamed in outrage; pigeon haters accused the authorities of not going far enough — why feed the dirty little bastards at all?

The code drawn up failed to stipulate just what "humane disposition" meant, although it judiciously approved the idea of a pigeon sanctuary, provided it could be built without public funds. At this point, an organization named the Bird Guardian League announced plans for constructing a $50,000 pigeon aviary in Golden Gate Park to house about fifty thousand of the birds in a futuristic structure of steel mesh and concrete to contain birdbaths, mating salons, automatic feeders, drinking fountains, and wading pools. For pigeon haters a special concession had been made by the architect: roosts of such large-meshed screen that eggs automatically would fall through it to smash on concrete below — instant birth control.

The Recreation and Parks Commission published a list of authorized feeding sites for pigeons — none of them within a mile of downtown San Francisco. This proposal aroused the San Francisco League of Pigeon Women. Its president, Mrs. Dorothy Schlegal, said sarcastically to the commissioners, "While the pigeon has superlatively good vision, it will not be able to read your directives, and will therefore remain fully uninformed as to the legal areas."

The Wildlife Emergency Council was next to be heard from. Its chairman, James A. Schroeder, stated unequivocally, "No force on earth can keep people from feeding pigeons."

A public meeting on the subject held at City Hall was almost as bombastic as those of 1960 when the House Un-American Activities Committee was there in full swing conducting open hearings. The grandiose proposition of the Bird Guardian League had failed to materialize and a superior court judge had just upheld the city's right to destroy pigeons as a public nuisance. "You hate God!" cried one irate woman as she stalked from the jammed gallery. "You are a pigeon pervert!" screamed another. An especially vehement participant shouted at the judge, "You bald-headed ignoramus, you'll wear your sick smile to your grave, and I hope it's soon." Naturally, someone called him a Communist. The judge chastised the pigeoneers for near contempt of court and curtly advised them that their benevolent impulses might better be directed toward their own species, whose health might be imperiled by pigeons. It all ended with the judge instructing the Society for the Prevention of Cruelty to Animals, as the operator of the city's pound for seventy-five of its ninety-eighty years of existence, to dispose of the foul fowl.

The SPCA said that it would not kill a single pigeon, not even humanely, but would find a home for each one in the country. It seems that a rancher up north had offered to take all the pigeons the organization could supply. On his property they would have the run of fields and streams and mingle freely with the birds and butterflies. Before this benevolent offer could be taken advantage of, the citizens of the town nearest this good samaritan's ranch rose up on their hind legs, grumbling that the pigeons would eat their crops; an orgy of pigeon pies was threatened in retaliation to the move proposed by the rancher. He hastily withdrew. However, another good soul came forward anonymously with a similar offer for a free pigeon preserve. So now, twice a month, the SPCA conducts a pigeon roundup and ships the catch to this Shangri La. Thus far the program has relocated about eight thousand pigeons at a cost of roughly eighty cents each.

It is amusing that such public outcry is made whenever the scruffy pigeons of our cities are threatened in the slightest, while the more beautiful ones of the wild are slaughtered by the thousands each year with no one bothering to bat an eye or raise a finger against the assaults.

In California, Washington, and Oregon close to half a million bandtail pigeons — said to be the fastest of all game birds — are bagged each year (daily limit eight per man). At one time the bandtail was so sought after by hunters that it was feared to be going the way of the passenger pigeon to oblivion. Just as that bird did, the bandtail female lays but a single egg at a setting. Then a bandtail mama must spend eighteen days hatching it and four weeks pumping the little squab full of pigeon milk until it can be pushed from the nest to make way for another egg. The bandtails were saved from extinction by their tendency to nest spread out across forests, rather than in vast numbers together as passenger pigeons had done, thus making themselves easy targets for commercial hunters. A ban on killing bandtails — in effect from 1913 to 1932 — also helped keep them alive, as did their phenomenal speed.

In the Southwest, the exquisite *paloma morada*, the mulberry-colored common pigeon of Mexico, is considered fair game for any hunter. This bird is one of the loveliest ever created — plump and compact, yet gracefully and smoothly fashioned, a little heavier than the American domestic pigeon. In color the *paloma morada* is a deep violet-pink; the feathers are a combination of wines, mauves, deep blues, violets, and they have a varied iridescence. The iris of the eye is a bright red-orange, circled in scarlet, and the pupil is dark. The base of the large bill is scarlet; legs and feet are a deep rosy pink. Naturally, its murder is justified by its killers — as is the cutting down of the flower of youth in war. Men who drop pigeons with rifles talk about the great outdoors and all that, gets a man out of the house, makes him forget the old office or factory, makes a man feel good to get his gun off — like a real man should.

Real men who also are wealthy men go in for a pigeon-shooting sport that has more pizazz than does chasing over hill and dale after the elusive birds. It's a dubious recreation called *Colombaire*-style live-pigeon shooting. Imported from Spain by way of Mexico, it somewhat resembles skeet or boxed-live pigeon shooting, except that it's faster, more competitive, more colorful, more daring, and it costs participants much more money — from $500 to $1,500 for a three-day shoot. *Colombaire* freely translated means "pigeon thrower" and that is the key to the game. A man throws live pigeons into the air to be shot at by the player. The bird is propelled with the speed of a big-league pitcher's fastest ball well into the second half of the gunner's 45- to 50-yard effective range before the pigeon needs to resort to its wings. This kind of pigeon shooting is popular in Mexico and Texas; in that state an estimated $3 million and 150,000 pigeons are involved annually. The dead birds usually are donated to orphanages and prisons, and the ones that get away mostly are grabbed up by Mexican kids waiting around to take them home to dinner. In Texas *Colombaire* shoots sometimes are staged as benefits. A regular beneficiary there has been the Southwest Research Institute, a foundation for medical research (famous for its "baboonery") which was set up by San Antonio's multimillionaire oilman, the late Tom Slick.

New word from San Francisco states that there is little danger of that city's pigeons slipping into oblivion — the pigeon eradication program is going to cost $60,000 and take five years to get all the unwanted pigeons out of town, assuming population estimates were correct, birth and death rates remain constant, none of the pigeons flies back, and no fanatic starts breeding them in his attic.

The absolutely final word came recently from a U.S. Public Health Service researcher at the University of California, who asserts that if the city substantially reduces its pigeon population a biological vacuum will be created into which other pigeons will be drawn, and if not pigeons, something much worse — such as starlings.

Starlings, too, have gotten a fair amount of attention from civic uplifters. The people in Syracuse who clobbered so many pigeons also went after starlings — killing as many as eighteen hundred in one day (gassed in traps by exhaust fumes from an automobile).

The starling is a pest chiefly because of its gregariousness, a trait common to all starlings. They roost in large flocks, nest in colonies, and love to be around people. Even in summer and late fall, starlings which usually feed in open country up to seventy-five miles from their roosts prefer to spend their nights in trees and buildings of residential areas rather than in isolated uninhabited woodland tracts equally as attractive. When colder weather comes, starlings seek shelter in barn cupolas, pigeon lofts, ventilators, on building ledges, and inside church towers. It is then that this bird is most troublesome. As many as three thousand starlings have been counted in a single church steeple. Starlings may be so thick on the face of a building that sidewalks below become slippery with their droppings in a matter of minutes after the flocks alight. Accumulations of droppings on roofs and gutters of a single building may weigh several tons; the uric acid of this fecal matter not only stains buildings badly, but corrodes metal gutters and flashings.

The starling doesn't look like a dirty slob. It is a compact bird, with short round body, square short tail, thick neck, short and pointed wings, and an inch-long pointed bill that turns bright yellow in spring. Normally the starling walks or runs on its rather long legs with alternate steps, seldom making two-legged hops as do so many other birds. In size it is between a sparrow and a pigeon. Mostly the starling is dark and iridescent, although some species are dull and one is a murky white. There are 103 species belonging to the family Sturnidae, of the passerine birds, which are songbirds of perching habit that range from titmice to ravens to birds of paradise, and include more than half of the world's birdlife. The well-known talking bird, the mynah, is a starling from India, and oxpeckers of Africa are starlings (genus *Buphaga*).

Starlings normally produce two broods each year, the first leaving the nest early in June. A hatch of from four to five eggs is usual, but as many as eight have been recorded. The eggs are bluish-green, not white as are those of most birds that nest in dark cavities. Incubation lasts from eleven to fourteen days and the young leave the nest two or three weeks after hatching, fully fledged and capable of strong flight. This rapid and complete development before leaving home gives young starlings a high survival rate. The young are fed almost exclusively on insects.

The starling is a curious bird. Its feeding habits make it both enemy and friend of man. What infuriates men most about starlings is that they are so fond of cherries, blueberries, strawberries, corn on the cob, and other farm and orchard products. But we tend to overlook the fact that starlings help control cloverleaf weevils, strawberry-crown girdlers, bluegrass billbugs, shorthorned grasshoppers, crickets, cutworms, armyworms, the larvae of the cabbage butterfly and Japanese beetles. Of this bird's annual food consumption, 57 percent is animal matter, the rest vegetable. In April and May there is a 90 percent consumption of animal food, principally insects. Even in the cold months — December to March — the animal content of the starling's diet is remarkably over 30 percent.

The starling was a tremendous help in cutting down the Japanese beetle, which attacks 275 different plants. It was largely brought under control by a patented method of the distribution of spore-forming bacteria in an insecticide having as essential active ingredients *Bacillus popilliae* and *Bacillus lentimorbus*. The bacteria grow and sporulate in the blood of living larvae of those beetles and give it a white color, whence the name of the affliction, the milky white disease. The system was devised by Samson R. Dutky, a bacteriologist with the United States Department of Agriculture. The diseased larvae are unable to move themselves vertically downward and so remain at the earth's surface, prey to starlings. These birds eat the infected grubs, with no ill effect, and by means of droppings redistribute them often miles away to contaminate other Japanese beetle larvae, thus achieving widespread dissemination of the control method.

The starling we have in this country is *Sturnus vulgaris*, introduced successfully from Europe in 1890, after a previous aborted attempt in 1850. The man responsible for bringing us this messy pest was Eugene Schiefflin, who was motivated by the desire to introduce to his fellow Americans every bird mentioned in the writings of Shakespeare. Schiefflin released sixty European starlings in Central Park, New York City, just before the advent of spring in 1890, and followed them with forty more in April of the next year. They thrived. By 1900 starlings were reported from New Haven, Connecticut; Ossining, New York; and Bayonne, New Jersey. By 1908 they had gotten to eastern Massachusetts, and in 1916 they were reported up and down the coast from southern Maine to Norfolk, Virginia, and inland as far as Ohio. By 1929 starlings had reached Texas and ranged the Gulf of Mexico.

In that year planners of the presidential inauguration of Herbert Hoover found starlings a major hazard of the parade route. The problem has persisted. The route of march for President Johnson's inaugural parade had to be starling-proofed at a cost of $10,000. Almost one hundred trees from the Capitol to the White House were treated with a gooey substance that supposedly irritated the feet of the birds. The stuff, odorless to humans but decidedly offensive to starlings, was guaranteed to repel them for one full year. The use of ultraviolet light has been tried to no avail against starlings. It was supposed to give the birds a ghastly appearance, so that they'd frighten each other. Instead they soaked up the light as if it were Miami Beach sunshine. When mirrors were set up to discourage starlings they admired themselves in the glasses. When bombarded by recorded music of electric guitars they huddled closer.

The starlings' filthy habits make them one of our most repulsive city pests, but it is their noise that most people object to. The din of their cries and shrill squeals is almost unbearable. President John F. Kennedy found starlings disagreeable White House companions, and attempts were made to keep them from disturbing the presidential slumber by playing at dusk taped recordings of starling distress calls. The device was not notably successful. An official of the Audubon Society explained why: "They shouldn't have sent out the *distress* call, because when birds hear any other bird in trouble they come to help. Birds from all over Washington flocked to the White House to see what was up when they played that thing."

The use of sonant effects against starlings has not worked well partly because the sounds directed at the birds have been those that man hears well, and starlings are insensitive to most of such tones. In experiments conducted at Cornell University's Laboratory of Ornithology in 1939, it was found that starlings have a tonal range of less than five octaves, compared to man's nine, and the loss is in the lower or middle range at frequencies where man's ear functions acutely. The birds do not hear middle C, nor the C an octave above it. Only the three highest octaves on the piano are audible to starlings, but they also are sensitive to almost two octaves above the piano range. Starlings can hear up to 16,000 cycles per second (about the same as the average human), but only as low as 600 cps. (The highest note on a piano is 4,138 cps. and the lowest 27 cps.) The hearing range of a pigeon is much lower than that of a starling. The pigeon's range of sensitivity is from 7,500 cps. to 200 — not really a low note, being about the G below middle C on a piano.

Starlings may not be able to get the message of man in every instance, but no one can be within blocks of a roosting flock of these birds and not be aware of them. People who frequent downtown Washington, D.C., know the sound well. It is estimated that one hundred thousand starlings congregate there each evening and each one is a compulsive chatterer.

In summer the birds disturb every downtowner's sleep — from slum-dweller to visiting tourist to President and his lady. The White House still has starling trouble. A recent feature story in a New York newspaper told of various methods used by grounds-keepers to drive the birds away from Johnsonland. Each day at dusk one of the groundsmen would walk around the lawn beating on a box with a paddle. Passersby sometimes thought it a bit odd, but most tourists simply accepted the peculiar behavior as typical of high-level statesmanship. Occasionally the bird chaser varied the routine by beating the grass or a tree trunk. "Whitey" Williams, then chief groundskeeper at the White House, is quoted as saying, "I used to try to chase them by clapping my hands, but they got pretty sore." (And then there always was the risk of bringing LBJ out onto the balcony to make a speech.)

Regarding dispersal of the birds, a pamphlet from the United States Department of the Interior's Fish and Wildlife Service has this to say: "Almost any disturbing noise or action will do, such as banging tin pans, strings of bells, hitting tree trunks with baseball bat, etc. More effective is the use of shotguns, carbide thunderclap cannons, automatic acetylene exploders and fireworks, particularly Roman candles, two-shot hand crackers, or rope firecrackers." Also recommended were "inflated paper bags or balloons, imitation snakes, feather dusters, fire hoses, rags on strings, and off-key organ music." Let's see — they left out Jack-in-the-boxes; automatic umbrellas; dirty socks swung on a long pole; a drunken peroxide blonde at an Elks' convention; roaring lions or liberals; Irish tenors; a clutch of Hell's Angels and stampeding elephants.

Starlings and other birds are a great hazard to flying aircraft. Airline pilots report an average of 300 bird collisions a year, while private pilots average 500 annually, according to U.S. Air Force spokesmen. In one year Air Force pilots reported 839 bird strikes. The starling is the chief offender, although sea gulls, snow geese, sparrows and blackbirds also create problems to aircraft. Mynah birds, the finch and three species of parrots living wild within the city of Los Angeles are expected to be aviation bird problems of the future. Collision with a pair of good-sized swans once caused a plane crash in which seventeen persons were killed. A grave danger to jet aircraft is that birds will be sucked into the engines. At the Boston airport starlings were pulled into the air intake of a prop-jet plane and sixty-three persons died in the crash.

Because garbage disposal at airports is not always ideal, birds are attracted to restaurant areas there, but the feeding of starlings by sympathizers is not a problem at air terminals or anywhere else. No one is so enraptured by this nasty noisy bird as to feel like scattering corn or bread crumbs for it. It rants and jabbers and screeches and says "*feeee-uuuuu*" and other dirty things that I'll not repeat. The pigeon, now — so pretty pearly opalescent, cooing softly, wooing coyly, eyes so ruby — well, that is another matter. Pigeons are fed so much that in most cities there are ordinances against doing it. In New York City pigeon feeding comes under the general head of littering, but since the city's administrative code does not specify birdseed as litter it is difficult, if not impossible, to convict apprehended pigeon feeders.

Nothing makes a pigeon zealot more defiant than to be told that he cannot feed his or her beloveds. It is advisable to steer clear of frustrated pigeon feeders. When the law runs against them they dip underground. Wealthy matrons have been known to pay taxi drivers by the week to drive slowly through Central Park early each morning while blithely tossing birdseed to the pigeons living there. Innocent-appearing financiers and business executives carry buttered enriched breadcrusts in their briefcases for surreptitious transfer to favorite pigeons. A prominent Madison Avenue haberdasher once carried birdseed in a false bottom of his derby; sweet old ladies secrete grain in parasols, gloves, knitting bags, shawls, and the folds of the *Christian Science Monitor*. Militant young mothers hide pigeon feed under their babies in perambulators; I know of at least one flat-chested one who substitutes it for the foam-rubber falsies in her brassiere.

Defilement of property certainly is the strongest factor in all the majestic disturbance over the lowly pigeon. In our country, however, the chief official justification for the pigeon pogroms is the fact that the birds are suspected of spreading disease. The Communicable Disease Center of the United States Public Health Service asserts that nine diseases attributed to pigeons directly or indirectly are capable of infecting man, although chances are extremely rare with the exception of cryptococcosis and histoplasmosis, both systemic fungus diseases of humans. Ectoparisites such as kissing bugs, louse flies, bedbugs, fleas, lice, soft ticks, and mites live off pigeons and add their bit — and in some cases their bite — to our discomfort.

Most of the row seems to be over cryptococcosis, for that disease, if severe enough, can lead to meningitis, an inflammation of the brain covering that still is regarded in the public mind as being absolutely fatal. Actually, since the advent of the antifungal drug amphotericin B, the fatality from cryptococcal meningitis is down to about 30 percent of its victims — but still, that's a lot. The disease is caused by inhalation of spores of *Cryptococcus neoformans*, found in the dust of bird droppings. It has become smart to refer to the disease as CN meningitis, although there is no scientific basis for such an abbreviation. Pigeon droppings furnish a rich culture for the fungus, so the pigeon has become the patsy. The furor over this new menace to the general public was set off in October 1963 by Dr. Maxwell L. Littman, a specialist in fungus diseases and chief mycologist of the New York City Health Department's Bureau of Laboratories, when he reported that a fifty-year-old man and a teen-ager had died because of the pigeon-dung fungus.

"Everyone is inhaling it," said Dr. Littman reassuringly, "and the susceptible get sick."

It was intimated that the city's multitude of air conditioners incredibly was sucking in the deadly spores, and that no one was safe from infection. Naturally, even non-thinking, shallow-breathing, non-air-conditioned people became upset. New York City statisticians had placed the five boroughs' pigeon figure at five million. The conception of deadly fallout from that many birds was just too much for anyone to contemplate without a tremor of panic. (The figure was astronomical, of course, for if each pigeon consumed only three ounces of dry food daily, 468 tons of provender would be required to feed that many birds — an utter impossibility in a concrete metropolis. Richard Ryan, a naturalist of the Bronx Zoological Gardens, an authoritative member of the Linnaean Society and an experienced pigeon-population estimator, put the number more realistically at under five hundred thousand, and more likely one hundred fifty thousand.)

Champions of the pigeon arose to its defense. A Mrs. Sarah Elisabeth Sagus, seventy-nine, of East 75th Street, Manhattan, an inveterate daily feeder of sixty-five pigeons (ninety-five on Sundays and holidays) in a newspaper interview termed it all a "dastardly lie"; people, not pigeons, carry diseases, she is reported to have said, and added that the story (in the New York Times) had been "concocted by the same people who want fluoridation," and that she never liked the Times anyway.

From Italy Professor Mario Girolami, director of the clinic on tropical and infectious diseases at the University of Rome, put his oar into the melee (in June, just in time for the opening of the tourist season) by defending the honor of Italian pigeons against besmirchment he believed aimed specifically at them.

"The germs found by Littman," said Professor Girolami, "are common. They were found in 1894 in Sardinia in the juice of fermented peaches, and subsequently in other fruit juices and in many animals including cows, horses, dogs, cats, pigs, chickens, and no doubt the American eagle. Why then pick on pigeons?"

The squabble ended up with Dr. Littman's getting a grant of $74,000 from the Health Research Council for further study.

The fungus of histoplasmosis, a similar disease, is found in pigeon droppings but thrives very well also in the dung of chickens, which are more contacted by humans than are pigeons. Histoplasmosis is one of the least frequently recognized but most widely occurring infections in America. Each year five hundred thousand of us suffer from it, but only a third are ill enough to require medical attention. An estimated thirty million United States citizens have been afflicted with histoplasmosis, according to the results of skin tests given during 1958–1961 to 306,000 white, male Navy recruits between the ages of seventeen and twenty-one who had lived all of their lives in this country. Many people never realize that they have histoplasmosis, as the symptoms — fatigue, slight fever, chest discomfort, and possibly a cough — often are diagnosed as the flu or a common cold. The disease can be contracted from bat dung, and therefore is known to speleologists as cave sickness or bat fever.

However, even histoplasmosis is hardly worth all the hysteria that's been generated over our cities' pigeons, for even in New York, one of the world's largest cities, the incidence of cases of the disease is only two per year per million inhabitants, despite the fact that about fifteen tons of feculent dust from forty-six tons of wet pigeon ordure is added daily to the air, a goodly portion of it drawn into living quarters.

The wild attacks by Americans on their domestic pigeons recall the historic barbarity that brought about the extinction of the passenger pigeon. In 1908, after fifty years of brutal, unrestrained butchery by frontiersmen, Indians, and commercial hunters, the total *world* population of passenger pigeons was down to exactly seven: four males in Milwaukee and two males and one female in Cincinnati. The Cincinnati males either were too feeble, too lackadaisical, or too infatuated with each other, or else the female (Martha, by name, after Mrs. George Washington) was sterile, frigid, or otherwise disinclined to mating, but anyway by 1910 there remained only poor, lonely old Martha living at the Cincinnati Zoo in shameful obscurity, with very few visitors. Shortly after lunch at 1 P.M. on the afternoon of September 1, 1914, Martha cooed her last and passenger pigeons at that moment became extinct. She was aged twenty-nine. Martha was promptly frozen within a three-hundred-pound cake of ice and forwarded to the Smithsonian Institution in Washington, D.C., where she remains — stuffed, mounted, and gathering dust — a poignant reminder of man's inherent bestiality.

Thus it is fitting that the best-known term of the underworld, "stool-pigeon" (an informer), derives from the decoy bird used by our ancestors to lure wild passenger pigeons to the nets. A live bird, with its eyes sewn shut, was fastened by its feet to a perch (stool) that was made to move up and down so that the captive's wings would flutter in the manner of a bird alighting to eat.

It is unfortunate that the pigeon has gotten itself such a tarnished name, for it has done a few nice things for mankind, much as I hate to admit this. Back in ancient history pigeons were helpful as strategic message carriers. The very first such recorded (by

Ovid in his *Metamorphoses*) was one dyed purple sent by Tauros-
thenes to inform his father in Aegina of victory at the Olympic
Games. Brutus and his soldiers, held within the city of Modena by
Mark Antony, were greatly aided by pigeons. Of this, Pliny, the
historian, wrote: "What service did Antony derive from his
trenches and his vigilant blockade, and even his nets stretched
across the river, while the winged messenger was traversing the
air?" French and Venetians, storming the city of Ptolemais in
Syria, intercepted a pigeon bearing a message to the besieged
troops from their Sultan, promising forthcoming military aid; for
that ray of hope, the attackers substituted words of despair and
released the pigeon, who thereupon delivered the sad tidings and
caused the town's defenders summarily to surrender. In the year
1574, when William the Silent and the Netherlands people of Ley-
den were pinned down in a six-month siege by the Spanish under
Philip II, carrier pigeons delivered orders to cut the sea dikes so
that ships carrying provisions could sail across the flooded land to
the beleaguered city.

Pigeons figured importantly in both world wars. One named
Mocker, born in 1917, was the most famous. He had a prominent
beak (like an eagle, some said), clear, keen eyes, and red feathers
splashed with white (but no stars). His job was to carry important
documents between the front and the rear. After he'd come
through a hellish German artillery barrage with a shrapnel-gashed
head, clipped tail feathers, and one eye shot out, Mocker was
awarded the Distinguished Service Cross and the Croix de Guerre.
When he died, at age twenty-one, Mocker was given a military
funeral; he didn't quite rate a plot in Arlington, but at least his
mounted body was placed on exhibition in the Post Library at Fort
Monmouth, New Jersey. Another notable pigeon courier of the
First World War named President Wilson eventually retired with
the Purple Heart for chest wounds and loss of one leg. In the Second Great Debacle, a pigeon named Yank carried the first news to
the world that American troops had recaptured Gafsa on March
17, 1943, and that the Italians were retreating. The first British war
correspondent into Normandy on D–Day, Doon Campbell, a Reu-

ters man, sent back across the Channel by carrier pigeon news of the invasion gathered from reporters who'd landed by parachute with RAF airborne troops. Other famous pigeons of World War II were Caesar, G. I. Joe, Burma Queen, Jungle Joe, Captain Letterman, Mollie MacArthur, and Priscilla Patton.

At medical centers throughout the country pigeons sometimes lend themselves to valuable research. Scientists at the University of Maryland's Naval Medical Research Institute use pigeons to study the effects on the human eye of sudden brilliant flashes of light, such as might come from a nuclear blast. Pigeon-pox virus is used to immunize laying hens against chicken pox (and I always thought that chickens got people pox). When a federal agency received a shipment of parasite-ridden rye grain containing an element essential for the production of a blood-clotting drug, the problem arose of how to separate the healthy grain from the ergot-laden. It was solved by pigeons who ate all the good grain leaving the diseased but medically useful kernels.

Racing pigeons will have nothing to do with bearing messages or performing other good works and look with scorn upon fellow pigeons who get roped into such affairs. The racer is the aristocrat of pigeondom — the poor man's racehorse. Racing pigeons give much pleasure to many people and keep a lot of husbands out of bars on weekends. The sport, however, costs about as much or more than bar attendance. To breed and train these specialized pigeons equipment is needed — carrying baskets, timing clocks, nets, special feeds and vitamins, a loft for housing the birds, and who knows how many six-packs of beer and other bribes to keep neighbors on a noncritical keel. Then there are club dues, entry fees, and transportation costs to and from the releasing areas — often several hundred miles from the lofts. Meets are held under the auspices of the American Pigeon Racing Union, Inc., a national organization of more than ten thousand members. A man can spend forty dollars a week on his pigeons during racing seasons, and about a thousand dollars all year round on a hundred birds, the usual number kept by a first-class handler. Some racing birds are worth as much as five hundred dollars. A lot of cash changes hands in the betting pools that accompany every race, therefore a pigeon racer always has the chance of getting some of his expenditures back in prize money.

In races these pigeons generally fly about fifty-five miles per hour, although under very favorable conditions — with wind and weather just right — racing pigeons have gone as fast as ninety miles per hour. Several pigeons have flown almost six hundred miles in twelve hours; one once was clocked at an average speed of seventy-two miles per hour over a two-hundred-mile course.

Some pigeon fanatics use motherhood ruthlessly to coax maximum speed from their racers. A setting hen suddenly will become aware that one of her eggs, which she'd calculated to be several days from hatching, has mysteriously become almost *qui vive*. Without realizing that there has been a switch, the bird is taken abruptly from the nest and transported to the race's starting point. Once released, she makes a beeline with all possible speed back to her precious pulsating egg.

The big problem with racing pigeons is that they can get beat down by the weather and take a year or more to make their way back home. Or they can become hopelessly lost. A pigeon might start out from La Brea Avenue in Los Angeles and end up (as one actually did) in the Panama Canal Zone. One racing pigeon released in Brooklyn turned up lost on the box-office line at Radio City Music Hall in the company of one of the infamous Times Square pigeons (they rarely get up before sundown and hardly ever go higher off the ground than that square's bronze statue of George M. Cohan). Another pigeon released in Fargo, North Dakota, to fly two hundred miles southeast to Minneapolis, Minnesota, got caught up in a violent rainstorm and ended up instead across the river in St. Paul, where it waddled through an open window of a beauty salon and was found there the following morning huddled under a hair dryer. One of the great pigeon disasters of recent times occurred in September 1964 when nearly six thousand racers belonging to the North Jersey and Central Pigeon Combines, each made up of thirteen homing pigeon clubs, were lost during a storm while racing from Remington, Virginia, and Breezewood, Pennsylvania, back to the home lofts in North Haledon, Elizabeth, and

Paterson, New Jersey. Once lost, a pigeon is forever useless to racing; his confidence is shredded.

A racing pigeon may get drenched and bewildered in a storm, but it always has a cozy warm cote to come home to and never has to scrounge for food or suffer being clouted over the head by a baseball bat or being shot at by cannon big and small, and it never lives in fear of having its sleek feathered neck twisted bloody in a dirty burlap sack by a pigeon poacher. Yet who has the more satisfactory life — the pigeon kept for competition or one free to ride the winds wherever they carry him and free to choose his own perils and pitfalls? I wonder.

The Bat

Toward blue sunset from attic crack
a black shadow shivers out.
Her child rides fixed to milky sack,
soft mouth in infant pout.

Oh, whistling girls and crowing hens
and flying nursing mothers
can surely come to no good ends,
for they're not like the others!

In such supreme serenity
is bigotry composed —
in so much squared security,
could bias be supposed?

5

The Ugliest Ones: *The Bat* People seem able to take pigeons but not to leave them alone. But with such domestic villains as rats, cockroaches, bedbugs, lice, and fleas there seldom is any question about which side the public is on. Most of us stand firmly against the more disgusting household pests. No one cares to suffer the stigma of harboring these lowlifes. Even silverfish, moths, and rug beetles are considered marks of a slovenly housekeeper, and no housewife cares to wear that label. Citizens who write or phone to the United States Department of Agriculture for literature on the control of the especially abhorrent home infesters usually request that information be mailed to them in a plain wrapper. And hardly anyone cares to have an exterminator's truck parked in front of his door for all the neighbors to see.

The only person I've ever known who doesn't give a good damn about such matters is a Haitian we call Phil, who lives in a town

near my home — about forty-five minutes out of New York City.
His true name is Philomé. It's unlikely that anyone but his family
knows his last name — not even the postman, for Phil doesn't get
even junk mail. He's on nobody's list. He hails from Jacmel, a tiny
seaport in Haiti, just over the mountains from Port au Prince.

Philomé was brought to America by his youngest son, who works
in one of the town's garment factories. The son had his father's
rotting teeth fixed, deloused him, and fitted him with eyeglasses.
Beyond those concessions, the old man hasn't been assimilated by
our culture. He still believes firmly in *vodun*, the mystic Haitian
religion, and lives alone in a shack without electricity or telephone
and heated primitively by kerosene stove; the walls are papered in
the style of his homeland with colored cutouts from magazines.
Phil lives simply, happily, earning just enough to get by, scorning
welfare and unemployment benefits.

One day the bank teller, for whom Philomé performs various
small services, informed me that Phil had got himself a pet — a
bat. He had been given the creature by a neighbor along our road
who'd called on the old Haitian for advice in clearing out an infestation of bats that had built up over the years in the loft of an old
barn which was to be renovated into living quarters. Phil, it turned
out, had recommended driving out the bats by a complicated series
of primitive cabalistic rites involving various *ouanga* charms, gourd
rattles wound with snake vertebrae, cockfeathers dipped in blood,
hatpins, corset steels, mirrors, candles, and an elaborate shield
made of a garbage can lid onto which had been affixed a collage
made of Tootsie Roll wrappers, the fronts of cigarette packages,
strips from supermarket cash registers, pairs of truly honest eyes
snipped from the faces of political campaign posters, silk ribbons,
and sundry scraps of gaudily colored fabrics.

My friend finally decided not to go through with the ritual; instead, he and his eldest son shot the bats one by one by rifle fire, a
method that took considerable time, but afforded more peace of
mind than Phil's proposal promised.

"I didn't object to having to provide a baby goat," my neighbor
explained, "but I drew the line when he asked for a hummingbird.

Besides, the only snakes we could find were copperheads; he didn't care too much for them, and I certainly didn't. I'd rather have bats."

After his dismissal as bat consultant Philomé declined the proffered fee, and asked only that he be allowed to take one of the bats home with him. The request was granted gladly. The barn's owner would have been happy to hand over a gross of the hideous things. But Phil wanted only one. After a long spell of mumbo-jumbo he made his choice from a group hanging cozily upside down from one of the lower rafters.

I once asked Philomé why he'd chosen a bat for a pet, and he replied, "Because it is he, and because it is I," which seems as good a justification of friendship as any I've ever heard.

Philomé was not unique as a bat fancier. There are many throughout the tropics — in cities, as well as backward areas — and there also are bat lovers among Anglo-Saxons. Russell Peterson, a mammalogist at the American Museum of Natural History in New York, in his *Silently by Night*, tells of his adopted bat Freddie that liked to go motoring in New Guinea in a Land Rover. And Alan Pryce-Jones, in his review of that book, remembers a certain Prince Murat in Paris, who adopted a bat, which he named Uranie. She used to come down to dinner, perch on his wife's shoulder, and was partial to chocolates. Whenever Uranie felt the urge for exercise or food less princely, she would dart out for a brief spin about the garden, but always returned to her master. Uranie eventually perished when, while fast asleep, she was rolled in a rug by mistake by a nearsighted housemaid. While poking around in a secondhand bookstore one day I came across *The Life of a Bat*, by Charles Derennes, published in London, a delightful treatise, though slightly adrip with the sentimental naïveté of the period 1925. It recounts that French scientist's experiences with many bats observed at close range, and especially of his favorite, which he named Noctu, for nocturnal.

A bat owner today won't be burned at the stake for being a witch, as was the case in the fourteenth century. Back then, people whose houses were overly infested with bats were summarily destroyed as devils. All during the Middle Ages the bat was considered the consort of demons. In England the word for bat was *bakke*, which compares with the Danish word *backe* and the Swedish *backa* — both derived from the Old Norse word *blaka*, to flutter. In those unenlightened times, serious believers in the corruption potential of the nocturnal flutterer swore that the daylight sky was full of enormous bats, invisible to the human eye because they were the same color as the sun and sky, and it was they whom the devil employed to abet his nighttime foul deeds. As for the bats that ordinary men could see at twilight, why they were nothing but the lingering shadows of the real ones.

In many rural areas of middle Europe men still nail a dead bat over their front doors to ward off misfortune, even though the premises are protected by a genuine insurance company. In bygone days such a grisly amulet mostly was to dissipate the evil eye, but it also prevented thunderstorms, preserved millstones from being struck by lightning (if there was a storm), discouraged rape on weekends, forestalled premature births of children, protected livestock from illness, and kept away marauders, unwanted relatives, servers of subpoenas and warrants and urinating dogs.

Being a mammal does not exempt a bat from abuse by its fellow mammal, man. Actually, we seem to relish tormenting our closest relatives of the animal family. Those mammals which most resemble the human get the most malevolence dumped on them. The whale has always had an unconscionable hard time at our hands; monkeys and apes seem too horribly like us — in appearance and character — not to be severely punished for the resemblance. However, the bat suffers from two other disadvantages besides that of being a mammal: first, its appearance, gruesome enough to frighten people into a blind rage against it; and second, automatic classification with the creeping, crawling things that repel nearly everyone and therefore must be stamped out.

Bats do not breed for the sake of beauty, as human mammals are prone to do. Not even the most charitable soul would call a bat charming. Bat faces vary enormously, each one uglier than the next

— they're the sort of thing you expect to encounter in nightmares, but fortunately seldom do. The noses often are a series of leaflike structures one atop the other; there are wrinkles and folds and great patches of naked skin. The number of bat teeth varies from twenty-four to thirty-two, according to varieties. The ears are all out of proportion to the size of the animal — some are bigger than the entire body. Often the main ears have within them repulsive smaller ears that repeat, smaller and smaller, almost ad infinitum.

The bat belongs to the order of mammals known as Chiroptera (from the Greek, meaning "hand wings"), and it is the only mammal equipped to fly. The bat's flying apparatus is the most imperfect and frustrating of the entire animal kingdom; the wings are so elastic and foldable (like umbrella sections) that the flight of this little beast is highly erratic and barely sufficient for the gathering of daily provender.

A bat's flight is a curious jumble of dizzying leaps and turns, headlong drops, collapses, jerks and spurts, breathtaking side slips and skids, incredible tumbles, and aerial somersaults to defy the most expert circus trapeze performer. In its ten-minute labyrinthian flight a bat will cover five miles of distance at a speed seldom clocked at more than thirty miles per hour. The greatest speed attributed to a bat is thirty-two miles per hour (the guano bat, *Tadarida mexicana*).

The vampire and flying fox bats fly with their bodies almost vertical — much as a dog swims in water — and with a languid wing beat of about three flaps per second.

People who have studied bats more thoroughly than I have claim that the ears are the most important element of the supertactile sensitivity which bats have that prevents midair collision with each other and with static objects during flight. A bat on the wing is said to emit an almost constant succession of shrill squeaks. Apparently the echoes from these sounds — a sort of primitive radar — enable the bat to avoid any obstacle, even such an insignificant one as the span of a single silk thread. The bats' squeaks are inaudible to man because their frequency of up to seventy thousand vibrations per second is much too high-pitched for our meager receiving equipment which is unable to accept vibrations beyond thirty thousand per second.

Dr. Donald R. Griffin of Cornell University, upon measuring these squeaks, found that each one lasts about one two-hundredth of a second and, in ordinary flight, is repeated about ten times every second.

The naturalist Ivan Sanderson found that bats which have their eyes taped shut can fly every bit as efficiently, but when an ear is folded down and attached by its tip to the face, a bat behaves peculiarly — going into abrupt tail dives and spinning erratically like an aerial whirling dervish.

It is thought that this bat radar system incorporates a distinctive wavelength for each bat, for if the echoes all were the same, complete confusion would result among bats flying in large flocks. Such a conception of individual wavelengths is strange only if we judge bat senses by our own, which at best are feebly developed. But, when you think about it, is it really that strange? The human auditory system, too, is highly discriminatory. Cannot each mother distinguish the voice of her own child amidst the babble of playground or nursery school? And we know that a blind person's ears are extremely receptive to familiar voices among a multitude.

The bat resembles both rodent and bird, but hasn't much in common with either. The rat and mouse are agile on the ground and have clever prehensile feet. The bat cannot even stand up while earthbound; its legs for all practical purposes are immovable. The bird not only can flap and soar majestically without fatigue for long periods of time, but on the ground is a serviceable runner, an admirable climber and jumper, and its beak is a useful feeding and preening tool. The bat, however, is a clumsy flier, can stay aloft only briefly, and has no beak for pecking food from vegetation or ground; it must capture its meals while in flight.

The hunting of an insectivorous bat is limited to no more than four daily flights of ten minutes each — or let's say an hour at most — as the flying creatures on which it feeds are not in the air for much longer than that after sunset (and, in the Temperate Zone, in only five months of the year). Since a bat tires after ten minutes of flight, it is relatively easy to capture one that has invaded your home. Simply wait until the bat hangs itself to rest on a beam, curtain rod, fold of drapery, or picture frame. Then it can easily be picked off.

There are nearly a thousand species of bats distributed throughout the world, most abundant in the tropics. Bats range in size from tiny ones of about an inch and a half in length to the giant fruit bat *Pteropus edulis*, or kalong, of Indonesia, which is a foot long and has a wingspan of five feet. In other places of the East it is called the flying fox. While in India I was told that the native flying-fox bat, when roasted, tastes just like chicken. I cannot vouch for this personally. Bats usually are dark brown, but one South American bat is white and a number of other varieties are marked beautifully with white and orange. Some bats are a bright red-orange.

I'm not going to confuse myself, or bore you, by delving into all the superfamilies and subfamilies of the bat. After all, how many bats does the average person encounter in a lifetime? To me, you see one bat, you've seen them all. I don't care if they are miserably misunderstood. I've other things to do besides getting involved with bats. I didn't even watch Batman on TV the first weeks. Suffice to say that there are two suborders of bats: Megachiroptera, the larger and vegetarian ones, and Microchiroptera, the smaller carnivorous ones — largely insect eaters and blood swillers. Most insectivorous bats, the ones we know best, live only four or five years. A bat doesn't lose its virginity until after its initial hibernation. Bats seldom have more than one offspring at a time. Being a mammal, the female bat has breasts for suckling her young, placed just as are those of apes, elephants, human mothers and sweethearts — but not nearly so attractive. As to varieties of bats: There are dog-faced, fruit, spinal-winged, epaulet, hammer-headed, tube-nosed, long-faced, flower, mouse-tailed, sheath-tailed, hare-lipped, slit-faced, horseshoe, leaf-nosed, javelin, spear-headed, centurion, long-eared, bent-winged, long-fingered, trumpet-eared, mastiff, free-tailed, false vampire, and true vampire bats. People want most to hear about that last one, the vampire.

Allow me immediately to correct one popular misconception: vampire bats do not suck blood; they lap it up with their tongues, much as a cat slurps up cream. *Desmodus* is the best known vampire genera; there are two much rarer, *Diphylla* and *Diaemus*. The most common vampire species, *Desmodus rufus*, is a small fellow about three inches long, not some great big scarey thing like Count Dracula.

Early travelers to tropical jungles brought back lurid reports of attacks by these bats on humans. Captain Jared Stedman in his *Narrative of a Five Years' Expedition Against the Revolted Negroes of Surinam*, published in the early nineteenth century, tells of his distress upon awakening at about four o'clock one morning in his hammock and finding himself weltering in congealed blood, without feeling any pain. He wrote:

The mystery was that I had been bitten by the vampyre spectre of Guiana, which is also called the flying dog of New Spain; and, by the Spaniards, *perrovolador*. This is no other than a bat of monstrous size, that sucks the blood from men and cattle, while they are fast asleep, even sometimes till they die; and, as the manner in which they proceed is truly wonderful, I shall endeavor to give a distinct account of it. Knowing, by instinct, that the person they intend to attack is in a sound slumber, they generally alight near the feet, where, while the creature continues fanning with his enormous wings, which keeps one cool, he bites a piece out of the tip of the great toe, so very small, indeed, that the head of a pin could scarcely be received into the wound, which is, consequently, not painful; yet, through this oriface, he continues to suck the blood, until he is obliged to disgorge. He then begins again and again, and thus continues sucking and disgorging, until he is scarcely able to fly, and the sufferer has often been known to pass from time to eternity.

Captain Stedman applied tobacco ashes to his wound as the best available remedy, and judged, from the congealed blood, that he'd lost about fourteen ounces of it.

Homeowners of America are much more apprehensive about bats since it was discovered that among bats the tropical vampires are not the sole vectors of rabies. Death by rabies is something no one would want to go through more than once. It is well described in a recent clinical study of a typical victim by D. L. Harris, medical director of the Pasteur Clinic in St. Louis, Missouri: "An excessive flow of thick tenacious saliva pours over his face and neck and becomes smeared on his hands and clothes and over the bedding and floor. These periods of rage are followed by moments of calm in which he usually shows anxiety for the safety of those around him and warns them of the approach of another crisis. Hyperesthesia of the skin to changes of temperature, and especially to currents of air, and increased sensitiveness to sound and light mark the progress of cerebral irritation. Convulsions are brought on by the least irritation and by the slightest current of air. . . ."

The fact that our native insectivorous bats can transmit rabies to humans was learned in 1951. In the fall of that year a west Texas cotton planter's wife, who had been bitten by a bat, was admitted to the Parkland City-County Hospital in Dallas with a tentative diagnosis of bulbar poliomyelitis, and died horribly within four days. An autopsy disclosed that the death was caused by "encephalomyelitis with demonstrable Negri bodies in central motor neurons." The presence of such bodies in the brain points to only one thing — rabies.

In the summer of 1953 the seven-year-old son of a Tampa, Florida, stockman was bitten by a bat which had swooped down from the sky where it had been circling ominously. The father killed the bat, and then on a hunch took the creature to the Board of Health for a laboratory examination. The findings were positive for rabies. The boy was given the Pasteur treatment and his life was saved.

In September of that year, the wife of an amateur ornithologist of Boiling Springs, Pennsylvania, a high-country resort about twenty miles west of Harrisburg, the state capital, was bitten by a bat while on a canoe trip with her husband. This bat also attacked without provocation or warning of any sort. The husband, being a naturalist, recognized the bat's behavior as abnormal, and within an hour the wife's wound had been cauterized and she had begun antirabies prophylaxis. Laboratory examination confirmed that the bat carried typical Negri bodies in its brain.

Two months later, in a Harrisburg tavern, a bat intruder fixed itself to the back of a patron's hand during the scuffle of chasing the creature from the barroom. This fellow was given superficial treatment for the wound at a local hospital and likely would be dead of rabies had not a reporter of the *Harrisburg Patriot*, while going home by cab that evening, learned of the gruesome accident. Doubting the credibility of the cab driver, the reporter on his way to work the next day checked the hospital records which verified the tale. Then, with the thoroughness typical of a good newshound, he dropped around to the office of the chief of veterinary public health of the Pennsylvania Department of Health. There he learned that the bat in all probability had been rabid. By luck Dr. Ernest J. Witte, the health officer whom the reporter contacted, had been involved in the case of the ornithologist's wife. And so the man that had been bitten in the bar also was saved from death.

A little more than two years after the last of these biting-bat accidents, the *Sante Fe New Mexican* carried a news story, authorized by the state Department of Public Health, with a six-column banner headline: CARLSBAD CAVE BATS INFECTED WITH RABIES. The account stated that Lieutenant Colonel Kenner Burns, chief of the veterinary virus laboratory at Fort Sam Houston, Texas, had found presence of rabies in 50 percent of the specimens of dead bats collected during a recent ten-day epidemic of bat deaths in the famous caverns.

Since that original Texas bat bite in 1951, the U.S. Public Health Service has undertaken an extensive investigation into the problem of rabid bats. Upwards of ten thousand bats have been bagged in sixteen different states; several hundred of them have been found definitely to be rabid. The government men believe that the Mexican free-tail bats of our Southwest are the culprits in the case, because they are known to migrate deep into Mexico's vampire country — in some instances even sharing the same caves with those bloodsuckers. Certain vampires of the tropics are known to be capable of transmitting rabies over long periods of time without showing the slightest signs of illness themselves. They're true carriers. It is hoped by all concerned that our native bats do not have that capacity. Remember Typhoid Mary?

When bats are inactive they often rest much as a dog or cat does, stretched out on their bellies with the muzzle hidden in the veils of their hideous little hands. During summertime naps bats dream just as dogs do — their wings flutter or shiver convulsively and sometimes a bat will talk in its sleep — but during the long slumber of winter nothing at all happens. The bat then is in a deathlike state with all action and thought suspended. It is not cold but hunger that causes the insectivorous bat to hibernate. Its food supply runs out and the bat must spend the winter living off a reserve of fat piled up during a short hunting season of but a few months. A bat hibernates only in a hanging position, upside down, with membranous wings arranged so as almost to conceal the muzzle.

In spring bats become fully awake in less than twenty-four hours — drawing in their wings, stretching muscles and bones, recognizing each other again with soft pipings and chatterings. Some, however, do not move — nor will they ever move again. They didn't store enough food before entering their winter torpor, and at some time during that season of total withdrawal they simply died, but remained hanging in position. Upon being touched, these slightly mummified bats crumble to silver gray dust. Sometimes only the stirring of the wings of the departing bats is enough to blow away these victims of winter sacrifice.

Bats turn up in odd places. In July 1966 at Hardwick, Vermont, in the Jaudevine Memorial Library, Mrs. Wanda Ainsworth, librarian, was washing her hands in the ladies' room when a bat emerged from the sink drain. As more bats followed, Mrs. Ainsworth hurriedly departed, and consequently the library was shut down two weeks for fumigating. At the recent New York World's Fair in the middle of one summer afternoon a bat swooped down from one of the light stanchions and bit a six-year-old Brooklyn boy. At the country auction in the Amish country around New Wilmington,

Pennsylvania, a bat flew out of a wicker hamper and sunk its fangs into one of the Pennsylvania Dutchmen's buggy horses.

Chimneys are a frequent roosting place for bats. The most effective way to get rid of them there is to seal off the chimney's bottom opening with wet paper packing, then drop two or three tablespoonfuls of Cyanogas-A dust down from the top, and quickly seal off that opening with a tight cover. To prevent reinfestation, install a screen over the chimney's top.

As denizens of the netherworld, bats are not alone in being greatly misunderstood. Many harmless snakes suffer our unthinking attacks (I've always suspected a lurking penis-envy); countless innocent insects, and a good many noninsect creatures as well, are caught up in the universal human hatred of anything that is small and crawls. Some of the noninsect fellow sufferers — for instance, the scorpion and centipede — deserve, if not annihilation, at least a precautionary approach, but prominent among them is one that doesn't warrant the cruelty we inflict. It is the spider. After the bat, it is the most feared and least acceptable mini-guest in our homes.

The Spider

Black widow's instincts guide her:
dark dusty trash will hide her
and appetite decide her.
Love's change has been denied her.
But no one's here to chide her —
no husband to deride her.
It's true he can't abide her:
he's stewing there inside her.

Part II

The Ugliest Ones: *The Spider* Whatever minor toleration there is of spiders is due largely to their historical reputation as healers of the sick. Once spiders were believed able to charm away all sorts of ailments and diseases. Crushed spiders were rolled into pills, mixed into ointments, and made into medicines. Healing potions were made of spiders brewed in alcohol. Warts, gout, jaundice, and even communicable diseases often were treated by concoctions made of dead spiders. Fevers reputedly were reduced by powders made of ground dry spiders, a remedy that dates back to the sixteenth century. One late eighteenth century prescription for fever was to swallow a spider that had been "gently bruised and wrapped up in a raisin or spread upon bread and butter."

A very early medical appraisal of the spider stated that: "The running of the eyes is stopped with the dung and urine of a House Spider dropt in with Oyl of Roses or one dram of Saffron, or else laid on alone with Wooll: whereby you may know that there is nothing so filthy in a spider that it is not good for something."

Belief in the therapeutic value of spiders prevailed until well after the end of the American Revolution, and as recently as the late nineteenth century a spider encased in a walnut shell was considered good insurance against many ailments. Such spider amulets had long been highly regarded. An eighteenth century spider enthusiast named Eleazer Albin wrote, in his *Natural History of Spiders and Other Curious Insects* (1736): "I have cured several children of malaria by hanging a large spider confined in a box about their necks, reaching to the pit of the stomach, without giving any internal remedies."

Spider silk once was a staple in household remedies, and still is in China, where it is widely used as an aid to blood clotting.

The spider is an arthropod, just as the insect is, but of a different class, Arachnida. Although bearing certain superficial similarities, the spider physically is quite unlike an insect. A spider has eight legs instead of six, two "hands" (palps) rather than antennae, six or eight simple eyes instead of complex ones, a body divided into fewer than the three parts characteristic of insects (head, thorax, abdomen), and no caterpillar-chrysalis stage in its life history.

The earliest known spider, *Palaeocteniza crassipes*, occurs in a fossil peat of Middle Devonian age (about 370 million years ago) in what is now Aberdeenshire, Scotland.

The spider, having a million or more different family members and twenty-five thousand varieties, is one of the earth's most numerous creatures. There are so many spiders in existence that a one-acre field of rough grass in late summer can support as many as 2¼ million spiders. In ten days that many spiders could spin one continuous thread that, if not broken by the clutter of satellites now orbiting the earth, would reach to the moon. Only one day's spinning could encircle the earth at the equator, according to W. S. Bristowe, England's most profound spider scholar.

It is characteristic of spiders to have vastly different habits, appearances, color, feeding patterns, and homes. Spiders are found from the arctic to the tropics, from sea edge to mountain snowline;

in desert and jungle, on the ground and vegetation; in forests, meadows, swamps, deserts, human domiciles, and caves. Spiders have been discovered alive at a greater altitude than any other land creatures. At the height of twenty-two thousand feet on Mount Everest jumping spiders (Salticidae) have been collected, and certain spiders live deep in coal mines.

Because spiders like tranquillity, they seldom are found in pinball machines, computers, discothèques, or sessions of the U.N. However, once a spider took up residence in our television screen. It perished one Tuesday night while Johnny Carson was simpering through a dog-food commercial, and now all that remains of that arthropod individual is an indelible brown speck in the upper right-hand corner of the picture tube.

In size, spiders range from those able to canter easily through the eye of an embroidery needle to tropical monsters with a leg spread twice the width of a man's palm and strength enough to vanquish small birds. The tiniest known spiders are the *Orchestina* and *Cepheia longiseta*, each of which is less than one-thirtieth of an inch in length. The largest known spider is the *Theraposa blondi* of the Guianas, South America; it is three and a half inches in body length with a leg span of ten inches, or about 105 times the size of the smallest spider. The rarest of all spiders are the primitive burrowing ones of the genus *Liphistius*, found in southeast Asia. The fastest spider is the *Tegenaria arrica*, clocked at 1.73 feet per second.

The only common denominator of spiders is their voracious appetite for insects. In its lifetime of eighteen months a single wheel-net spider, for instance, may destroy an average of two thousand insects. The estimated spider population of England and Wales, $2\frac{1}{5}$ billions, is said to consume 220 billion insects annually, their total weight supposedly exceeding that of all the humans in those two countries.

To my knowledge, such a compilation and comparison, typically British, has not yet been made in our own country, but it is acknowledged that spiders here gobble up an astronomical total tonnage of insects each year — much more than do birds, which get all the credit, principally because people are so foolishly fond of birds and so adamantly against spiders. Spiders should be better appreciated, for they do a yeoman's job of keeping down destructive hordes of gypsy moths, pea aphids, cotton worms, and those filthy little creeps, the houseflies. Spiders are pretty good on bedbugs, too, and are a major factor in the control of insects that damage forests. (A biologically sound forest has from fifty to 150 spiders per square yard.)

Spiders predigest most of their food by liquifying it with a powerful digestive fluid discharged on the prey. One African species can liquify a two-inch-long fish in less than three hours. After biting into an insect that has an obnoxious flavor a spider often will stagger to the edge of its web and throw up — a fluid actually oozes from the spider's mouth and the residue is rubbed away against a twig or leaf. Oddly, only a few varieties of spider will eat an aphid. The honeydew ooze so relished by ants is repellent to most spiders. Truly a case of one man's mead being another's poison.

Spiders have so many detractors that it is nice to be able to quote the spider's greatest admirer of all time, an early seventeenth century minister, the Reverend E. Topsell, who wrote of it: "The skin is so soft, smooth, polished, and neat, that she precedes the softest skin'd Mayds, and the daintiest and most beautiful Strumpets . . . She hath fingers that the most gallant virgins desire to have theirs like them, long, slender, round, of exact feeling, that there is no man, nor any creature, that can compare with her."

I don't imagine the good reverend was ever bitten by a spider. No one who has suffered through a serious spider bite could feel so lyrical about the little beasts. Actually, there are fewer spider nips than is commonly supposed. We are faithfully told by those who champion spiders that they don't bite us often because they love us so. Rubbish! In truth, it's more because our hides are too tough to be punctured by any but the largest spiders, and besides all spiders are exceedingly shy; when danger threatens, they will beat a retreat if at all possible. We are the aggressive ones.

Often we are so aghast upon being confronted by a spider that its size becomes greatly exaggerated. A classic instance of this magnification by fear is a report in 1751 of the slaying of a monstrous spider that had been lapping up the altar lamp oil at the Cathedral in Milan. The slayer preposterously claimed this spider weighed four pounds — about the size of a large Pekingese dog. No spider ever was that big. Even spiders in the three-inch range have trouble existing because their respiratory apparatus is much too small to cope efficiently with serving such a great body volume. Those reports of extraordinary church spiders no doubt were fabricated by thieving sextons to cover up their own filching of altar-lamp oil. Actually, spiders can't stand anything unctuous, including church sextons.

The word *spider* goes back to Old English *spinnan*, to spin, which acquired in Middle English the derivitive *spithre*, pronounced *spy-ther*, literally a spinner. The myth that a visit by a spider to one's garments is sure to bring a financial windfall goes back to ancient times when it was thought that if a spider, being such an expert weaver, was found running over one's clothes it had come to weave new ones, and that indicated imminent good fortune.

Relatively few spiders use their spinning abilities to build snares for capturing prey. The majority of spider species use their silk in constructing egg cocoons, sperm webs, molting sheets, burrow linings, hinges for entrances into lairs, and so forth.

Only spiders that make webs intended to capture insects produce silk having adhesive droplets — strung like beads along each strand. The largest web of the wheel-net cross spider, measuring sixteen inches, bears about 120,000 of such adhesive nodules on its myriad of strands. An insect trying to escape from a spider's web is comparable to a man knee-deep in snow attempting to outdistance a ski-borne pursuer. The spider herself does not become entangled in the sticky spirals of her own web because her feet are slightly oily.

The most complex webs are those of the geometric orb-weaver spider, of the family Argiopidae. A Great Smokies mountain spider, the *Hypochilus thorelli,* builds an unusual web shaped like a cone which hangs, apex up, from the underside of rock ledges.

The most nozzles for web spinning that a spider can have are four pair, found only in spiders named *Liphistiomorphae,* familiarly known to other spiders as "Big Squirts."

Web silk enables tiny spiders to travel great distances through the air, carried on trailing gossamer strands to landings on ship masts hundreds of miles from shore. Because it was the finest thread available, spider silk once was widely used as crosshairs in optical and surveying instruments, microscopes, and telescopic gunsights. Today, however, platinum filaments and engraved glass are considered superior.

In 1714 the Society of Sciences at Montpelier, France, was startled by the report of one of its members, M. Bon, that silk could be spun from webs of the *Pseudo-scorpiones* spider better than that made by silkworms. The Duke de Noailles promptly ordered a pair of spider-silk stockings to be presented to his lady friend, the Duchess of Burgundy, who had beautiful legs. The hose turned out to be so extraordinarily elegant that plans were laid to put spider-silk stockings into limited commercial production. The experiment ended unfavorably when it was discovered how difficult it was to breed this species of spider; that, at any rate, it would take 388 spiders to furnish as much silk as one silkworm; that 663,552 spiders, working night and day, would produce only one pound of such silk; and that anyway very few women of that day, except the Duchess, had legs nice enough to be sheathed in spider silk.

Instead of a web, the European and Asiatic aquatic spider, *Argyroneta aquatica,* builds a bell-shaped tent home, fills it with air, and submerges it in water. (The wolf spider *Lycosa purbeckensis* is able to dive under water carrying a bubble of air beneath it.) Land spiders often make tents about themselves in which to winter or to care for their broods. Western trapdoor spiders do not make webs at all but live in earthen burrows measuring from two inches to nearly a foot in depth, depending upon the size of the individual. These spiders range from one no bigger than a bee to one about as large as the upper joint of a man's thumb, and with a leg spread of two inches. Most remarkably, they make with spun silk perfectly fitted trapdoors for their underground homes — a marvel of engineering.

Recently a pair of scientists at the State University of New York at Syracuse, Dr. Peter N. Witt and Dr. Charles F. Reed, conducted a series of experiments purporting to prove that spiders, by means of their webs, can give to psychologists and pharmacologists (specialists in reactions to drugs) important messages that no other creature can match for subtlety, nuance, and reproductibility. By this work it is hoped to gain insight into many baffling problems concerning chemical effects on the central nervous system of the human body.

In the first of these spider-spinning studies the subjects were altered by the administration of drugs — tranquilizers, barbiturates, and hallucination compounds — but finally a laser beam was acquired for the work. It was able to burn out a tiny spot of spider nerve tissue one-thousandth of a millimeter in diameter, causing minor damage to the brain comparable to that made in the human brain by a slight stroke. Since the laser cooks as it pierces, sealing the hole as it is made, this method of nerve wounding has a great advantage over the use of a piercing needle. Even the most ultrathin one jabbing through the spider's hard outer skeleton would make an opening through which all the insect's vital juices would drain, thus causing it soon to die. The laser's lenses can focus the beam precisely on the desired spot, and the job is accomplished in one-thousandth of a second, therefore it doesn't matter at all if the spider moves. The two scientists believe that they are quantitatively measuring behavior in a way previously impossible.

Dr. Witt, in a newspaper article, explained his inclination to the spider as a research animal: "We pharmacologists are always looking for more eloquent members of the animal kingdom. Wire recordings of the brain waves of an anesthetized cat, the combativeness of Siamese fighting fish, and the restlessness of a mouse have all been used and are being used to show behavior changes produced by chemical compounds. But they are extremely crude compared with the fine variations in a spider's web produced by drugs, leg amputation, or by a tiny wound in his nervous system."

Psychologist Reed had this to add: "It takes a remarkable coordination of its eight legs for a spider to spin a web. When we remove one of his legs, he loses his zest for spinning, his spirals grow tighter and his web smaller."

That reference to the spider losing its zest for spinning reminds me of the apocryphal story of the psychologist who is testing a flea. He removes the legs one by one, commanding the insect after each amputation to "Jump!" It does each time. But upon removal of the final leg it no longer responds to the command, and the psychologist concludes that, "With all its legs removed, *Pulex irritans* loses its sense of hearing."

When Dr. Witt was asked whether any of his or Dr. Reed's work indicates that spiders have emotions or apprehensions as humans do, he smiled regretfully. "Emotions," he said, "are beyond our range."

So much for the various spiders' homes and spinnings. I now shall endeavor to explain the sex life of the spider although I'm not so sure that I fully understand it myself. I am not a Peeping Tom regarding spiders, and so can only set down here what I've learned by reading in the *Encyclopaedia Britannica*, which I regard as the Empire's noblest contribution to general obfuscation.

To touch on first things first: the reproductive organs of the male spider differ from those of all other animals. His copulatory apparatus is unique, because it is completely separated from the reproductive system proper, which in both sexes is situated in the abdomen — of all the hard-to-get-at places.

The female has two ovaries, two oviducts, a single very short uterus; on each side of it is an additional genital opening. These two openings lead to sperm receptacles, and in the more highly developed spiders are also connected with the uterus by special fertilization ducts. The male has the usual testes and a pair of deferent ducts leading from them to what I suspect is the penis, even though it is called the "common ejaculatory duct" by (A. PH.) the writer of the erudite *Britannica* article (who turns out to be, when I look him up in the contributors' listing, Alexander Petrunkevitch, Emeritus Professor of Zoology, Yale University, and not some old British funky-dunky as I'd assumed. Ah, but he's Russian). You've got to pay attention. The male genital opening is in the same position as that of the female. However — and now it gets pretty tricky — the organs of copulation customary to males (penis and testes), being inside the spider, have no way of directly contacting the female's reproductive mechanism, which lies within her body. So this is what spiders do to woo, as near as I can gather from the *Britannica's* muddle-through prose. It's a sort of artificial insemination deal. First, the male spider engages in a weird kind of internal masturbation to get up enough sperm to present to his lady love — a pumping-up process that takes from forty-five minutes to two hours, and leaves the poor devil so debilitated that he dies soon after courtship and mating have taken place. Now then, after he's got this great life-giving supply ready, he ejects some of it into a little special sperm web that he's woven all by himself. Then he transfers droplets of the sperm from the web to what are termed "pedipalpi," which I gather are the palms of his two "hands" (replacing the antennae of an insect). On each of them is a bulblike, spouted receptacle which accepts and holds the sperm. It is from these pedipalpi bulbs that the sperm is placed — in quick darts — on the female's genital openings to impregnate her. Once this is done the male takes off and is never seen again by the female — unless he gets caught in her web while escaping and is trapped. In that case she waits until she is hungry enough and then at her leisure eats him, pedipalpi and all.

Traditionally, spiders have been regarded as poisonous, and rightly so, for only two spider families, Uloboridae and Heptathelidae, have no poison glands. The old Anglo-Saxon name for a spider was *attercop*, or "poison head"; an ancient English proverb says, "Where the bee sucks honey, the spider sucks poison." Spiders' jaws do inject a poison able to kill small creatures, but there is considerable difference in its effect on midge and man. To humans an ordinary spider bite is not much worse than that of gnat or mosquito.

The most innocent-looking spider likely is the one we call the daddy-longlegs, a member of the order Phalangida, and also known as the harvestmen, harvester, harvest spider, shepherd spider, haymaker, pseudo-spider, and (in northern New York State) grandfather-graybeard.

The two commonly most dreaded spiders in the world are the tropical tarantula and the black widow, the popular name of an American spider (more properly called *Latrodectus mactans*, of the family Theridiidae) distributed from the central belt of the United States to Patagonia, and occasionally found as far north as the southern belt of Canada. Repeated bites by the Australian funnel-web spider of the family Agelenidae, and of the red-backed spiders *Latrodectus hasseltii*, also sometimes have lethal results.

The tarantula lives in a cylindrical burrow one inch in diameter which thrusts into the ground for a distance of about one foot. The first four or five inches of descent are vertical, then there occurs an angular drop followed by a horizontal turning elbow, after which comes another straight-down section. The burrow's orifice usually is surmounted by a shaft lip, wider than the opening and made of clay or dry wood. This protective edge prevents flooding of the burrow, aids in trapping prey, and keeps things from accidentally falling into and clogging the hole. The tarantula can be attracted from its lair by placing over the shaft opening a bottle in which a bee is entrapped. Country people of southeastern Italy ensnare tarantulas by blowing plaintive squeaks through an oat stalk into the burrow entrance, in imitation of an insect's vocalization. The tarantula ordinarily does not hunt from the comparative safety of its lair's anteroom. It is a night prowler, roaming the countryside on foot looking for prey, a skillful murderer attacking its victims with accuracy at the cervical ganglia, the nerve centers of the neck. The prey must be located, however, by touch, for although this marauding spider has eight pairs of eyes, its eyesight is so poor that it cannot tell night from day. These spiders are exceedingly cannibalistic. To put two of them together is akin to locking a Negro Phi Beta Kappa in the same room with a Mississippi Ku Klux Klan redneck.

The name of this spider derives from the ancient Roman city of Tarentum, where a European variety was particularly common. A dance was named for it — the tarantella. That came about back in the witchcrafty days of the Dark Ages when people feared their own shadows and firmly believed in evil spirits. One prevalent superstition was that sure death would result from a bite of this southern Italian tarantula. It was found that the usual treatments for the moribund — bat-dung poultices, powdered-toad pills, purée of owls' liver, or three mice teeth taken four times daily in a glass of Chianti — were to no avail against the bite of this spider. People so wounded developed an uncontrollable itch and rushed from their homes to thrash about madly in the public squares. Those who had not been bitten began greatly to admire what they considered a new dance form. Small bands were rustled up to accompany the frenzied twitchings, and eventually special music was composed for them. Everybody — spider-bitten or not — began doing the tarantella.

The true tarantula (*Lycosa tarantula*) for which the now-famous dance is named, is much smaller than our Western spider of that name (actually a wolf spider), which is so harmless that children of our Southwest Indians enjoy them as pets on leashes of string.

In South America, a giant spider, the *Grammostola*, is known as the tarantula. This tropical fiend is a dark, ugly, hairy horror, with gruesome curved tusk fangs that spurt sickening poison. It is so big and fierce that it dines regularly on birds, frogs and snakes — seldom bothering with such puny fare as insects. These tarantulas' main defenses against enemies are stiff fine hairs which cover their bodies. When angry, the tarantula scrapes some of them off with its legs and brushes them onto its attacker. If they get into folds of your skin you are in misery for two or three days. Chopped tarantula hairs are the principal ingredient of the itching powders sold in novelty stores to practical jokesters. Dan Mannix, the well-known witty observer of natural history, and one of the few Americans who have kept tropical tarantulas in captivity, once got a brushing of these hairs on his hand as an aftermath of smuggling a pair of the South American spiders past United States Customs officers. One of them had chewed out of the box in which it had been imprisoned in Dan's pocket, and was roaming loose when he went to retrieve it for transfer to a better carrier during the long drive from the airport to the Mannix farm. Mr. Mannix recounted the experience in a magazine article: "There are exactly 58 gas stations on the way home. I know because I had to stop at every one to wash my hands in a desperate attempt to get the hairs off. If you have ever run several semi-microscopic filaments of glass wool into your fingers, you have a dim idea of the sensation — especially if the wool had been dipped in whatever a mosquito uses to make its bites itch."

Mannix had picked up his tarantulas at the National Institution of Microbiology in Buenos Aires, Argentina, from Dr. Addalberto H. Ibarra-Grasso, who keeps a collection there of more than one hundred of these spine-chillers. He regards tarantulas with the affection most men reserve for dogs or horses. One of the most curious and most dangerous of this man's extraordinary collection is a tarantula called *Araña homicida*. Its venom is both neurotoxic and hematoxic — that is, it affects both the nervous system and the bloodstream — and it will leap onto a man to bite him.

Dr. Ibarra-Grasso also makes money from his dearly beloveds, by milking their venom for sale to serum manufacturers. In milking a tarantula her fangs are held over the edge of a small glass vial, and the last segment of the spider's abdomen is touched lightly with two live electrodes. The hot shot sends the venom squirting out in a torrent.

Since a tarantula's life history may take at least twenty-four years to complete, very few researchers choose this spider as a laboratory subject. I know of only one tarantula specialist in this country, Professor William Baerg, of the University of Arkansas, Fayetteville, Arkansas, who has devoted thirty-nine years to the study of this little-appreciated spider.

The tarantula is considered to be as intelligent as a goldfish —

which isn't saying much — but it is doubtful that the tarantula will ever replace it, the canary, or lovebird as a pet in American homes, even though, unlike birds, these spiders don't seem to mind confinement (possibly because being all but blind they're never really aware that they are in captivity).

That other public-enemy spider, the black widow (*Latrodectus mactans* of the family Theridiidae), is as repulsive as the tarantula in a different way. It is shiny jet-black, about as big as the end of a man's little finger, square, with an unattractive gash of mouth flanked by two revolting hairy fangs having nasty hooks on their tips. The underbelly is marked by a scarlet patch shaped like an hourglass.

This villainess is less ferocious than she looks. When disturbed, she does not attack but tries to remain in concealment or to escape. The black widow will bite only upon great provocation, but when it does the pain is intense, accompanied by tears, profuse sweating, constricted breathing, dizziness, convulsions, general prostration, and a vow to rejoin the church. The black widow's poison — strongly neurotoxic — is fifteen times greater than that of the rattlesnake (proven by comparison tests on rats). Indians of our Pacific Northwest used to make poisoned arrows by dipping the points into a paste made of freshly killed black widows; a deer, merely scratched by one such arrow, lasted no more than five minutes. An overseas cousin of the North and South American black widow called *Latrodectus tredecimguttatus* (one of the chief enemies of the migratory locust) likes to bite barefoot field hands in Italy and southern Russia. An effective antitoxin to the black widow spider's poison was discovered in 1942 by Dr. R. R. L. Sampayo of Buenos Aires.

When I was a boy, the black widow was the scariest spider of them all. You'd just sneak up behind your mother, aunt, grandma, or the lady next door and yell, "BLACK WIDOW!" and they'd jump a mile and scream *holyjesus!* It turns out that we were a lot more apprehensive of the black widow than we should have been, for, according to Dr. W. J. Gertach of the American Museum of Natural History, there have been less than fifteen hundred verified cases of black widow spider bites reported in 240 years — from 1726 to 1966 — and over that lengthy stretch only sixty-one were fatal.

The black widow as bugaboo has become passé. The other day I yelled "BLACK WIDOW!" behind a couple of ladies in hair curlers and toreador pants who were fingering bananas in the local A & P. Neither one turned a hair. I don't believe they'd ever heard of such a thing as a black widow spider — probably thought I was some kind of civil rights nut. The store manager still gives me peculiar looks and I'm just lucky that he continues to accept my checks.

The black widow is not a house spider, but prefers to live in places from which there is easy escape, such as: animal burrows, culverts, lumber piles, deserted outbuildings, rock piles and crevices, hollow logs, under loose bark of trees, in crotches of large tree branches, on palmettos and cacti, in embankment holes, in beehives — although occasionally one does roost in a little-used cellar or some other deserted corner of a home. This spider never spins a wheel-shaped web, but lives in a tunnel of coarse cobweb, a dusty funnel usually running into and under trash piles; she never bothers her ugly head over such romantic nonsense as sunlit lace embroidery spun gently over silver staircases. Much of the black widow's time is spent hanging — upside down — in the circular doorway of her cylindrical burrow — the better to tempt passing prey with the hourglass on her belly.

The black widow lives only about three months. Its babies are born from eggs which their mother places in a specially woven cup of webbing that is fastened to the outside of the nest; the eggs, about four hundred in all, hatch in three weeks, and then the spider mites begin eating each other — strong versus weak. Whenever the weaklings are all gone, the cottony ball of baby spiders splits open and out they swarm to join the world of grown-up predators. Before the year is out there will be three more crops of these little horrors — unless a Coquillett fly gets to the sack first. That rare California insect is a black widow baby eliminator. It lays its own eggs in the tiny pouch and when they hatch in three days the fly larvae make short work of the embryonic spiders. Curiously pigeons, wasps, and chickens are able to eat the black widow spider without ill effects.

About ten years ago a Midwestern brown spider (*Loxosceles reclusa*) began to be known as a serious biter of humans, although it had been around a long time without attracting undue attention. It is yellowish to dark brown in color, with a body about one-quarter of an inch long, and is related to the South American spider *Loxosceles laeta*, which has been identified as the cause of gangrenous spot in humans. The bite of the brown spider was found to be much worse than that of the black widow, which has a neurotoxic venom (affecting the nerve centers directly). Recovery from a black widow bite is rapid, although the victim suffers great agony while in its grip. The brown spider's venom is necrotoxic — that is, it causes destruction of tissue at the site of the bite. In a day or so after the bite has been inflicted, the area around it begins to look like a blister filled with blood, and after several days the center of the bite turns black and finally sloughs off, leaving a deep ulcer that may expose underlying muscles and take several weeks, or even months, to heal.

The Wasp

In humming teams of two
wasps ramble in the eaves —
leave and enter turban houses
hid by lilac leaves.
Soft organdy houses
shelter these enamelled pairs.

Pleated leather strips
make fan-folded wings —
banded stems hold golden leg-wisps —
quadrilateral stings.
Now! clinging wasp-lisps —
mouths of wounds show, marked in squares.

Part III

The Ugliest Ones: *The Wasp* The bat and spider are feared out of all proportion to their danger, but there is one frequenter of our domiciles — the wasp — that fully warrants alarm. It is widely regarded as being only mildly dangerous, although the U.S. Department of Agriculture gets over ten thousand requests for wasp information each year; over seventy-five thousand copies of its wasp leaflets have been distributed in the past five years.

Entomologists and even some doctors more or less ignore the importance of wasp stings, and the public is inclined to look upon them as a source of amusement — a fit subject for comic strip joshing. But, to the victim of a wasp sting, the situation is far from amusing. A person bitten by a wasp may become seriously ill, be hospitalized, and even die from just a single sting.

I have before me three newspaper clippings of three deaths by wasp sting — all of them in my immediate vicinity: a middle-aged

portrait artist and dance orchestra accordionist of North Tarrytown, New York, died from stings of yellow jackets that were dislodged while he was shingling the home of a friend; in Coopers-
town, New York, a surgeon forty-nine was killed by multiple stings
of hornets encountered while removing vines that had overgrown
the windows of his summer home; in North Tarrytown again, a
carpenter forty-four was fatally stung by wasps that attacked him as
he worked on a roof. As another example of the lethal qualities of
the wasp, I cite a Reuters report from Hong Kong of November 29,
1966, that tells about a barricade of hornets' nests placed on a
highway by Vietcong guerrillas to block an advance of South Vietnamese government troops.

Wasps kill more people each year in the United States than do
snakes, spiders, or scorpions. Of human deaths from venomous
animals, wasps are responsible for 40 percent, poisonous snakes 33
percent, and scorpions and other venomous animals 27 percent.
Data on this subject are very difficult to obtain, however; the figures likely do not include all deaths due to wasp stings, since some
hospitals do not separate the causes of death into particular
venoms but lump them all together simply as "venomous." Reaction to wasp stings is not even a separate category in morbidity
reports. Many physicians do not recognize the symptoms of wasp
sting; many coroners are not aware of anaphylactic shock as a cause
of death, and thus quite a lot of deaths from the sting of a venomous insect are listed as resulting from heart attacks or heat stroke.
Also wasps' stings cause more deaths by automobile accident than
they are given credit for. Even a minor reaction to such an attack
will dangerously distract a motorist. A report of the North Vietnamese press agency states that a Vietcong peasant, Doan Van Chia,
has trained regiments of wasps to act as "winged guerillas" in attacking enemy forces. For his work, Mr. Chia was awarded the title
"Rudimentary Weapons Engineer."

Wasps are so brave that they attack not only people but the
dreaded tarantula spider. Only two strategic thrusts are used to
immobilize it. In the first one, the wasp's stinger darts lightning-
swift straight down the throat of the spider, right between its

gnashing, poison-drooling fangs. For supreme daring there is nothing like this in the annals of insect combat. In a flash the fangs hang limp, their power gone forever. Next, the wasp strikes exactly the right spot on the tarantula's hairy body to paralyze its legs. The frightful hulk crumples, now fit only for wasp food. An egg will be laid on this living inert body of the spider, and in due time the grub will hatch and begin to feed on the live flesh. Oddly, this small, blind speck of life never attacks the vital organs of its meal ticket, and the immobilized spider lives on, though it is being gnawed to pieces bit by bit, day by day.

The term wasp is broad and covers many kinds of Hymenoptera, but usually is limited to predominantly carniverous forms, muddaubers, and noncarniverous gall wasps. Solitary wasps are the greatest enemies of the spider; to many of them it is their only food.

Most wasps are of this loner type. Of the wasps' total number of species, ten thousand (with twenty-five hundred in North America, but only fifty of them troublesome to man), about eight hundred species are social insects (i.e., living in colonies) of the family Vespidae. In our country the most prominent of the social wasps are the hornet, yellow jacket, and the *Polistes*. Our solitary wasps — the diggers and tunnelers — include the mud-dauber, noncarniverous gall wasps, and the parasitic wasps. Two of the smaller parasitic wasps like to nestle in beds, the *Eypris californicus* and the *Scleroderma macrogaster*. An attack from one of them at a strategic moment will most certainly add to a man's reputation as a bedchamber athlete.

Aside from their stinging potential, wasps are friends of man. They feed mostly on other insects. Yellow jackets eat vegetable matter, such as overripe fruit, and soft-bodied insects, feeding the juices to their young. Both this wasp and the *Polistes*, larger mahogany-colored ones, kill such garden pests as the corn earworm and the army worm. The *Polistes*, most valuable recruit in the war against the American tobacco hornworm, kills over 60 percent of these tobacco fiends. The thread-waisted and digger wasps are the tarantula killers and horse guards (they catch horn, horse, and stable flies that pester livestock). Parasitic wasps combat all kinds of destructive insects, though they do not confine themselves to injurious ones. Some of these wasps are so small that several may develop within an insect egg no larger than a pinhead; others have a body length of two or more inches.

In American folklore, the wasp is strongly associated with Cupid — possibly because that cherub's arrow is of the same potency as a wasp's sting. In the hills of Kentucky, any maiden stung by a wasp in the spring is sure to lose her virginity before winter's first frost. A sting to a married woman indicates a coming pregnancy, and/or a surprise visit by an illicit lover. Young girls of the Ozarks once made a practice of pinning wasps' nests to their underwear to attract men. The come-on, I suppose, was, "Why don't y'all come up to the cabin and see my wasp nest?" In Tennessee back country if the postman is stung by a wasp that means he'll soon be bringing bad tidings — possibly news of a death — to the family on whose property he was attacked.

A wasp actually was the attacker in that insidious nursery rhyme about Little Miss Muffet. I daresay that a disclosure at this late date concerning Little Miss Muffet will have little effect on a world preoccupied with technology, and engulfed in automation, psychiatry, outer-space rocketry, and the foolish fervors of sex, religion, chauvinism, racial integration, and xenophobia — but since it concerns the wasp, I pass it along for what it is worth.

Little Miss Muffet indeed "sat on a tuffet, eating her curds and whey," but she was frightened not by a spider, but by a whole slew of wasps. The real-life counterpart of the young lady of the famous nursery jingle was a Miss Patience Muffet, daughter of Dr. T. Muffet, author of *Theater of Insects*, an addition to the 1658 edition of the famous British natural history classic *History of Four-footed Beasts and Serpents*, by Reverend E. Topsell. It seems, according to Dr. Muffet's recently discovered diary, that the incident occurred during a picnic in Epping Forest when the party, including Miss Muffet, was forced to flee in panic by the attack of a horde of wasps who'd come to feed on the picnic baskets parked by a tree under their nest. Dr. Muffet very likely had some difficulty rhyming "wasp" with "sat down beside her" and settled on "spider" instead. Well, that's the way things go in the writing trade. You've got to roll with the punches.

Household Pests and Exterminators

Bedbug, rugbug, moth and weevil —
terminate those lives; they're evil
dedicates to mastication,
callous to all supplication.
Unregenerate, these vermin!
Piety, their ends determine!

6

When They Crawl, Call: *Household Pests and Exterminators* Fortunately a host of professional exterminators stands ready to advance against any and all invasions of miniature monsters. About five thousand such firms operate in this country, employing approximately twenty thousand people (mostly service personnel); the annual volume of business exceeds $225 million. Colossus of the lot is Orkin Exterminating, of Atlanta, Georgia, which has outlets in thirty-five states. It is the elephant among turtles. In 1966, Orkin hit a gross of $71 million, with a net of $4.2 million — and that adds up to a powerful lot of rats, mice, and cockroaches that will never see the sun go down again.

That competition in the pest control business is keen can be seen by turning to the *Exterminating* listings in the Yellow Pages of the telephone book of any major United States city. Even Key West, Florida, the southernmost and most remote point in the

States, lists two exterminating services (one of them, Orkin). Dallas advertises 159 companies specializing in pest work; St. Louis has 78 and Phoenix, 57. Chicagoans pestered by cockroaches or rats can call for relief on any one of 162 outfits; in Detroit there are 83 available; Washington, D.C. boasts 100. The San Francisco total is 37; Los Angeles, 123; Miami, 78; Pittsburgh, 49; and Philadelphia, 168. In New York, Manhattan listings number 157; Brooklyn, 179; the Bronx, 89; Staten Island, 14; and Queens, 147; for a grand total of 586 firms in the five boroughs.

New York pest control men go to extraordinary lengths to be at the head of the Yellow Page listings. In Manhattan the first company in line simply is A, followed by AAAA AAron Exterminators, and then in succession there are AAAA ABBEY; AAA Exterminating and Chemical Corporation; and A ACE Purina Von Damm, Corporation. In the Brooklyn spread, AAAA AARON gets bumped to second place, superseded by AAAA AABBA Pest Control. A few of the Manhattan firms seem to cater to ethnic groups. There is the Fumigadora Latina Compania and the Oriental Exterminating Corp., as well as Sure-Pop Exterminators, who could be wooing business from young newlyweds.

From perusing the Yellow Pages as I've moved about the country (the lousiest motel pastime I know of), I'd gotten the idea from exterminator ads that termites were the big thing in this business. It wasn't until I'd talked to some genuine live exterminators that I learned the fallacy of my thinking. It's rats, mice, and roaches all the way that make the most dollars for pest control men. Like a litany, exterminators chant, "Rats, mice, and roaches. Rats, mice and roaches." Termite control constitutes only about 30 percent of an exterminator's total business in the Northern states and about 50 percent down South.

One of my most interesting meetings with pest control men was with Walter Blank, the first fellow I called upon. Mr. Blank is head of the Abalene Pest Control Service, Inc., New York's largest upstate exterminating firm, in Poughkeepsie, not far from my home. Walter turned out to be quite different from what I expected. Not having had much truck with exterminators in recent years, I guess I was still hung up in the oldtime bedbug-cockroach-rat syndrome of regarding these people as shady, slovenly characters about on the intellectual level of garbage collectors. Apparently my wife also retained such a conception, for before I'd left home to drive upriver to Poughkeepsie, she'd said, regarding the name of Abalene's head man, "That can't be his real name. He probably doesn't want it to be connected with bugs. He's hiding behind a fake one."

"A pestdonym?" I suggested. "Come off it, this is the space age."

Yet, as I drove along the Dutchess Turnpike looking for Abalene's street number, I did half expect to find the company established in some dingy storefront or holed up in the parlor of one of those terribly tacky, front-porched houses that prevail in Po'keepsie — which is about as dreary a town as I care to visit, despite the recent spiritual and facial uplift engendered by the influx of IBM enterprises.

When I finally found Abalene I wasn't prepared for the modern elegance of its plant and offices. They seemed more suited to a stockbroker than to my preconceived notion of bug buster. The spacious room into which I was welcomed was tastefully furnished, indirectly lighted, and handsomely paneled in a glowing dark wood. There were no portraits in oils of rats, no heroic hand-painted plaster models of cockroaches. No one sprayed me as I entered. Trim business machines clattered, clicked, and shifted for themselves; neat girl clerks bustled about and secretaries with nice gams and lacquered fingernails tapped discreetly on electric type-writers. Mr. Walter Blank himself sat in an inner office, casually behind a large neat-looking desk.

I'd sort of expected someone on the order of Eliza Doolittle's father, but this fellow was slim and young — early thirties, I judged — with a broad, rounded, pleasant face, snub-nosed. His eyes crinkled almost shut whenever he smiled, which I soon found to be often. His hair, a stiff, sandy-red brush, swept forward like the prow of a ship. I liked this bug battler immediately, and wished that I could tell him of some place that had millions of cockroaches and rats just dying to be exterminated.

I should have said "controlled," as exterminated is not a word that modern pest men like to hear. Those who hold checkrein on our pest population feel the term no longer applies accurately to the industry, as 90 percent of the work today is preventive. The term "pest control" seems a better description of the overall operation.

"We do mostly contract work here," explained Walter, in beginning our dialogue, "hardly ever have what we call 'cleanout' — one-shot extermination jobs. We handle very few individual residences — mostly business and industrial accounts. Almost all our work is preventive, involving monthly inspections and treatment. We handle IBM, for instance, Vassar College, and a lot of big first-class establishments like them, but the bulk of our business is with much smaller outfits and food establishments, such as cafés, bars, and restaurants."

The shift in emphasis in the extermination trade, he explained, was due to increased public enlightenment regarding sanitation. Except in slum areas, American homes no longer are filthy. Modern materials and construction methods make them easier to keep clean.

"It used to be," Walter explained, "that roaches and rats were taken for granted. Today, now, if a food establishment spots just one roach, we get a call right away to come down and check the place out."

I was led to the shipping room and shown stacks of cylindrical cardboard cartons — each about a yard long and six inches in diameter — that contained an anticoagulant rat bait.

"We use about eighty-six thousand pounds of it a year," said Walter, "to keep down the rat population."

"What do you recommend for flies?" I asked.

"Best seller for flies," he replied, "still is the good old aerosol bomb. It still kills the most, although one company now makes a resin strip — looks just like a big yellow taffy bar that releases an organic phosphate gas, DDVP, very slowly over a period of three months. It kills flying insects by knockdown. It's what we call space treatment."

After kindly translating DDVP as dichlorovinyldimethylphosphate, Walter went on to say that the biggest single change in the business since he broke into it as a boy is in fumigation.

"There's one thing you don't see much of around pest control establishments any more," he said, "and that's cyanide boxes. There's just not that much fumigation being done today. Oh, maybe once in a great while some freight cars of grain will get fumigated, but that's about it. Why, when I was a boy I remember that my father brought home enough wooden cyanide boxes to make me a backyard fort that finally got to be about three stories high. I got to like it so much that I wanted to take it with us when we moved, but my father wouldn't let me."

Another significant change in the pest control business is the recent introduction of organic phosphate insecticides such as diazinon, malathion, entex, ronnel, dicapthon, delnay, and DDVP. They have come about largely because of the resistance to chlordane that has developed in the German cockroach, which is the key to general pest control.

The cost of pesticides used by pest control firms amounts to approximately 10 percent of their gross business. The most used chemical is chlordane, important in both general pest and termite control. DDT comes next in usage by professionals, followed by diazinon, lindane, dieldrin, aldrin, and heptachlor. Diazinon is the chemical most favored now against cockroaches.

An odd killer of insects was suggested by a Harvard University professor, Carroll Williams, of the Department of Biology, who succeeded in isolating from copies of newspapers (the *Boston Globe, Wall Street Journal,* and *New York Times*) a hormone that can effectively kill insects. "There is enough of it in the Sunday *Times*," said Professor Williams, "to kill, literally, billions of insects." The hormone is manufactured by the balsam fir, the *Abies balsamea,* which is used to make newsprint.

On occasion commercial exterminators are called upon to annihilate mosquitoes. In 1964 it was reported that mosquitoes were a peril to the building of the huge rocket that will be used in an attempt to land a man on the moon. Day-biting mosquitoes from the salt marshes around the Michoud, Louisiana, plant of the Boeing Company were so bad that wives of the engineers did not dare let their children out to play, and the enforced confinement created domestic tensions that were destroying the efficiency of the plant workers. Indifference of local residents, accustomed to Southern mosquitoes, added to the exasperation of the Northerners.

I asked Walter Blank how he, as a dealer in chemical pesticides, regarded Rachel Carson's sensational best seller *Silent Spring*.

"I believe," he said, "that a lot of people bought it that didn't bother to read it through, and I think it was somewhat misleading in a good many places. For instance, there's one place where she speaks of parathion poisoning in one paragraph, and then starts the next one talking about malathion, so that a casual reader might lump the two together or be confused over them. Parathion *is* lethally dangerous, but, shucks, I'd be willing to bet I could drink a water glass full of malathion and it wouldn't affect me too much — might get a little sick, is all. And the whole book was like that — full of half truths and scare statements that maybe you could prove and maybe you couldn't."

I suggested that the pest control business must be almost unbearably competitive.

"Around the big cities it is bad," conceded Walter. "There if you do a contract service for five dollars, you'll always find some joe willing to do it for four — then someone else will take it on for three, and maybe even two dollars or a buck."

"But what can anyone do — about rats, for instance — for just one dollar?" I asked.

"For a dollar about all you can do," replied Walter, "is to swing open the front door and yell, 'All right, all you rats! ALL rats OUT!'"

I learned that an annoying and little-publicized problem faced by pest control operators is that of insect phobias, or pest hallucination. Often the pest control man is called in by a client who is convinced that he is a victim of an invisible infestation that is causing him painful itching or other discomfort. Usually nothing, not even the most diligent examination of the premises, will convince the sufferer that no insects or bugs are present. Unscrupulous exterminators sometimes will take advantage of such a situation and chemically treat the areas in question, perhaps hoping to effect a psychological victory over the problem, but an honest firm will recommend that the customer consult his family physician. Very few are daring enough to send the sufferer to a psychiatrist.

Most people feel quite capable of banishing from their households such irritating intruders as spiders, wasps, flies and fleas, clothes moths, carpet beetles, bedbugs, silverfish, ants, and the various other pantry pests. The casual, homespun approach to their control by means of window screening and store-bought sprays and dusts, while often inefficient, frequently is successful if the invasions are of a minor nature.

"Usually," said Walter Blank, "it's only when things get out of hand that a family will call us in to get rid of the more common household pests."

Pest control service appeals to people who don't want to take the time, trouble or risk to do the work themselves. Often they don't know how to start or where to look for the hiding holes. Neither do they have thorough knowledge of insect life or necessary and proper equipment.

General pest control (more specifically, structural pest control — concerned with pests in or around buildings) represents from 50 to 60 percent of the total exterminating business. Of primary concern in this division, as already stated, are roaches (especially the persistent German cockroach), rats, and mice. Flies, ants, fleas, moths, and carpet beetles are of subordinate interest. Control of wood-destroying organisms accounts for 35 percent of the commercial exterminators' gross business. The termite is the most potent pest in this category, followed by powder post beetles, old house borers, wharf borers, and carpenter ants. Other services of lesser importance to the pest control industry include: mothproofing, fumigation, pest-bird control, control of pests bothering ornamental plants, weed control, tree spraying and pruning, and the sale of pesticide products to the general public.

From Walter Blank I learned that since farmers seldom call for help in ridding their buildings of bats, and because serious infestations of them occur so rarely in towns and cities, they are not a major problem to commercial pest control operators. The bat is not even listed in the Serviceman's Manual of the National Pest Control Association, an alliance of one thousand of the most reputable professional exterminators in America, with headquarters in Elizabeth, New Jersey.

The names of most exterminating firms are fairly conservative, but I've culled a few from the NPCA membership list that seem to have lost their cool: Guarankil Co., Inc.; Breth-O-Death Laboratories, Inc.; Askus Pest Control Corp.; Adroit Chemical Pest Control Co.; Ailing House Pest Control; Paradise Pest Control; and A.A.A. Aabaddon Exterminating Co. Of all those I've come across, my favorite remains either: "Buggie" Bales (Spraying by Appointment Only), or Nighthawk Co., Inc., "Willie, the Bug Man" (We Use Unmarked Cars). Both firms are in St. Louis. The three runners-up in my league are: Getz Gets 'Em, No Squawkin's, Call Lawkins, and Roaches No More with J. Narmore.

From Naples, Florida, the millionaires' town (thirty-six in residence during the winter season), a nonmillionaire friend has passed on to me what I regard as the most appropriate name a pest control man ever could have — Seymour Roach, who does business at that resort haven. In some areas of the Deep South cockroaches are a badge of prestige; if they inhabit your house, it means that at least you're eating well enough to support them.

Cockroaches, rats, and mice cause a ghastly share of household destruction, but the most costly predators of all are the fabric pests: principally the carpet beetles, the tapestry and clothes moths. Between them they cost our nation about half a billion dollars annually in damages and expenditure on control.

The most destructive carpet beetle, and possibly the greatest damager of woolen fabrics in the world, is the black carpet beetle, also known as the buffalo moth. It came here originally from the Orient about 150 years ago and is most prevalent in our Northern states. Feeding on both plant and animal protein, it likes to cuddle up in wool and many other woven materials, and relishes such things as horsehair furniture stuffing; furs; feathers; horn; dried meat; dead insects, animals and birds; kid leather; milk powders and bookbindings. Although the introduction of synthetic fibers in rugs and clothing has greatly reduced their food potential, wall-to-wall carpeting remains a superb haven for the black carpet beetle. The advent of the disposable paper container for vacuum cleaners eliminated one of this beetle's long-standing habitations — the dusty cloth bag. However, modern duct work for heating and air-conditioning has furnished new and more ingenious hideouts.

The carpet beetle likes to be associated with housekeepers who dust indifferently, who favor rugs that are tacked down and therefore seldom shaken out, who vacuum infrequently and listlessly without moving the furniture. These sluggards are inclined to consider the results of beetle banquets merely as ordinary wear and tear on the old broadloom.

Black beetle larvae are scavengers of materials having high protein content, and often are found in the dead bodies of insects and rodents, or in the nests of bees, wasps, animals, or birds after the beetles have abandoned temporary stopovers there. Larvae started in those locations readily migrate into the living quarters of a building. There they are able to thrive on lint and dust within, under, or behind furniture; in such appliances as radios and record players and television sets; in rugs and the felts of pianos; around floors or their baseboards; and inside furniture and air ducts.

Equally destructive as the carpet beetle are the tapestry and clothes moths. Few Americans escape paying tribute to them in riddled clothing, drapes, and bedding. It isn't the little moths themselves that do the damage however; killing them will give you nothing more than a sweet taste of vengeance. It's their hungry larvae that do the trick. These wormlike things, when newly hatched, are one thirty-second of an inch long and no thicker than a man's chin whisker. They survive on what organic materials they can find in food, beer, bloodstains, and other common soil on clothing. Like the black beetle, they are tickled to find fur and feathers.

These ravagers do poorly on clean feeding grounds. When one hundred eggs are deposited on a clean piece of wool, only one may live and it may only partially develop. That it lives at all is only because it feeds on the bodies of the other ninety-nine brothers and sisters. Therefore dry-cleaning, followed by mothproofing, is the best preventative against fabric pests. It is well to remember that a cedar chest or closet in itself is not mothproof, but affords excellent protection for stored materials simply because its joints are airtight enough to prevent the infiltration of dust and lint on which moth larvae feed. Don't rely entirely on the snugness of the chest or closet for protection, but also put flakes of naphthalene or paradichlorobenzene — a pound for every one hundred cubic feet of space — inside the chest or closet at its top, because the moth-killing fumes seep downward. Sprays that include DDT, lindane, and fluorine compounds also are effective in protecting woolens against the pernicious moths.

Another troublesome household beetle is the powder-post beetle, long familiar to farmers who find them in fence posts and barn timbers. These wood-damaging beetles migrated to cities and suburbs in the great post-World War II building boom by hitch-hiking on the millions of feet of lumber used in construction. Because of the inordinate demand for wood, often it was not practical to give timber proper care during production and warehousing, and the beetles thus were encouraged to enter it. Some of these beetles even bore into the wood while it is still green in forest or lumber yard. Once established, they tunnel in every direction, chewing the wood to a fine dust, weakening it with hidden chambers and tunnels. The larvae of these beetles remain in the wood for from one year to as long as eighteen years, before emerging as adults.

Wood already infested presents difficult eradication problems, but almost any finish — paint, varnish, wax or even an oil coat — will prevent these beetles from originally piercing a piece of wood. There are five groups of them, but the *Lyctus* beetle probably is the best known because it fancies the hardwoods used in home floor construction and furniture manufacture. It is a slender, inch-long beetle, dark brown or black.

The longhorn beetle, known as the "old house borer," doesn't necessarily confine its destructive activities to old houses. The name refers to the fact that it takes this beetle up to seventeen years to reach adulthood. The sapwood of pine, spruce, or Douglas fir timber is this borer's prime target. An adult enters the wood by drilling holes that measure one-quarter to a half inch in diameter, and then lays its eggs in the shafts. From egg to adult stage commonly takes from three to seven years, with the grubs merrily tunneling away all that time. Just thinking about it is enough to give a builder nightmares.

Many of the insects and other arthropods that bother homeowners are not indoor pests, but simply come inside to enjoy a winter holiday. Ever since man devised steam heat and insulation, more and more insects have caught on to the Sybaritic advantages of civilization and are spurning their usual cold-weather haunts of hollow trees, fallen logs, and other such shelters. Also, man's migration from city to suburb and country has brought perfect winter quarters right into the insects' own territories.

One of the most pesky of these winter moochers is the clover mite, a relative of the spider. It is tiny (no bigger than a pinhead), measured in microns, and it doesn't bite humans or eat their food, yet it is a nagging nuisance. Lush green lawns are its natural food and when the grass disappears in the fall the clover mites, seeking warmth, desert it and crawl cozily into the houses that surround those carpets of green. An invasion of clover mites can bring as many as a quarter of a million individuals into one room. They are impossible to pick up (except very gingerly with a high-powered vacuum cleaner), to sweep out, or dispose of otherwise without leaving blood-red stains where their bodies have been crushed.

A common pest, especially in brand-new houses, is the silverfish, an extremely shy, swift-scurrying insect, half an inch in length, found wherever there is moisture. The silverfish loves to live in the damp cellars of a newly constructed home. Its new lumber, with high moisture and sap content, furnishes a readily available supply of sugary resin that can be converted into the starch upon which this insect thrives. The silverfish also will take this nutriment from bookbindings, the filler of drapery materials, and wallpaper paste. Silverfish are able to eat the starchy-sized coated surface off a sheet of paper — writing, or printing included — without ever drilling a single hole in the sheet itself.

Pantry pests often are a great nuisance to housewives. These are the insects with a fondness for food staples — flour, pastry mixes, cereals, grain, dog foods, nuts, and tobacco, spices, paprika, celery seed, and herbs. Among these dreary little creeps are: the bran beetle (family members include the red, saw-toothed, and confused flour beetles — so-named because entomologists are confused in properly classifying it; the cabinet beetles and relatives, collectively called the dermestids (they have drilling equipment able to bore through sealed packages); the drugstore and cigarette beetles, with such low-hanging heads they sometimes are termed the "modest" beetles; the weevils (bean, rice, and granary); food moths, especially the Indian meal moth; hide and larder beetles that have a wide taste range from hams, bacon, cakes, and cheese to garbage. The answer to pantry pest control is either scrupulous cleanliness or a rigidly adhered-to program of eating in restaurants.

The bedbug (*Cimex lectularius*) is considered the most shameful of all household pests. Most people would rather be caught dead than in bed with a bedbug. It is one of man's most unpleasant insects, and it's been with us a long time. Many a high-class pest control firm got its start with bedbugs. "We first began to grow," I was told by one young second-generation pest control man whose family firm now is one of New York State's largest and most respectable, "when my father got the contract for bedbugs in the old CCC camps up in the Adirondacks." (*CCC: Civilian Conservation Corps, a work-camp aid program for young men back in the depression Thirties.*)

In some areas the bedbug is called a chinch bug, or a mahogany flat, or a red coat. Unfed, it is flat and papery looking, a spade-shaped thing, dark red in color and about a quarter of an inch long. It looks like a discouraged Negro ladybug. After feeding, the bedbug is as plump as a new pillow. Bedbugs feed on animal blood, preferring that of humans to the blood of chickens, mice, rabbits, guinea pigs, and rats, which they also relish. Once a puncture is made by the elongated beak, this insect injects a fluid to prevent clotting, so that there is a free flow of blood for the three to five minutes needed to fill its tank with food enough to last several days. Older bedbugs sometimes go from two weeks to two months without nourishment; under ideal conditions, a bedbug can live a year or longer without dining out.

Bedbugs have always been associated with the depressed and deprived. And, like every other meager possession of the poor, the bedbug has been forced to contribute maximum usefulness. In big-city slums at the turn of the century, a favorite energizer and courage stimulator was a mixture made of sorghum juice, black beans, garlic, rum, and seven freshly killed bedbugs. Among the penniless, bedbugs long were advocated as certain cures for sore eyes, wax in the ears, ingrown toenail, itching navel, runny nose, and quartan plague (a fever recurring every four days). Even hysteria has been treated by applications of bedbugs; the acrid smell of these insects often was considered sufficient to relieve a person suffering hysterical suffocation. In the benighted bayous of Louisiana, to dream of a bedbug is a sure sign of impending illness. But to find one in the negligee of your loved one is indication of imminent incredible good fortune or a sign that she has dirty underwear.

Repulsive as they may seem to us, bedbugs love each other. Uniquely, the female is not impregnated by way of the vagina; instead, the male injects his spermatozoa into a copulatory pouch called the organ of Ribaga, beyond which is a tissue known as the organ of Berlese. After passing through these two organs, the spermatozoa reach the genital tract by wandering through the general body cavity. Seems a little haphazard to me, but they seem to know what they're doing.

A decade ago the bedbug encountered DDT and was started on its way to extinction. In the years following World War II that chemical was so effective against the little bloodsuckers that scientists at times were hard put to find live specimens for laboratory study. However, nature's persistence in continuing a species influences insects to develop, from occasional exceptionally strong individuals that survive various chemical poisons, strains that will survive such killers. That happened with the bedbug. It soon became immune to DDT and made an alarmingly swift return from the road to oblivion. Again it became an embarrassing bedchamber nuisance. In some areas, infestations multiplied as much as sevenfold and resistant strains spread nationwide. The resurgence was not for long. Two new antibedbug chemicals, using malathion and pyrethrum, were devised and to date there has been no indication of bedbug resistance to them. They are highly recommended by the U.S. Department of Agriculture.

Pharaoh ants will rid premises of bedbugs, too, but then you've got a bunch of sassy fat ants on your hands. It's simpler just to drive to the next town where you're not known and, after donning dark glasses and altering your voice, walk, and mannerisms, go to a drugstore or hardware emporium there and buy enough bedbug spray or powder to do the job. If the infestation is overwhelming, better call in a professional exterminator — but make him promise to drive up in an unmarked sports car, carry an attaché case and dress like a Bible salesman.

The harboring of fleas also may bring neighborhood excommunication down upon your happy home. Householders owning pet dogs or cats often are plagued by fleas. The infestations frequently come as an unpleasant surprise upon a family's return from a vacation, during which the house pets were not in residence. While they were around the animals were used as a feeding station by the fleas, who laid their eggs around the pets' bedding or favorite snoozing spots. Fleas do not make nests or provide for their young; eggs simply are dropped at random. In the thick jungles of rugs, the folds of threadbare carpets and the crevices of floors and furniture, the eggs hatch and the larvae feed on whatever bits of organic matter come to hand. The development from egg to adult stage of a flea in humid warm weather is just about the length of time covered by the average family summer holiday — two to three weeks. Newly hatched fleas can survive at least that long without food. In the absence of proper hosts (dog or cat), a new generation of fleas will lie dormant, to be awakened by the vibrations of returning residents moving about the house. The new batch of fleas then will swarm out — sometimes as many as two thousand per square foot — lusting for blood, and begin feeding voraciously on any flesh available, whether it be of dog, cat, man, woman, or child.

Fleas belong to the order Siphonaptera (*siphon*, for their tubelike sucking mouth parts, and *aptera*, meaning wingless). Some people find it encouraging that there are less than a thousand different kinds of fleas. I do not. Nor do I appreciate the fleas' peculiar habit of not sticking to their properly assigned animals. They defy the will of God — or perhaps merely lack discrimination.

The most common household fleas, the dog (*Ctenocephalides canis*) and the cat (*C. felis*), are indistinguishable except to each other, and blithely exchange their dining hosts; both of them also bite man. The sticktight flea (*Echidnophaga gallinacea*) annoys humans as well as poultry. Rat fleas (*Xenopsylla cheopis*, the Oriental type, and the European, *Nosopsyllus fasciatus*) also attack ground squirrels and people. These fleas act as carriers of bubonic plague and murine typhus, which in numbers of cases outweighs plague as a worldwide human disease. (It has been reported recently, in Mexico and Manchuria, brought to man by lice after establishment by fleas.) You will find more about these sinister fleas in this book's chapter on the pests of wartime.

The chigoe flea (*Tunga penetrans*) is an especially irritating tropical flea. The females bury themselves in the skin, particularly of the feet, and cause persistent, ulcerlike craters, from which the fleas have to be removed before the wound can heal. This flea is not a disease carrier, and is not to be confused with the chigger (also chigre or jigger), which is not a flea, but a mite.

An occasionally seen wintertime insect frequently mistaken for a flea because it too is wingless, is the springtail, a thysanuran (tassel-tailed) insect of the order Collembola, not of the flea order Siphonaptera. The springtail popularly is called the snowflea, because stimulated by cold it likes to swarm on snowbanks, invade refrigerators, and climb along brine coils and pipes.

The so-called human flea, *Pulex irritans*, is a major problem insect of the Mississippi Valley and the Southwest. It feeds on human blood, but does not engage persons as hosts, preferring to live in furniture, rugs, and other cozy out-of-the-way places. *Pulex irritans*, brownish to black and shaped like a bee, is never much longer than one-eighth of an inch, frequently less. This flea weighs from one-twentieth to one-fifth of a grain; therefore it would take 2,187½ to 8,750 fleas to weigh one ounce.

It might be well to repeat here some flea facts given to me by the late Professor Leroy Heckler, a second-generation trainer of fleas and America's most renowned master of that unique art form, at the time I wrote about his famous Hubert's Museum Flea Circus in *Wild Tigers & Tame Fleas*. *Pulex irritans's* legs are very strong because this insect's leap is its main protection when being pursued. If a human's legs were comparatively as strong, a man could broad-jump seven hundred feet and leap into the air 450 feet — higher than the Statue of Liberty by 145 feet or just clearing the great Pyramid of Cheops. *P. irritans* can do a broad jump of thirteen inches, a high jump of eight. This type of flea can kick a ball three times its own weight farther comparatively than a man can bat a baseball. It can lift 150 times its own weight. A wagon pulled by a horse is three to four times its weight; this flea can pull a vehicle weighing three hundred to four hundred times what the insect weighs. The flea that operated Professor Heckler's tiny merry-go-round was pushing an object 2,187½ times its own weight.

I'd like also to set down again, for the benefit of those who might have missed it the first time around, the great Professor's flea credo, inherited from his flea-trainer father: "Even the small are great in the eyes of those who understand them." And I'll pass along Roy Heckler's favorite flea jingle: "Great fleas have little fleas/Upon their backs to bite 'em,/And little fleas have lesser fleas,/And so, ad infinitum."

The most innocuous home invaders are the cricket and the ladybug. Hardly anybody ever bothers the ladybug except to chant at her, "Lady-bird, lady-bird, Fly away home./Your house is on fire/Your children may roam"; even grown men do it. How that bit of puerile poesy ever got started, I've no idea, but I do know that the lady bird beetle got its present name in the Middle Ages, when it was called the "Beetle of the Blessed Lady." It does no harm whatsoever to humans or their possessions, and in fact is a blessing to them, for it consumes hordes of harmful insects, including a variety of plant lice and the larvae and eggs of the destructive corn borer. An Australian ladybug, the vedalia beetle, first imported to this country in 1888 — only twenty-eight in the shipment — is responsible for the elimination of the cotton-cushiony scale, an insect that was destroying our citrus groves.

In the United States the black field cricket is the commonest and most widespread member of the Orthoptera order, a vast group numbering one thousand species in North America and 22,500 in the world. There are many other kinds of crickets, including pale green tree crickets, a burrowing mole cricket, and the straw-colored house cricket, *Gryllus domesticus*, immortalizd by Charles Dickens in *Cricket on the Hearth*. Snowy tree crickets are the symphonic musicians of the realm; they chirp in unison, but of course they never attempt anything very profound.

The cricket is an old friend of the homesteader. Its chirrup is welcomed in almost every one of our states. Many Americans regard crickets as omens of prosperity and good fortune, but it is wise to remember that while the cricket on the hearth adds a delightfully cozy touch to a room, the little beast may also be delightedly nibbling away in the kitchen as well as voraciously attacking clothing and other fabrics. The crickets of Malaysia are respected because they are thought to be spirits of the departed, but to the Chinese crickets are very much alive and are matched in sporting fights, much as the game cocks are in Latin countries. Everyone reads his own meaning into the cricket's chirp. In California, it indicates "no smog tomorrow"; in Iowa, it signifies that the corn will be extra high; in Minnesota, it brings good cheese; in western Pennsylvania, it presages extra good Christmas anise cookies and *Liebküchen*; in Naples, upstate New York, it predicts that the grape pressings will create superlative wine, fit for the *Chevaliers du Taste-vin*; and in the dingy skid-row hotels of New York's Bowery a cricket's chirp simply means that "some sunabitchin' noisy bedbug is wakin' up the whole goddam joint an' somebody had better *do* somethin' to make it shut up *gah-DAM it!*"

One moonlit night while on a Caribbean cruise, my wife and I were touchingly surprised by an echo of home — a cricket chirruping from the depths of a lifeboat on the promenade deck. "That means," commented a passing fellow passenger, female, "that there will be good shopping bargains tomorrow in Curaçao." To me it meant that the lifeboat hadn't been used for some time and, very likely, leaked.

The Termite

In the cellar I tap the seams
which, leaking, give up tiny streams
of pulp. A horde of termites teems,
perhaps, through spaces where the beams
     have stood.

In the selva your thousand trees
daily drop, made soft as cheese.
Your full queen calls — you rush to please —
pray gifts you take on trembling knees
     be good.

Hard to frame an empathy
for all your eager urgency —
your one-two-three-four destiny —
at last! a surge of sympathy!
     Knock wood.

7

An Inside Job: *The Termite* Our nation's blackest insect villain is
the termite. It does more damage than lightning, tornadoes, arson,
and frugging teen-agers combined. Almost two million of the
roughly fifty million dwellings in the United States have been
spoiled enough by termites to send their owners scurrying to an
exterminator.

Termites are found in every one of our states except Alaska, according to Dr. Thomas E. Snyder of the Smithsonian Institution.
Although he states further that "what once were isolated pockets
of infestation in Northern states are now spreading out," the major
problem with termites still is throughout the South, where damage
from them is traditional and expected. No one down there would
think of constructing a wooden home without taking every precaution against termites, and no Southerner is more than mildly astonished by catastrophes caused by termites. Happens all the time with

old buildings, so why get excited? I have before me, contained in a clutch of clippings from several Dixieland regional newspapers, evidence of a half-dozen odd dilemmas in which people have found themselves due to the nibblings of these voracious pests.

In Wookerton, South Carolina, a wedding party, after being herded into a local photographer's studio to pose for a traditional group portrait, was all set to say "Cheese" when the floor collapsed. Bride, groom, the respective parents, the best man, matron of honor, and an assortment of bridesmaids and ushers were tumbled pell-mell into the basement — in a confusion of silks, satins, laces, and rented tuxedos. Only the ring boy, nimbler than the others, was able to leap clear at the crucial moment. He was peeled off the back wall where he hung to a painted cloud on the canvas backdrop. Termites were the culprits.

In Magnolia, Mississippi, the town band, while playing a concert during the revival of a long-dormant Fourth of July celebration (renamed the Festival of White, Red and Blue), was plunged through the floor of the bandstand that had stood unused for too long. Integrationist termites were blamed.

In Sneedy, Tennessee, American Legionnaires, in order to upset a peace rally being held by a youth group in front of the courthouse, scheduled a "trooping of the colors" flag ceremony at the same time, and while marching militantly in close-order up the courthouse's wooden steps, they collapsed, sending the chauvinists into embarrassing disarray. The destruction was widely attributed to Communist termites, although more levelheaded members of the assemblage thought it might have been simple inner decay.

The worsening in the North of the termite problem largely is due to four factors: more houses today are built on cement slabs or low foundations — or have raised planting beds — which make termite entry easier; more new houses have attached patios, decks, breezeways, and garages — all of which encourage termite entry; almost all new homes are built of sapwood far more susceptible to termite attack than heartwood; and lastly, better central heating creates favorable conditions for termite activity on a year-round, rather than a merely summertime basis.

A Forest Service termite map of the United States indicates the least intensity of infestation in Wyoming, followed by Montana, the Dakotas, Wisconsin, and Michigan. The greatest clusters of map dots indicating termites fall along the California coast (these insects love sandy and rocky soil), the Mississippi and Ohio rivers (but oddly, not along the Missouri), the New England coast, the shores of Long Island, New York, the Jersey shore, the Chesapeake Bay area of Maryland, both Florida coasts (Atlantic and Gulf), the Gulf coast extending from that state west to the Mexican border, and are fairly heavily sprinkled throughout east Texas, Louisiana, Arkansas, Alabama, Georgia, and South Carolina.

Termites have been around for a long time. They've been found in Eocene rock and Miocene shale; some termite fossils go back in time 50 million years. These insects often are mistaken for ants, which they resemble somewhat, except that termites all have thick midsections and look like middle-aged men who should join the gym, learn to swim, and lay off the booze.

There are two main types of termite — Subterranean and Nonsubterranean. The first are the kind we think of when we hear about pianos crashing through to cellars and of people leaning through termite-eroded walls. Ninety-five percent of termite damage is done by the Subterranean species. They are the only ones ever seen by inhabitants of our country's interior, for the Nonsubterraneans are found chiefly in the warm coastal areas of North America — normally only as far north as Northern California, although there is a local infestation at Tacoma, Washington — and along our Mexican border.

There are several kinds of these aboveground termites, the most common being the dry-wood termite called *Kalotermes*. Another dry-wooder is the powder-post termite, *Cryptotermes*. Rotten wood appeals to the termite known as *Zootermopsis*; damp wood attracts the *Paraneotermes simplicicornis* and *Neotermes castaneus*.

All of these nonearth-burrowing termites fly directly to and bore into wood. They attack living trees and other woody plants; poles used for telephone, telegraph, and power lines; wooden derricks; piled lumber; woodpulp, fiber, and other insulation boards containing cellulose; and a myriad of household objects, including furniture, pianos and their keys, clocks, picture frames, books, children's toys, sewing machines, dust brushes, trunks and chests.

Because they are able to live in objects that frequently are moved about, the scourge of these termites is easily spread. Many times they are found well outside their usual range, as far inland as Kansas and Ohio, and north to Canada. Some of these termites have traveled to Washington, D.C., from Cuba, where they are so plentiful that building codes prohibit the construction of wooden floors in city buildings. In Colombia, Guatemala, and Mexico damage from these aboveground termites has been found as high as eight thousand feet.

Among Nonsubterraneans there is no worker caste — only reproductive and sterile soldiers. Work is done exclusively by young nymphs before they mature — an idea I sometimes wish our society could adopt. The soldiers, large and wingless, have powerful jaws with teeth along the inner edge, in contrast to their Subterranean counterparts, which are toothless.

Colonies of these Nonsub termites grow very slowly; old ones seldom contain more than a few thousand individuals.

Only those termites that go for damp and rotten wood require moisture, and some may leave their wood domiciles to get it. The dry-wood termites of these species do not need water and live entirely in the wood throughout their lives. Strange but true, one of them once was captured in a trap attached to an airplane flying at nineteen thousand feet, but probably he was just some adventuresome oddball who'd been chewing on a Jules Verne book and was trying to reach the moon, and is not to be taken seriously. Ordinarily, these termites prefer quiet places.

The reason termites can take on so much wood is because their digestive tracts carry colonies of microscopic one-celled protozoa that break down the cellulose of the wood into a form of nourishment the insects can readily assimilate. Whenever these protozoa — so essential to breaking down the wood into digestible matter — are killed by intense heat or cold, the termite is unable to live any longer. All of the boring termites can be killed if the furniture they infest is held for an hour and a half in 150-degree heat, but there is some risk of burning down the house as well. Extreme cold of minus 150 degrees Fahrenheit for four days also is an effective killer, but with a chair in the freezer for that long a time, it might be difficult to prepare meals, so generally this method is not really recommended. One lethal pesticide for these wood-inhabiting termites is trichlorobenzene; very volatile, it kills as it vaporizes. California's public service poles, infested with dry-wood termites, are treated by dipping them in special vats filled with two-hundred-degree hot coal-tar creosote; each vat can handle four poles at once.

All termites are stone deaf, so there is no point in cursing them for the damage they've done. If you feel the need of vengeance, a pneumatic trip-hammer would shake them up considerably, since termites are quite sensitive to vibration. For that reason they never invade railroad ties, or the woodwork of factories containing heavy machinery, or bass fiddles. They steer clear of bowling alleys but are not averse to billiard parlors.

Subterranean termites use three basic routes to enter a house: they attack wood which directly contacts the earth (stair risers, trellises, siding run too close to the ground); they enter through cracks and voids as small as one thirty-second of an inch in slabs, foundations, and piers; they construct tubes of mud across materials through which they cannot penetrate. Such tubes often are hard to locate due to this termite's preference for dark places.

The only time termites are attracted to light is during their dispersal flight. Its sole purpose is to spread the species and to establish new colonies. Termites, unlike ants and honeybees, do not mate while airborne, but wait until they've landed and broken off their wings before pairing up to carry on the race. While swarming, termites are easy pickings for dragonflies and birds. In North America, fifty-two species of birds are fond of termites. The champion bird glutton of these insects is an unnamed flicker collected by a Georgia ornithologist named Eustis P. Bearfoot, who found in its stomach 1,109½ termites. In the tropics, armadillos and anteaters wreak considerable havoc on termites, but our domestic ones face extinction on the ground principally from lizards and warrior ants, and people armed with poisons.

Except for the winged reproductives that swarm, the Subterranean termite — blind, grayish-white, and wingless — shuns light and air. It shrivels and dies when exposed to dry air, because the soft body, devoid of a hard cuticle, loses moisture rapidly. The winged ones that emerge once in their lifetimes on dispersal flights are protected by harder bodies that are darker in hue and less sensitive to dryness.

Subterranean termites spend their entire lives within the protective network of channels through wood, underground galleries and the mud tubes that run between those two locales. These termites do not remain constantly in the wood into which they have chewed, but travel regularly back through the tubes to their underground burrows for water. They must have moisture, since they can thrive only in an atmosphere of high humidity and warmth. In poorly built houses termites may find enough moisture so that they needn't return to the ground. All the water needed by a colony, which can number up to 250,000 members, often is supplied by condensation in walls without vapor barriers, unvented crawl spaces, water dripping from plumbing leaks, or in moisture from faulty flashing. Termites once were found living on the eleventh floor of a hotel in Silver Moon Beach, Florida, getting all the water they needed from a leaky ice-cube machine and an elderly tenant's rheumy Pomeranian that suffered an impatient bladder.

The best termite protection begins with sound construction. In building a house intended to be safe from termites the most essential considerations are the separation of wood from earth and maximum dryness of the structure. Be certain that construction site and the backfill have both been cleared of all wood on which termites can be nourished — tree roots, stumps, wood debris, scrap lumber, form boards, grade stakes, and spreader sticks. No wood used in construction should come directly in contact with the ground. There should be proper grading, guttering, and foundation drains to keep moisture away from the building. Adequate flashing of windows, doors, chimneys, valleys, etc., should be provided to keep water out of walls. Soffits, attics, and crawl spaces should be well ventilated or equipped with vapor barriers to prevent condensation.

Termite shields, which are flanges of metal inserted between concrete or block foundations and a home's wooden superstructure, once were considered the best possible barrier against termites. They are widely credited to the ingenuity of the aforementioned Dr. Snyder, who now feels that widespread careless installation has reduced their effectiveness. R. J. Kowal, an entomologist of the Division of Forest Insect Research of the U.S. Forest Service, is another expert disenchanted with this method of termite protection. "Perhaps 95 percent of all shields installed to date," he has said, "have been ineffective, and the money spent on them completely wasted."

A University of Georgia survey made in 1961 of 310 shielded houses found 1,423 serious defects — involving improper joints; poorly installed corners; breaks caused by pipes or ductwork; noncoverage of the entire foundation; flat, instead of bent-down, edges; and not enough clearance of the foundation before bending downward. The author of the study, James B. Cobb, concluded that "metal termite shields, as they are installed in this area, afford little protection. Not one single house had termite shields which met FHA standards."

"You just can't get the builders to put them in right any more," I was told by Edward C. Stearns, New York regional representative of the Bruce-Terminex Co., Inc., world's largest termite control outfit.

Pressure-impregnated lumber gives a homeowner more peace of mind regarding termites than any other method of their control. It sometimes costs more than soil poisoning, but has the added advantage of making the house decay-resistant, a valuable factor where dampness and condensation are serious problems. Maximum pressure-treating protection can add from 2 to 2½ percent to the cost of a house. All kinds of pressure-impregnated lumber are commonly available in most areas — sheathing, siding, flooring, decking, planking, framing, millwork, fencing, glue-lam timbers, and plywood (from a quarter to one inch thick). Pressure-impregnation forces the poison deep into the wood and it should not be confused with painted-on preservatives or preservative-dipped lumber, which generally costs less, but is not acceptable by FHA standards for termite protection. Heartwood of three species — foundation-grade California redwood, Southern tidewater red cypress, and pitchy Southern (lightwood) longleaf pine — are very resistant to termite attack, but even their naturally toxic qualities do not afford the protection offered by wood that has been poison-impregnated under pressure. Eastern red cedar is a heartwood less resistant to termites.

One symptom of advanced termite infestation is the sudden pronounced settling of a house. Unless you are a keeper of elephants, such a phenomenon should be investigated immediately, lest you find your bedchamber suddenly transferred to the basement in the middle of some dark night, along with the piano, refrigerator, the living room furniture, hi-fi, the color TV, and your wife.

There isn't much that is safe from termite attack. Termites have been known to try their teeth on such seeming impervious substances as stainless steel, hard plastics, the enamel of refrigerators, and false teeth. The most formidable termite likely is one known by the scientific name, *Cryptotermes niger*. It gnaws through lead sheathings on cables, and even can work its way through quite a thick concrete slab if the mortar mix contains sand in which there are fragments of seashells able to be dissolved by a powerful chemical excreted by the insect. Fortunately, this termite has not yet discovered America; it is native to Barro Colorado Island in the Panama Canal Zone.

Protection of a house by soil poisoning, and treatment of those parts of the structure that are in contact with the ground, often is the lowest cost method of positive termite protection. To treat the average custom-built house, covering an area of from twelve to fifteen hundred square feet, costs upward of $150, depending of course upon the problems encountered in each individual situation; the average job runs three hundred dollars. Treatment of

development houses while in construction runs considerably less
—from fifty to seventy-five dollars per unit, although if the controller can treat more than one in a single day the cost may be even
further reduced.

In this method the termite barrier is established by saturating
both sides of the foundation with poison, and by also treating voids
in hollow masonry walls, piers, utility lines, entrance areas, and all
other possible points of termite entry, including soil under porches,
carport, breezeway slabs, and subfill under the floors of slab houses.
The accepted chemicals used in this work, and their recommended
percentages in a water emulsion, are: aldrin (0.5 percent); benzene hexachloride (0.8 percent); gamma isomer, chlordane (1.0
percent); dieldrin (0.5 percent); lindane (0.8 percent) heptachlor
(0.5 percent). There also are certain proprietary products, most of
which include one or more of the above chemicals. The FHA lists
chemicals in oil solution as well, but these rarely are used in residential work. For normal soils, termite experts recommend: one
gallon per ten square feet under slabs, porches, garages, etc.; four
gallons per ten linear feet, per foot of depth, on both sides of foundations, piers, etc.; and two gallons per ten linear feet to voids in
masonry. Some manufacturers say their products will protect a
house up to fifteen years, but reputable exterminators claim that a
more realistic figure would be from five to seven years. (For more
detailed information concerning termite prevention by soil poisoning, write to the U.S. Department of Agriculture for its Home
and Garden Bulletin No. 64, *Subterranean Termites, Their Prevention and Control in Buildings.*)

To the public the most important factors in a termite control
contract are its guarantees that provide not only for additional
treatment should the initial one not produce 100 percent elimination, but also up to $25,000 indemnity for any building damage
inflicted after the treatment. The guarantees usually run for a five-
year period and can be continued thereafter upon payment of a
reasonable annual fee of say twenty-five dollars, which includes a
yearly checkup, additional treatment, and damage repair, if any.

The American Museum of Natural History has more termites

than any other establishment in the world — more than a million individuals (fortunately, all of them pickled in alcohol), the collection of Dr. Alfred E. Emerson, emeritus professor of the University of Chicago and a research associate at the museum. The Emerson collection boasts 80.7 percent, or 1,645 of the 1,802 known living termite species. Of the fifty species known to the United States, only one is indigenous to the New York area, *Reticulitermes flavipes*. It swarms in May, June, and sometimes in the fall.

No termites in this country build their nests aboveground, but this is the usual practice in tropical countries. These nests often contain enormous populations. There are records of from 750,000 to 1,806,000 individuals in one nest of the Australian termite, *Nasutitermes exitiosus*. A nest of the termite *Nasutitermes surinamensis* was found that contained three million individuals.

Termites are natural-born warriors. Certain tropical ones, known as the *nasuti* ("nosed ones"), are capable of making chemical warfare attacks on their enemies from long frontal protrusions that do indeed look like noses, but actually are a development from a primitive eye. From these openings a sticky, stinky, thick fluid is exuded in stringy threads, and sometimes is spurted for a distance of about one inch. It has strong corrosive properties when applied to metals, and is able to gum up other insects into immobility.

Some tropical peoples eat termites. When toasted they are said to taste like popcorn. The Bantus of South Africa enjoy them that way, not realizing that toasting takes out all the vitamin B. In the East Indies, the queen termite is considered a delicacy. It also is given to old men to relieve stiff backs, and to young men as an aphrodisiac.

One of the great admirers of the termite was Maurice Maeterlinck, the famous Belgian-French dramatist, poet, and natural history observer. To my knowledge, he never ate any termites. He loved them in an ethereal way. Maeterlinck's passion for the termite is not surprising, for he leaned strongly to mysticism; his work largely was concerned with indicating mysteries which lie barely out of sight, just beneath the surface of ordinary life. He wrote of people who lived nonglorious lives, somewhat removed from the robustness of the competitive world — such withdrawn characters as aged guardians of desolate castles, orphaned princesses, and banished Arthurian knights, pale rather than powerful. In the intensity and consistency of the termite's life, Maeterlinck found a spirituality that he associated with deep mysteries of the human soul.

In his *The Life of the White Ant*, Maeterlinck wrote concerning the termite: "From several points of view, this civilization, although fierce, sinister, and often repulsive, is superior to that of the bee, of the ant, and even of man himself."

Ah, but would he have been so in love with the occultism of the termite if he'd ever leaned against the kitchen wall of a pre-Revolutionary house and crashed through it onto the cellar stairs, fallen tail-first to their bottom onto hard cement, to get up with a badly spilled bourbon-on-the-rocks and a cracked rib? Down with termites, I say. Down with all decay behind bravado façades.

The Rat

Toward the drain
fur love clips along the floor —
scrapes pink to a scaled tail
and lifts, in sweet mammalian illusion.

Doubly tubed,
caste-locked, out of touch with sun,
blood beats in the round damp:
two dental gleaners stir the fur occlusion.

8

In Darkest America: *The Rat and Mouse* From the top of the Empire State Building you can't see any rats at all. They're down there by the thousands, jammed in their burrows, waiting for dark to begin its nightly stumble across the city. When the sun goes down the rats, avid for water and fresh spreads of garbage, crawl furtively from their hiding holes — underground, under the floors of tenements, inside the walls of rooming houses, and deep within rubbish heaps. Across the slums they skitter until dawn — through sewers and a network of gnawed tunnels connecting one dank unkempt cellar to another to another. Cheeky rats climb water pipes to emerge from jagged holes in dilapidated planking under leaky kitchen sinks, greasy gas ranges, and old-fashioned four-legged bathtubs. Following drip trails of milk, rats slither into the cribs of sleeping babies, onto the wet beds of children. Sopping rats pop unexpectedly out of toilet bowls. And the screams of the people are all silent ones.

There have been many educated guesses regarding the number of rats in New York City—from 250,000 to a half million to 1,600,000. The smallest figure is the deduction of a Johns Hopkins mammalogist; the second estimate is that of Dr. George James, former Health Commissioner of New York City; and the high figure comes from the U.S. Department of the Interior Fish and Wildlife Service, based on its belief that rats equal one-fifth the number of people in cities, equal the populations in our towns and double that on our farms. New York City is said to have comparatively fewer rats than any other waterfront city in the world. According to some authorities only 1 percent of the city's twenty-two thousand eating establishments are rat-infested (the national figure is 10 percent). Yet there are some New Yorkers who claim that the city has one rat for every person — eight million. Incredible? Perhaps. No one really knows the right number; no one ever will.

Surprisingly, few people in this enormous city ever get to see a genuine common live rat. Commuters never do. Some blue-collar workers — especially men working on demolition and excavation for new buildings — manage to glimpse one every now and again, but office toilers mostly remain unfamiliar with the filthy beasts. The sleek new steel-and-glass skyscrapers of midtown Manhattan are not sympathetic to rats. There are none in gleaming high-rise apartment houses — none at least beyond the basements, for rats don't usually leave cellars and ground floors, and seldom get above a building's fifth floor. In no instance do rats haunt places that are clean. They prefer filth.

While unsanitary conditions are not exclusive to the slums, rats find life much more agreeable there. Slum-dwellers know well the rats' greasy trails, spindly footprints, and the dragmarks of rat tails. The poor of New York know what a rathole looks like, and do not cringe at rat droppings. Yet, even in the most dilapidated parts of town, live rats seldom are encountered face to face. However, when one does turn up there is no panic, for those who must live with rats lurking in the shadows have been conditioned to them from the cradle. They are accepted stoically as just one more problem of the degraded life.

The rat must gnaw, gnaw, gnaw constantly to wear down his four incisors — scimitar-like teeth that grow six inches a year. They are nature's most fearsome tools, for if not kept in check, these teeth will curve back and fatally stab their owner in the throat and brain, or wedge the rat's jaws permanently ajar so that he dies of starvation. It is the bite from these terribly sharp teeth that people fear most. The wound is a nasty one.

Comparatively few New Yorkers have felt the jaws of a rat closing over their own flesh, the fangs sinking in. Those who have would like to be able to forget it. In New York City only about five hundred persons are bitten by rats each year. From 1960 to 1963 the average number of rat bites annually in this city was seven hundred. In 1964 there was a sharp decline when the Department of Health began going after rats in dead earnest.

On January 21 of that year the Board of Health passed its now-famous "rat resolution," which for the first time in city history put some real power into the law against harboring rats and resulted in the formation, in February 1964, of The Bureau of Pest Control, now headed by a genial soft-spoken gray-haired pipe-smoker named Murry Raphael, who first came to the Department of Health in 1939, stayed for nine years, and then went into private industry as a public health consultant for fifteen years. He returned to city employ in 1964 to organize the Bureau of Pest Control and subsequently was implored to remain as its first director. He is a happy crusader against rats and feels strongly that he is making a definite contribution to the betterment of humanity.

"The rat problem," Mr. Raphael told me when I first went to his office at 93 Worth Street in lower Manhattan near City Hall, "is really a human problem — all tied up with the behavior of people. I, personally, seldom meet any of the people that we're trying to help, but I know they're out there — spread all over the city farther than I can see from this window up here. The answer to rat control is simple — you deprive a rat of food, water, and shelter and he'll perish. But the solution to that answer is loaded with convolutions, because you're not dealing just with rats alone, but with people, and they are not nearly so predictable. It all comes down to getting them to have enough pride to keep themselves and their living quarters clean — and usually that is very difficult because so many things today are out to grind down the pride of the poor."

The Pest Control Bureau makes a valiant effort to educate its constituents in how to keep clean and discourage rats. Every Saturday somewhere in the city there is a block demonstration in sanitation by the combined forces of the sanitation, police, and fire departments. The police barricade the street and remove illegally parked cars; the firemen point out fire hazards; the sanitation department men remove accumulated garbage and rubbish and hose down the street. Pest control men announce their purpose from a loudspeaker atop one of the bureau's trucks and make a house-to-house canvass, door to door, taking complaints, which they channel to the departments having jurisdiction over them. Antirat literature is distributed, printed in both English and Spanish. Some of the leaflets are elementary, like the one titled "The Rat That Didn't Have a Chance, *La Rata Frustrada*" which reads like a second-grade primer. Others are more sophisticated and carry specific information *para acabar con RATAS* (to get rid of rats). One gimmick to enlist the youngsters in the clean-up campaign is an elaborate certificate that makes a kid a Volunteer Junior Sanitarian (a handsome badge goes with it). Talks on rat control are given regularly at school assembly programs, and the Welfare Department, in cooperation with the Department of Health, instructs slum mothers in home hygiene.

"I don't expect to eliminate all the rats in New York in my lifetime," Murry Raphael told me, "but I think we stand a pretty good chance with the young generation coming along. They're catching on to what it's all about."

When I asked Joe Mazza, a young Department of Health sanitarian, what he considered the worst aspect of his job as a rat chaser, he said without hesitation, "The stink. A rat has a peculiar kind of dry, musty, putrid smell that's hard to describe, but once you ever smell it you never forget it. And, of course, dead ones are even worse. We don't see many live rats, but we sure meet a lot of dead ones. All kinds — bloated ones, some that's half decomposed, and others that are just a kind of fur-and-bones stain on the floor."

"But with these new poisons," I asked, "don't they go outside to die?"

Mazza just smiled and said, "That's what everybody thinks. Some do die outside, but rats'll die wherever the trumpet blows for whom the bell tolls — inside or out. We had one garage, I remember, where they all died inside the walls — hundreds of them — and that guy could hardly stand to work there for almost two months. But he said the stink was worth it just to get rid of them."

I first met up with *parfum du rat* when I accompanied a crew from the Pest Control Bureau of the City of New York on one of its regular daily swings through Harlem, that predominantly Negro section of Manhattan stretching from 96th Street north to 168th Street between the Hudson and Harlem rivers.

Along about 10 A.M., at the bureau's headquarters on the tenth floor of 93 Worth, I met my escorts for the first leg of my exploratory trek, two genial young fellows, Bill Pelligrini and Al Castrulli, who were to drive me in one of the bureau's official trucks to a rendezvous in Harlem with a crew already in the field. The bureau trucks are small Chevy vans, painted white, with unadorned light blue lettering on the sides that says: BUREAU OF PEST CONTROL (HOUSING) *Department of Health, City of New York.* There are ten of these vehicles. Most of them are outfitted to carry a normal crew of four with squeeze-room for one more, but this particular truck had no rear seat, so Castrulli casually squatted in back, bracing himself on a large carton of rat poison.

It didn't take us long to get uptown because the boys, after a brief discussion of the risks involved, decided to take the West Side highway, the Henry Hudson Parkway, on which trucks are forbidden by law. En route, after recovering from their initial surprise that someone not an exterminator could be interested in rats, the boys relaxed and passed along some impressions of their unusual profession. I learned that the sewer under fashionable Park Avenue is "loaded with rats," also that they inhabit the city's subway system, and that there are plenty of rats in Chinatown, but it is not true the Chinese put rat meat in their chop suey.

"You be surprised how many people still think that," said Castrulli. "The thing is, down there, nobody will give you access; they won't let you in to distribute the bait. They're all very cagey, especially about anything to do with the city." There are rats, I was told, all over town — not just in the slums. Every once in a while a few will turn up in Times Square, Wall Street, around Grand Central Station, or at the New York Public Library on Fifth Avenue. The city's worst rat regions, I learned, are: the south and southeast Bronx; Harlem and the Lower East Side of Manhattan; and in Brooklyn, the Brownsville-East New York, the Bedford-Stuyvesant, and the Williamsburg neighborhoods. Queens and Richmond (Staten Island), the city's most recently developed boroughs — therefore having fewer slum sections — suffer very little from rats. In Manhattan the heaviest infestations occur between 90th Street and 110th, with the most troublesome areas in the northwestern part of that section and nearest Central Park. Castrulli told me that one of the oddest cases he'd ever been on was that of a Mott Street eccentric who kept a menagerie of several dozen big brown sewer rats as house pets.

"What'd they do to him? Well, I'll tell you, we cleaned out the rats and he was hauled off to Bellevue for observation — what else? He was some kinda nut to be livin' with rats. He cried when we took them away, but what're you gonna do? The law's the law. It says you can't harbor rats in a human habitation, especially if the other tenants complain — and did they ever. They said it sounded all the time like babies cryin'."

Both of these young rat assailants concluded that the best way to rid premises of rodents is to clean them up. "It's like when you put a man on a desert island," said Castrulli. "If he's got no food, he'll automatically die in time, if not sooner. What you gotta remember about rats is they're like a lot of people I know; all they want out of life is food, drink, shelter, and sex."

The crew that I was to join was waiting for me, pulled up to the curb on Broadway at 109th Street on the lower fringes of Harlem. Pelligrini and Castrulli turned me over to a pleasant-looking stocky Negro, a bit older than they were and dressed neatly in a business suit. He said his name was Peeples, Solomon Peeples.

"You must be a wise man," I ventured.

"That's what my grandfather used to say," he replied, smiling broadly, "but not my wife now. She'd rather I was in some other branch of civil service. There's a lot more jobs that pays a lot better, believe me. But I believe in this work. I know we're doing some good for people that can't do much to help themselves. In some ways a pest control man is almost as important as being a doctor. I tell my wife, would she be ashamed for me to be a doctor? And then she sees how I feel about killing rats and she thinks better about it."

On the rolls of the City Health Department Peeples is listed as a Public Health Sanitarian, a job with a wage scale of from $7,100 to $8,900 annually. (According to civil service regulations, a permanent appointee benefits by five "mandatory increments," what we ordinary civilians call "raises.") The Pest Control Bureau's sanitarians number ten regulars, four senior, and one supervising (a female, who does not go out into the field). The bureau employs forty-five active exterminators, earning from $4,850 to $6,290 per year. There are ten motor vehicle operators and a dispatcher for them. An educational program involving training in rat sanitation for others and school children is managed by a Community Relations Coordinator, who, by civil service designation, is a Senior Public Health Educator.

On this day Peeples was acting as an inspector and supervising the work of two exterminators, Bernard Schinz, an easygoing, heavyset Jewish fellow from Canarsie, Brooklyn, and a well-upholstered, mahogany-colored chap named C. L. Williams. ("I have a real name," he said, "but downtown that's all they ever call me — C. L.") These fellows were more casually and roughly attired. I was introduced, with a little bantering byplay involving the similarity of my family name to that of a famous distiller of Scotch whiskey.

"He hasn't brought any samples with him," said the supervisor.

"I'd be more interested in Mr. Ballantine's cousin, Cutty Stark," said Williams.

He was busy at the back of the truck, standing in the street and working through the vehicle's open back doors, measuring out rat poison that looked like pink circus sawdust, from a large carton into shallow square cardboard bevel-sided dishes that were about the size of a man's cupped hands. On the containers poison warnings were printed in large black letters. ANTICOAGULANT DO NOT TOUCH N.Y.C. DEPT. OF HEALTH MADE IN U.S.A.

"He's making bait stations," explained Peeples. "We put them around in apartments — a minimum of four, usually two each in the kitchen and bathroom — and in cellars and basements about three to four feet apart — maybe twenty, thirty, or even as many as fifty if the place is big — mostly against walls, because that's where rats usually travel, along the walls. You'll hardly ever see a rat run across a room or come out into the open at all. He seems always to got to have a wall to his back. Feels more secure that way."

Mr. Peeples introduced the truck's driver, Mike Egan, who used to be a cab driver and knows the city like an altar boy knows the laces of his parish priest. Peeples spread out a stack of official forms on the truck seat alongside Mike.

"All right, Mike," he said, "we'll do it this way. Try this one first and then go uptown to a-hundred-forty-fifth. Then to two-twenty-four west a-hundred-twenty-third, then to one-twenty-fifth, and then the Eighth Avenue stops. Get some continuity to it. It's not as haphazard as it seems. I know where they are."

The first stop on Peeples's list was a doddering Victorian brownstone residence that had been converted, during the housing shortage of World War II, into a rooming house. It was almost directly across the street from a police precinct station and at the curb in front stood a horribly wrecked, faded red Cadillac sedan that the police had towed there and parked. A dour hawk-nosed photographer was taking pictures of it from various angles. He ignored us as we entered the building.

We went first to the landlady's quarters on the ground-floor front. She met us in the sitting room, a claustrophobic box that had a heavily draped window facing the sidewalk. Behind the closed door to what I judged was the bedroom, a dog slavered and raged ferociously. The room was dismally decorated with shabby secondhand furniture and smelled musty. On one wall hung a large paper map of the world printed in colors; beneath it stood a gaudy plaster figurine of Jesus Christ. Behind Jesus there was what appeared to be a large rathole. On a shelf above was a glass-chimneyed oil lamp. Peeples said that a rat bite had been reported here, but the landlady, a tall raw-boned Negro woman about forty, denied this.

"No rat bite here, mister," she said in a flat voice. "Somebody got hit on the *haid* upstairs Saturday night, but ain't nobody got bit by no rat."

Peeples went to the tiny kitchen to probe with his flashlight. The drainboards flanking the sink slanted like ski slopes; the sink was propped up with a board and its drainpipe was heavily bandaged by black electrical tape. The landlady followed us.

"How come I don't see them when I goes down to the cellar to turn on the steam?" she asked querulously.

Peeples ignored the question and went on into the alcove called a bathroom. Through the open door I could see a bathtub so narrow that an adult boa constrictor would have trouble turning around in it. The landlady spoke then directly to me. "If I see one of them rats I have a heart attack, because I'm death afraid of them."

We went down the narrow stairs to the basement and sure enough there were two fat dead rats, each about seven inches long, not counting the tail, and both on a narrow stone ledge that ran around the walls.

"You have dead rats down here, fellows," Peeples called to Williams and Schinz, adding to me, "We don't get too close to dead rats ever. They're likely to carry disease."

We went back upstairs and Peeples reeled off to the landlady all the things she was to do to make her building ratproof.

"You've got to plug up all the holes and fill the cracks so's no rats can get through. You'll have to fix that broken window down there, and the leaks in the sink and bathtub, also that big opening under the stairs has got to be boarded over, and you clear out the rubbish out of the cellar, and see to it that the sewage drain gets unplugged, and you've got to mind that the garbage is always covered up and taken away regular and don't let anybody leave it in the building overnight."

"Mister," said the landlady wearily, "you gonna have to write all that down for me."

Back out on the sidewalk a man waiting alongside the truck asked Peeples if he could have some rat poison for his building.

"I'd be delighted to give you some, friend," Peeples told him kindly, "but it's against the law. Everything in the city is budgeted, and we have to work under our appropriation, which isn't nearly enough as it is. You'll have to call up the Department of Buildings and tell them you have a problem of rodents and they'll come and certify the building and then we'll come and treat it with poison."

The man accepted this calmly, said thank you, and what was that number again down there to call? After he'd gone, Peeples said to me, "He's afraid that by putting poison in the rooming house we're going to drive the rats across the street to his building. And they might just do that. If a rat is impeded in any way he'll either find or make some other holes to a new source of food."

"They don't need to cross the street," commented Schinz. "They've probably got regular six-lane express highways between all the buildings in the row, all down the block, and restaurants and snack bars at every crossroads."

"About fifteen years ago," added Williams, "I used to work in this area as a private exterminator, and once I seen a rat tunnel that went the whole block long."

Peeples looked up from his papers and said, "She was right. There was no rat bite there. She wasn't hiding it, like they sometimes do, because she was ashamed. The one we're going to next is the one that has a bite reported."

The next place we went to was within a block of the famed

"Sugar Hill" section of Harlem, where once the most prosperous Protestant whites lived in comfortable splendor.

"You can see," said Peeples, "what a nice section this used to be. Look at all the fancy stonework and decorations on these houses and how wide the street is. You can just imagine carriages rolling along, and people wheeling their kids in perambulators on Sunday afternoons. You had to be rich to live up here. These houses all are at least seventy-five years old now — maybe over a hundred — and all mostly going to pot. But you can see how nice they once was."

The building we went to, just around the corner from the broad avenue, had a heavy cross-hatched steel screen nailed to the front door. The super let us in and we climbed three flights to apartment No. 12, from which the rat bite had been reported. The hallways throughout were covered floor to ceiling by wallpaper the color of long-unwashed ladies' silk underwear and dotted with small golden shapes that looked exactly like scurrying cockroaches. On the painted-over windows of each landing were scratched such boasts as: *Beware of Ding the Great . . . Torch of 146 St. . . . Eddie of 145 St. . . . El Torrio Batman of 146 St. . . . and Batman Is.*

The complainant in No. 9, a rather pudgy woman, younger than the landlady we'd just visited, was reluctant to let us in until Peeples flashed his badge (City Health Department sanitarians all are peace officers). She seemed a little drunk.

"I got a dog and two kids," she said, "I don't want no rat poison in here."

"Is the dog well fed?" asked Peeples.

"Oh, yeah, he well fed, he sure is. Sometimes he eats better'n we do."

"Then he won't eat rat poison," said Peeples. "It's nonpoisonous to animal pets and children," adding aside to me, "but we always keep it out of the way of cats and dogs because then we don't know if the rats are bothering it."

"It don't do any good. It just *draws* the rats," the apartment occupant muttered, as we pushed in toward her kitchen and bathroom, the center of most rat infestations in residences.

"When was an exterminator here last?" asked Peeples.

"I don't even let them in," said the woman belligerently. "Why should I? The rats, they never gonna eat that stuff. They don't even eat the food."

Williams and Schinz began tossing their little boxes of poison under the bathtub and about the untidy kitchen, as the woman screeched hysterically to her children, "Get on outa here, you Derrick and Maw-reese, cause if any of you get it, it gonna be too bad. You *die* an' turn *blue!*" Then she again muttered, "It's not gonna do any good, no good at all."

Since this woman was listed as the wife of the super, Peeples asked her for the key to the cellar. She didn't have it, said that her husband had it with him in another building nearby.

"The law," said Peeples, trying to soften his admonition, "requires that the key to a cellar be available in the super's apartment twenty-four hours a day. That's the law, lady, and you are in violation of it."

The woman calmed down somewhat at this unexpected attack, but Peeples wasn't finished.

"Is there anyone in this apartment on welfare?" he asked.

"Yes," said the troublesome client. "Yes, there is someone here on welfare. Yes, there is."

With that, she quieted down completely, and didn't say another word. Neither did Peeples. When we left we weren't thanked, but neither were we cursed.

"With a noncooperative person like that, we have to place a little leverage sometimes," Peeples explained to me. "Otherwise, after we're gone she might just pick up all that rat bait and flush it down the john. And nobody's going to get rid of rats *that* way."

Out in the hallway, Peeples banged on the doors of the three other apartments on this floor. They were shoulder to shoulder, and he pounded them one-two-three, without waiting for responses, all the while shouting gruffly, "*Health* Department! *Health* Department! *Health* Department!"

From each apartment came the barking of a dog. An elderly

gent, wearing a sepia-colored silk stocking over his kinky gray hair, opened the door of No. 11.

"Do you want some rat poison?" asked Peeples, as though he were offering some rare viand. "It's free."

The courtly old fellow kindly declined the offer. "My dog kills them all," he said.

The tenant of No. 10 was a sweet elderly lady in floppy bedroom slippers and nondescript cotton wrapper, with her hair up in curlers. She said yes, she'd take some poison, but wait until she put the dog away. While she was gone from the door, No. 9 answered her knock — another sweet old doll. "We have mice," she said demurely, adding that yes, she'd be pleased to have some rat poison. "It's real nice for you to do this," she said appreciatively to Peeples.

Her door was at right angles to that of her neighbor, who returned, saying to Peeples, "The door is open; you can come on in anytime." No. 9 then said, "Good morning, Lavinia," to her neighbor, who thereupon asked me, "What did she say?" I replied, "She said, 'Good morning, Lavinia.'" No. 10 smiled wanly and said, "Oh, good morning, Petula," and I relayed this message to No. 9: "She said, 'Good morning, Petula.'" "Thank you," said Miss Petula. "Tell her I returns the greeting." I did and then we left.

As Peeples and I came out of the building we ran into Williams, who said he'd already found the super and baited the cellar.

"I saw a goddam rat down there the other day as big as I was," a bystander offered gratuitously.

When we got around the corner, Peeples called to me, "Come on over here, I want to show you what we call the Airmail Express." He led me into the building's rear courtyard to see a pile of rubbish and garbage that had been unceremoniously dropped from the windows of various apartments. "They think it's easier than trotting with it down all those stairs," said Peeples, "but it sure makes a delightful banquet hall for rats."

At our next stop we were pleased to find a very polite householder, a young woman on crutches with one leg in a cast from ankle to above the knee. I noticed there were no autographs scrawled on it or frivolous messages and cute drawings. She told us that she'd been in this apartment for "two years last August," and the landlord's exterminator had called only once. We baited the place thoroughly and she was extremely grateful.

"You know," Peeples remarked to me as we left, "rats can chew through plaster."

We went on to our next stop, a seven-story building with sixteen apartments. On the vestibule walls was scrawled: *Lil Terry the Stinker of 1966 through 1967.* Underneath, a message of deathless defiance: *Lil Terry the Lover There is no Other,* followed by, *Sock it to me by Dona.*

The super was out. A note on his door simply said, "Camel doen't live here." As we were about to leave we encountered a slim young hippie who looked like he'd been sleeping in a coal bin; he also resembled one of Mack the Knife's henchmen.

When Peeples asked if he was the super, he said, with great dignity, "Ah'm the super's helper, man. What can I do for you, man?"

He took us around back where electrical wiring was draped like black spaghetti all over the building's sheer brick walls. A leaking rainspout had formed a great stalactite in one corner of the en-closed area, and as we approached the cellar door a large live rat scampered from behind the ice mass.

"Did you see him?" asked Peeples excitedly. "In all my experi-ence that's the first and only one I ever saw outside in the open like this — the very first one." He was visibly awed, as though he'd seen a vision of the Holy Redeemer. "When you see an active rat in daytime," he continued, "that is a sign of an excessive infestation. It must be *extremely* heavy here. The burrow is so crowded that he was forced out."

"I see that un all the time, man," said the super's helper noncha-lantly. "That un, he is *so* bold, man. He king of the rats. Either it's him or another bold un, man, that I can tell by the difference way he look, man, but I didn' get no good look at him this time, man, but I *think* he the king."

A jet airplane roared across the patch of winter gray overhead, pushing perhaps for the West Coast, Arizona sunshine, or the warm sands of Florida. Water from the rooftops dripped, dripped, dripped as in a wet cave. Against one wall of this inner courtyard lay a waterlogged mattress topped by a spraddle-legged overstuffed chair upholstered in a gold-threaded fabric. From a distance came a faint chorus of squalling infants, and over it all flowed the heady passionate pleasures of soap opera coming from a dozen TV sets — unctuous male voice pleading with dulcet female, whining, being resolute and loving, hating, and all larded with the syrupy lugubrious wailings and bleatings of a sonorous pipe organ. We entered the high-ceilinged cellar, designated by a rusting plaque on the door as a "Fallout Shelter," and walked past the roaring furnace that had alongside it a pile of coal cinders that almost touched the ceiling. "All that snow and all the last couple days," the super's helper said, "we ain't had no chance to haul them out yet, but we gonna do it, man."

"Would you like an educated estimate of the number of rats you have in this building?" asked Peeples of the super's helper.

"Yeah, man, how many you say, man?"

"I'd say about two hundred and fifty rats, but it may even be double that."

"That's a hell a lot of rats, man. Must be all this dampness and shit attracts them."

Schinz and Williams methodically began tossing new stations of rat bait down alongside some very decrepit ones evidently placed a good long time ago by a private exterminator.

"Look at that tray," said Peeples disgustedly, kicking one of the moldering ones. "It's about as old as I am, and I'm forty."

He and I returned to the truck, where Mike Egan, the ever ready driver, was just winding up a conversation with a landlord, white.

"He was screaming about how much it costs to fix up a building," said Mike after the man left, "and how the rent controls keep him from raising rents, and how the tenants damages the property. One family, he says, that has been tenants a long time, pays only forty bucks a month rent, and they take in a roomer who pays them fifteen bucks a week. He figures they're making money on his property. Guess he could be right, at that."

At the next stopping place there was some confusion over whether we had the right street number. The building listed on Peeples's work order was a walk-up hotel of dubious nature, which sported in its tiny lobby a fireplace glowing carmine red with a frenetic electrically simulated fire. A pair of candleless candlesticks were securely bolted to the mantelpiece. The surly uniformed girl clerk denied the presence of rats, so Peeples had to phone in to the office to straighten things out. While Williams and I waited out on the sidewalk, I remarked on the perfection of his teeth, which were remarkably even, untarnished, and pearly white. When you're around rats for a while, you tend to think about teeth. He said yes, they were all fine except for one that he'd had knocked crooked when he was a young man trying to be a Golden Gloves champ along about the time Joe Louis was world's champion.

"I wanted to be somebody, have all my friends and neighbors think I was someone. I guess what they'd call today a search for identity, what we're all supposed to be looking for—even the rats, I guess."

As we chatted a little old gnome of a man tottered up, leaning on a cane, and injected himself into our conversation. Said he was Henry Fetterkoop—*cackle, cackle*—lived in the neighborhood almost all his life, born not here but in another country on the other side of the ocean, ninety-three years old—*cackle, cackle*—owned two buildings besides this one next door to the hotel, bought it in 1904 for $49,000, you want to buy it? How much you give me? *Cackle, cackle.*

Williams said to him, "Old man, nineteen-oh-four, you bought that building for two thousand bucks no more, and you know it."

The old man chortled.

Then Schinz asked him, "You have a girl friend?"

The old man guffawed with delight. These rat men were lots of fun.

When Peeples came back from the phone he said it was the hotel all right, and then asked the old man if he was Henry Fetterkoop, and if he was, he was cited for rat inspection too — the complaint has just come in downtown. Henry said yes, he was, and he did have rats in his buildings, and that they all came from all those butcher shops. With his cane he pointed out each one.

"I got private exterminator," said the old gent. "You know what they do? They do *nothing!*"

Peeples sympathized with him, and said they'd be back to treat his places as soon as the order came through.

"Then you gentlemen be back again and, if I am not here, you go into the laundry on the corner, my super, he has keys." Mr. Fetterkoop looked very pleased. I wondered if he realized that the visits of the city exterminators were going to cost him fifteen dollars apiece.

Peeples sent Williams up to the hotel clerk to get the key to the cellar door.

"Anybody live in that hotel?" asked Mike Egan, when Williams returned.

"There was some ac-*tiv*-ity up there," he replied, "but not what you might actually call *living.*" In the cellar we were struck with the strongest blast of rat stench we'd had all day, and soon saw the reason why. On the cement floor was a scatter of seven long-dead rats, their flesh completely gone. All that remained were large oval shapes of hairs with tails protruding and skeletons laid out neatly.

"Let's get outa *here,*" Peeples said to me, then he called up to his co-workers, "Got some mortifieds down here, fellows, and tons of excreta. Be careful."

"Come along, pal," said Williams to Schinz. "You are one of God's chosen people and you have been chosen for this mission."

"I'm not the chosen people," replied Schinz. "Not on *this* job."

After the cellar had been baited and we were pulling away in the truck, Peeples said to Williams, "We got to speed that paper up, so's we can get back here tomorrow to treat the building next door for that nice old man."

At the next stop, the whole block resounded with the raucous bounce of rock-and-roll music coming from hyped-up loudspeakers pointed into the street from the front of a variety store. A poster in

its window advertised the New Year's Eve Breakfast Dance of the
Le Grandeur Sporting Club, Inc., at the Renaissance Casino. The
place we were to bait was a mess. It had everything a rat desires:
kicked-in windows, rubbish, quiet environment, plenty of water
available, and all sorts of what Peeples called ingress and egress. A
door to the cellar had been torn off its hinges and the stairwell was
being used as a garbage chute.

"This is truly a magnificently disgusting place," was Peeples's
considered opinion. In an upstairs hallway, littered with rubbish, he
found an abandoned refrigerator and two defunct gas ranges blocking one of the doors of an apartment. Behind the door we could
hear drunken voices arguing. Peeples marked down the sanitary
violations and also promised to report the place as a fire hazard.

After that melancholy experience, we next came to a building on
a street lined with what once had been rather elegant residences.

"This was a real aristocratic neighborhood at one time," Peeples
commented. "You can tell that only one family lived in each
house, because there is not a one fire escape in front — only in the
backs. These people had maids and porters."

The super of the house, a tall straight sinewy man the color of
old mustard, talked so strangely unlike a Harlemite that I asked
him his origin. At first he said Washington, D.C., but finally I
learned that he was from the Caribbean, the island of St. Thomas.
The cellar in this building had a rotting false floor in one part — an
excellent refuge for rats.

"The super must have lived down here once," conjectured Peeples. "Rats can get under a floor like that and stay for years. You
tear that up and lord knows what you'll find — maybe even the
grandniece of the first duchess of Russia."

The man from St. Thomas just smiled dreamily. He was a long
way from home.

We drove from there around to Mount Morris Park at 120th
Street and Lenox Avenue. Wide streets again, and faded grandeur
brought more lyrical regrets from Peeples.

"Now I want you to stop here a minute and appreciate what

you're looking at," he said to me, as we got out of the truck. "This once was about as fine a place as you'd find anywhere."

I'd heard about Mount Morris Park. The big shots of Tammany Hall used to live here. In 1903, the *New York Herald* commented on this residential enclave of politicians, "When private homes in Harlem are spoken of, it is invariably the Mount Morris Park section which comes in for first comment."

The houses, heavy-browed brownstone-fronted ones like those that line Fifth Avenue in the Eighties, all face a low flat-topped hill in the center of a small park. The Dutch called the hill Slang Berg, or Snake Hill, because back then it crawled with rattlers. In 1776, the Hessians prevented a detachment of the Revolutionary army from crossing the Harlem River by setting up a cannon atop the hill and dominating the river's mouth.

Architecturally, the buildings that I could see from where we stood were a charming conglomeration of neo-Grecque, neo-Romanesque and some Venetian Gothic. Several of the homes sported stained-glass windows. I told Peeples that farther north in Harlem stands a building that once was the home of Alexander Hamilton, the renowned early American statesman.

"I bet now it's got rats," said Peeples.

The home we were to bait was a monthly-stop one. A sign on the hand-forged iron grillwork of the servants' entrance gate under the front high stone steps said: BELL IS WORKING UES IT!

"This building," said Peeples, with an air of mystery, "was certified for a very special reason, and in a minute I'll show it to you."

I couldn't imagine what he was driving at.

A comely, young and petite girl answered the bell and blurted, "Willie's not in," before she recognized Peeples as a Health Department sanitarian. When she did, we were admitted.

"Where's my sweetheart?" asked Peeples. The girl went into the bedroom and carried out a cuddly nine-month-old baby. The kid's hair had all been parted and plaited into a dozen tiny tufts; there really was only just enough to make one decent-sized pigtail — about an inch and a half long. The baby was wearing gold loop earrings; the young mother told me its ears had been pierced at two months.

After instructing the woman always to wipe the milk from her daughter's face and never to put her in the crib wet or with food of any kind, Peeples said to me, "You see now why I hate rats so much?"

On our way out, one of three men seated at a table in the living room, poring over a scatter of papers, called good-bye to Peeples.

"Yeah, good-bye, Willie," he answered.

"What do you suppose they're up to?" I asked him.

"I don't know," Peeples replied, "and I don't want to know. I don't wish to wear out my welcome."

We had three more calls to make. As we crossed the Fifth Avenue borderline into the Puerto Rican territory of East Harlem, Peeples said, "You need a club in both hands to come in here after dark. The big apartment houses — the public housing places — locks their front doors at ten, and if you come home gassed after that and don't have your key and can't rouse the super, you just either have to go to a hotel or sleep out in the street — and that I wouldn't advise my worst friend. You will get rolled, bounced, and whatnot else."

The building marked for baiting was one of a long row of very old houses. In the first-floor hall, we could smell the rats even over a sickeningly sweet perfume that had been doused about liberally, but we couldn't raise any life in any of the apartments either on this ground level or above. Everybody was playing possum. The only sound was that of an ultrafierce dog slavering at one of the doors.

"I should not want to tangle with him," said Peeples.

The door to the cellar was open, so we went on down.

"Watch out for your head," said Peeples, as he crouched to accommodate himself to the exceptionally low ceiling. "All of the buildings on this side of Harlem has low ceilings like this, and dirt floors."

We didn't find any dead rats, but rat bait was placed nevertheless.

"You know," I remarked to Peeples as we left Harlem to drive downtown, "with what the government is spending in just one month in Vietnam this whole glut of slums — rats and all — could be wiped out and rebuilt."

"Yes, I believe that it could," he agreed. "I saw in the paper what they lay out for those napalm bombers, each one. Wouldn't take too many to build a first-class hospital, or some better schools, or a nursery day-care center."

"But that's just foolish talk," I said, "a dream. The people at the Pentagon don't think that way. You go knocking at their door with ideas like that and they'd just lock the door."

"Just the cost of one load of bombs could do a lot of good," said Peeples.

"Only they'd want to dump them here instead of giving up the money," I said.

I recalled a *New York Times* UPI story in which the Defense Department stated that during 1966 the number of Negroes killed in Vietnam was proportionately larger than that of whites, and more so in the Army and Marine Corps than in the Air Force and Navy. In the Army, 14.5 percent Negroes, their death rate was 20.6 percent; the Marine Corps, with 7.5 Negroes, had a Negro death rate of 10.5 percent. When I mentioned the figures to Peeples, he said, "You know all those boys volunteered; they wasn't draftees."

"I know," I replied, "but they didn't do it because they're especially patriotic. It's just that in the armed forces they get a better break than they can here."

"I hate to have to admit that," said Peeples. "It's a terrible thing to say, but it's true. They got a better chance to be men in there, on an equal with other men — or at least more so on an equal."

The next to last stop was on Third Avenue in Yorkville, a building that was half a block long and had only one apartment occupied; all the windows but one were tinned over. Nobody answered the doorbell and we gained entry only after a scrawny, hatless, baldish, sandy-haired white man in two-tone shoes and a camel's hair topcoat that had seen better days, who was standing out on the sidewalk taking the wispy sun, kept whistling through his teeth at the single window until it was flung up and a middle-aged florid-faced woman stuck her head out to yell impatiently, "Whaddaya-want?"

Our final stop was a real surprise to me. It was midtown, only a few doors from a Third Avenue bar I used to frequent in my more roistering days. The place under certification was the cellar of a small storeroom. A greeting card entrepreneur had just set up business there; brave *Grand Opening* banners and bunting flapped from over the show windows, which were bedecked with displays of cards of all sizes oozing love and friendship. Inside the store display racks along one entire wall were loaded with valentines — thirty feet of lace-trimmed bleeding hearts.

Peeples went directly to the cellar through a metal door that lifted out of the sidewalk. The proprietor, a young snappily dressed hustler type, coatless, white, came bustling out of the store as if he were walking on molten lead.

"What's *this* now?" he asked pugnaciously, but Peeples's soft answer turned him off. He came with us to the cellar, very proud of what he'd done to clean it up. It was beautiful — all whitewashed, fluorescent-lighted, the floor spotless, all the merchandise cartons lined up along the walls and down the middle. "Didn't I do a good job?" the young man insisted, leaning into us for emphasis. "Didn't I? Isn't it perfectly swell down here now? And I did it all with my own money. Cost me over a thousand dollars. The landlord didn't pay a damn nickel. I asked my lawyer what should I do, and he said if you wait for your landlord he'll do just enough to get by, baby, and the city'll be after you again before you know it. That's what my lawyer said. So I did it all myself. Didn't I do a good job? Didn't I? I have to have it nice because my help has to come down here. It has to be nice. Isn't it nice now? Tell me you think it's nice."

Peeples quietly voiced approval of the accomplishment and then proceeded to tell the hard-sell fellow how to become decertified.

Schinz, Williams, and Mike Egan were not at the truck when we emerged from the greeting card shop. We found them next door in the pizza parlor making up for their skipped lunch hour. I thought how quickly the place could be cleared of customers if I would

announce that these three hearties stuffing themselves at the counter on pizzas and coffee were rat exterminators fresh off the trail.
Right now, dead rats were the farthest thing from the uncluttered
minds of these metropolitan gladiators. Their working day was all
but over, save for the ride back downtown and a little necessary
paper work at the office.

I left my comrades and went home to take a good long hot bath
and a hearty swig of good dark Haitian rum, *Barbancourt cinc
étoile*. Lying soaking in the tub, I was both disturbed and at peace
with myself. For I'd done what every honest American should do
at least once in his lifetime. I'd not only crossed the border into
that foreign land called a slum where no one needs a visa, but I'd
forged deep into its interior. And nothing terrible had happened. I
didn't find the streets running with snotty kids brandishing switch-
blades. Nobody sneered at me, "Burn, baby, burn!" Girls weren't
being sexually assaulted against every street-light stanchion. There
wasn't a dope addict or a stupefied drunk lolling in every front vestibule.

There was dirt and disillusion, yes, and passivity spread a blank-
ness like that of new-fallen snow. Signs of great stress were
apparent, but everyone was coping with intolerable situations as
best he could. Those slum-dwellers whose trails I crossed behaved
kindly toward each other; an odd politeness and consideration
passed quietly among them, a rough chivalry and kind of disassoci-
ated unity — if such a contradiction can be — that often is found
among the besieged or the doomed. Moving about Harlem, I
began to understand the true meaning of the hip term "cool," and
why it could only have originated there.

The rats that are raiding Harlem and other slum sections of New
York City are not the scurrilous black rats, *Rattus rattus*, that
swept through Europe from the fourteenth through the seventeenth centuries carrying the rat flea and the Black Death of
bubonic plague that wiped out twenty-five million European lives.
The rats that overrun American cities today are those commonly
called Norway rats, *Rattus norvegicus* (also known as brown,

wharf, and sewer rats). They did not originate in Norway. The true place of origin likely is Chinese Mongolia or the region east of Lake Baikal in Siberia. Great masses of these rats are believed to have swum across the Volga River after an earthquake, invaded Astrakhan, and thence moved inexorably — silent and invincible — across the European continent. Each nation tried to blame another for the invasion of these big, bold, brown predators. In Germany they were known as French rats, and in France as Dutch or German rats. When they reached England in 1730, they were called the Hanoverian rat due to the unpopularity there of the House of Hanover. The brown rat arrived in Norway in 1762 and was called the Swedish rat, a little later in Spain, and in Scotland about 1770. It didn't do too well in Scotland (not enough to eat), nor in Switzerland (too neat and clean), but when it was brought to Colonial America by the British Redcoats, this terrifying rat thrived and immediately began to massacre all the black rats that could be found. When the covered wagons went West, brown rats tagged along. They started for California with the Forty-niners but didn't get there until 1851 — there were so many fast wide rivers to cross and not many bridges. These rats didn't become established in the Rockies until after the First World War — from 1919 to 1923. Now they scamper all over America.

The Norway rat has the heavyset build of a well-fed burgher. It weighs about a pound usually, and has a slimy-looking tail shorter than its body. The fur varies between a sooty gray and reddish brown. The beady eyes are the kind you find in California politicians and certain country bankers.

First cousin to the Norway rat is the roof rat, which has a longer tail and ears and a more pointed snout. The roof rat is not prevalent in New York but quite common down South. In Florida it is known as the climbing, fruit, house, or Alexandrine rat. (I'd be willing to bet that last name was dreamed up by real-estate promoters.) Roof rats prefer to live in attics, roof spaces, hollow walls, and even atop palm trees and ornamental shrubbery.

Both these rat species are determined year-round breeders. The rat breeds in all seasons, but like man is more amorous in springtime. Rat gestation period is slightly more than twenty-one days; a female gives birth to as many as eight litters a year, with six to fourteen infants in each. The young mature rapidly and can mate successfully within three to five months. Unchecked, a single pair of married rats conceivably could acquire almost one hundred offspring in one year, and the clan, growing from the spin-offs of the original coupling, could in just five years reach a total membership of 950 billion rats, but for one thing — the extraordinarily high rate of rat mortality. If it weren't for that, we'd be up to our silly navels in rats. Fortunately, the average number of surviving rat young per year for an adult couple is only twenty.

Even under normal conditions, the rat has a short life span. By our standards, rats age quickly, since each rat year is the equivalent of thirty human ones. A rat is through breeding at age two, and from then on goes into a decline. So relax, and thank God for whichever celestial account executive He's put in charge Up There of universal interdenominational rat control.

Do not, however, underestimate the number of rats living among us. It's been said, by the Department of the Interior, that there are one hundred million rats in the United States. With that population figure as a base, and considering the rapid rate of rat reproduction, there would be about forty rats born in America every second, or roughly a half million daily. (Those figures come from a lecture delivered at a Chicago sanitation seminar by Walter W. Dykstra, assistant to the chief, Branch of Predator and Rodent Control, U.S. Fish and Wildlife Service.)

From January through August 1967 five different rat control bills were introduced in Congress. All of them either died in committee, or were killed or buried in some way, principally by procrastination. After the Sparkman bill was turned down in April, Governor Rockefeller of New York announced that in April of 1968, the beginning of the new fiscal year, $4.5 million would be appropriated by the state to its cities and counties for rat control and eradication. New York City's share of this allotment will be $1.5 million. In the interim $1.5 million was granted to cities and counties for use until the end of the current 1967 fiscal year, ending on March 31, 1968.

New York City's share of that rat control money was $750,000. That additional funding has enabled the city's Pest Control Bureau to step up its program considerably. In mid-November of 1967 a Congressional committee in joint session approved a bill as part of the Comprehensive Health Plan Act covering a total outlay of $589 million (Public Law 89–749) that will provide $40 million for rat control in two fiscal years if the bill is passed.

Big cities are very hospitable to rats, as none of their natural enemies of the countryside are there — the hawks, owls, foxes, ferrets, weasels, mink, and skunks who consider raw rat a delectable dish. Large frogs also are capable of eating rats — alive and whole. Snakes are marvelous rat catchers. They are very sneaky about it, so stealthily clever that the rat is fanged before it realizes what is happening. With one surprised squeal he dashes off, but in half a minute his enthusiasm over his lucky escape begins to flag. The rat pants; its heart thumps alarmingly and its legs grow numb. It sinks down to rest and never gets up again. The snake, at its leisure, slithers up and swallows the poisoned rat in one extended gulp.

In town, man is a bountiful provider and his poisons and traps are the rats' only enemies. In most instances attacks utilizing these tormentors are halfhearted and sporadic. The rat, being an exceptionally clever beast, soon catches on to them. The rat's intelligence is of a practical nature; he instinctively knows what is good or bad for him. Rats will not touch food or anything else that seems to be dropping fellow rats in their tracks. They will not go near a trap that has slaughtered one of their members. Before being set out again such a trap must be thoroughly cleaned and aired. Baits for trapping can include rolled oats, cake crumbs, or nut particles sprinkled over the trap trigger; whole nuts, apple cubes, raisins, dried fruit, candy, peanut butter, bacon squares, or smoked fish can be fastened to the trigger. Rats will not be tempted by the bait in traps if other provender is available. In such cases traps may be used without bait if they are placed so that they can be triggered by the rats while going about their regular rounds. A good way is to nail the traps to rafters or under beams at right angles to the paths the rats ordinarily travel, so that the triggers can be set off from either side of the trap without the rats becoming aware of it by running across it.

A single-dose poison for rats is red squill mixed with freshly ground meat or fish. Arsenic, phosphorus, and thallium sometimes are used to kill rats, but they are highly toxic and should be handled only by experienced exterminators. Rats can be controlled also by gassing their burrows and fumigating buildings which they infest. The material most commonly used is the dust form of calcium cyanide, which presents no hazard to pets and other animals.

Harsh poisons are outlawed in New York City, for it has been found that the most efficient rat exterminators are the anticoagulant chemicals of the type used by the city Pest Control Bureau exterminators.

Recently at a Pennsylvania laboratory a new rat poison, Norbormide, was discovered when a young Polish scientist, Dr. Adolph P. Roszkowski, in checking the potential as a diet-control drug of a chemical formulation that had been rejected as a possible aid to arthritis relief, found that six milligrams of the stuff amazingly killed laboratory rats but not mice. Roszkowski subsequently learned that the same dosage had no effect on dogs or cats, and when it was stepped up to thirty, one hundred, three hundred and finally one thousand milligrams per kilogram of body weight still no harm came to these animals. Thirty different species of animal and fowl — horses, cattle, sheep, chickens, pigs, rhesus monkeys, chimpanzees, and even goldfish — then were exposed to the chemical with no dire results.

Its effect is on the cardiovascular system and vital organs of the rat. Blood vessels and heart are constricted, the rat goes into shock, and starved for blood, its extremities turn white, and in about three minutes it is dead.

First tests of the new rat killer were made in Kansas City, Missouri, and the results hailed by pest control operators. Dr. Lloyd R. Gates, chief of environmental sanitation of that city, said, "We've been fighting the rat infestation for years. Our tests to date have convinced us that this is the safest, fastest killer we've ever seen."

But exterminators, ever skeptical, are watching and waiting. It is a new product and therefore suspect. The men who deal with rats on a day-to-day basis have been stung too often by miraculous rat eradicators, have seen the most rosy promises gnawed away by the persistent rats.

Cats, popularly regarded as terrific rat killers, are scorned by exterminators as being practically worthless in that capacity. "You put a cat in a cellar with heavy rat infestation," I was told by Peeples, the city pest control man who'd taken me into Harlem, "and you got yourself one very dead cat, believe me." Actually, a rat is a pretty fair match for a good-sized fierce dog, and a pack of rats doesn't hesitate to gang up on even such formidable opponents as a tiger or wild boar.

Not all rats are considered menacing enemies of society. There are some good-guy rats, the pink-eyed white ones employed in science and medical laboratories. They alone of the far-reaching rat family are respected. Yet, this rat differs from the loathsome brown rat only in that it is an albino and has been especially bred for laboratory environment. This white brown rat has made countless (though unwitting) contributions to public health. He has suffered his cunning brain to be bombarded by laser beams; he has ingested a variety of chemicals to aid in the development of our twentieth century wonder drugs; and he has patiently scampered through endless miles of mazes for the edification of psychology graduate students, learned professors, and the *Scientific American*.

It is surprising what these white rats can be taught if the instructor has enough patience. A famous white rat named Barnabel at Barnard College, New York City, once was trained to demonstrate in one minute, fifty-six seconds, the chaining process in learning — the system of one response providing stimulus for the next (committing a poem to memory is a good example of this). A written description of the process took up twenty pages of the classroom textbook. The circus-like routine to which the rat had become conditioned involved a complicated array of actions: bars were pressed by the rat's feet in order to sound buzzers and to flash signal lights;

there were staircases and ladders to be climbed; a tiny pennant was raised by the rat, pulling a halyard with its teeth; a small wheeled vehicle was pedaled by Barnabel; he slithered through a glass cylinder, and rode an elevator for a twelve-inch drop. The account in the *New York Times* of this spectacular rat performance did not state whether Barnabel, in order to get an extra handout of food pellets, had saluted his professors of psychology and pledged allegiance to cheese, but I wouldn't have been surprised by such canniness. For when food is involved, rats are mighty smart and fantastically ingenious.

A farmer neighbor of ours told me that once, to get rid of rats in his barn, he spread a layer of grain on the surface of the water in a hogshead. After the first half dozen or so rats drowned in trying to gobble the grain, the others avoided the big cask, but soon they nibbled a hole in its base so that the water drained out, leaving the grain on the bottom, which they promptly ate and then dined greedily on their dead brother rats.

I've heard of another instance of expert ratmanship. At a Tennessee distillery, rats gnawed just enough of a hole in a cask of aged sour-mash whiskey to enable them to siphon off a little at a time, replugging the hole on each occasion. Three of the rats were not permitted by their confreres to touch a drop of the booze. It seemed that they were kept sober so that they could lead the roisterers back to the burrow after their drunken orgy.

I once tested a rat's fondness for hard liquor when visiting friends on a horse farm upstate. I'd sat up late reading and in the stillness of the library about 3 A.M. a small rat appeared on the bookshelf within reach of my easy chair. I kept very quiet and, when it went away, opened a box of chocolates (which is likely what had attracted the rat), bit into a cherry piece, poured off the liquid, and substituted a splash of bourbon. The rat soon returned, ignored all the unrigged chocolates, and stuck his nose in the one containing the whiskey. He took a good snifter, leaped back about a foot, whirled around three or four times, shot like a bullet down the stack of books, crossed the floor, scooted halfway up the wall on the other side of the room and did a tremendous triple backflip to the floor. Then he disappeared and I didn't see him ever again. Maybe Ringling Bros picked him up.

Rats possess great curiosity. The movie theater in Fridelberg, North Carolina (where one of my cousins used to live), once was haunted by a rat that would creep out on the balcony railing and sit there for hours gazing attentively at the screen. He didn't applaud or anything like that, of course, but he did munch on popcorn, and everyone swears that he only appeared for the best pictures, and only on Tuesdays, somehow sensing this traditional weekly nadir of show business attendance. A rat that lived in the stables of a small racetrack at Sydelsport, Virginia, where we summered one year, often came out, as I did, in the early morning just after dawn to watch the horses being trained.

A rat is so adroit that it is able to steal even such a fragile, awkwardly shaped thing as an egg by rolling it along the ground. If you've ever tried to roll an egg you know how difficult that would be for a rat. Two rats together can hoist an egg up, over, and down a sheer wall as high as six feet. Rats can peel bananas and gnaw through the prickly scales of a fresh pineapple. They can tunnel through a watermelon or a salami, and open black walnuts without a nutcracker. They can uncork champagne by chewing on the cork — not, however, without causing a sudden bubbly geyser. A St. Louis baker reports that rats, after feasting on the icing of a five-layer wedding cake, made off with the crowning figure of the bride supposedly to use her little lace dress in their nest; the groom, carved of wood, was ignored.

In all the hullabaloo over the city rat its mean little brother, the house mouse, frequently is overlooked. People just don't hate mice as they do rats. The mouse has such a good public image — what with all the favorable publicity given Mickey and Minnie Mouse; that little Italian trick, Topolino, that appeared frequently on the Ed Sullivan show; Jerry, the animated movie mouse of *Tom and Jerry*; and, long ago, Herriman's comic strip mouse, Ignatz. They've all given to the public the impression that mice are cute, cuddly little things; physically, they are, but they're also horribly destructive. The common house mouse (scientifically known as *Mus musculus*) is the A-number-one pest of the food industry. One of fifteen hundred different rodents common to the United States, and one of the smallest mammals of North America, the house mouse is more destructive than any other of our three hundred different kinds of mice. Total damage inflicted by house mice exceeds that caused by any other destructive animal except the Norway rat; he remains the superdestroyer. Like the rat, the house mouse eats twenty or more times a day and spoils more than he consumes. He also gnaws just to keep his teeth in sharp shape. These mice destroy all sorts of things in order to get easily shredded material for their nests. While mice are not noted as disease spreaders, they do carry fleas, lice, and mites, and may harbor the virus causing choriomeningitis in humans.

The mouse is mentioned in the Bible before any other pest (Leviticus 11:29). The word mouse derives from the Latin *mus*, the Greek *mys*, and Persian *moosh*, which traces to Sanskrit *musha*, that is derived from a verb meaning "to steal." And that is why the house mouse is known as "the little thief." Scavenger mice are so bad in the slums of New York City that when I asked one landlord to suggest the best way to get rid of them he said laconically, "Burn the building down."

The mouse's original home was in Central Asia; from there it went south to India, west and on to northern Africa and the Mediterranean seacoast, where it arrived during the Neolithic age (8000 to 4000 B.C.). Later it spread to Europe and then, aided by shipping, over the rest of the world.

There are many more mice than rats in this country. If there are one hundred million rats in the United States, then the mouse population is close to one billion. At times there occur great mouse population explosions. During one such at Buena Vista Lake, California, in the autumn of 1926, the haul of dead mice from one ranch in a single night was eight wagonloads, or more than eight tons.

Although they don't get all the attention that rats do, mice are even more clever. They are the most popular laboratory animal. Usually, the white mouse is used for experimental purposes, but recently an associate professor of biology at Humboldt State College, Arcata, California, Dr. Daniel H. Brant, advanced the proposition that psychologists have been using the wrong rodent in their mouse-involved studies relating to the behavior of mankind. Dr. Brant tried using wild deer mice and found that they had a much more powerful motivational drive and were more curious than their overprotected white brothers.

"Our wild deer mice," Dr. Brant said, "will run through a maze we have built, covering three miles a night. They will climb three hundred and sixty feet in that time, making leaps fourteen inches high even though they have plenty of food and water in their home nest. They're explorers."

The maze box, about as big as a small foreign sports car, contained more than a quarter-mile of tunnels and mazes and 445 blind alleys. To go the shortest route through the labyrinth the animal had to make 1,205 turns and climb eighty feet. At the end he found nothing, yet he did it night after night.

But still I believe the wild mouse, like the wilder humans, will have a tough time making it with the Establishment. After all, it was a white mouse that pioneered for his race in becoming an astronaut. The first mouse into space was named Laska (for the then newly admitted forty-ninth state, Alaska) and later there was Wickie, named for a local young female radio reporter, Mrs. Wickham L. Stivers (then twenty) of Cocoa Beach, Florida, the launching site, who was a Reuters correspondent assigned to the missile beat.

Another achievement of the white mouse that makes things tough for any old brown or tan field mouse who tries to improve its image is a recent experiment in which white mice were able to breathe water like fishes. The mice used their lungs as gills to extract life-sustaining oxygen from liquid that had been heavily pressurized with that element. The water had salinity to match that of the animal's lung tissues. The project was undertaken by a Hollander, Dr. Johannes H. Kylstra, at the State University of New

York in Buffalo, in an attempt to develop techniques that would allow man to breathe liquids as an aid in two important realms of exploration: space and the ocean depths. A human astronaut could be protected from the destructive forces of a hard landing on another celestial body if he were enclosed in a cockpit filled with oxygenated fluid that he could also breathe. This would be analogous to the way mammalian fetuses are protected from physical shocks by the amniotic fluid in which they float before birth. Also, a free-swimming underwater explorer with liquid-filled lungs could dive deeper, stay longer, and ascend faster and more safely than a diver breathing a gaseous mixture of nitrogen and oxygen. At present, nitrogen narcosis, the so-called "rapture of the deep," is a limiting factor in underwater exploration; a diver is incapacitated by it at a depth of about three hundred feet. Breathing of an oxygenated fluid also would lessen the dangers of the "bends," decompression sickness. To completely flood both lungs with liquid, of course, would drown a person — unless, perhaps, the liquid were loaded with oxygen that could be extracted by the lungs to prevent asphyxiation. The mice used in this experiment all died after being taken from the liquid, so I guess we've got a long way to go before any of us can consider eloping with a mermaid.

The mice that are benefiting mankind definitely are in the minority. The malevolent ones rule the roost. Rats, however, still command the most attention from the public because as an enemy they are more dramatic. I found out just how shocking the rat problem can be, a week or so after my excursion to Harlem, when I rejoined Solomon Peeples and his Pest Control Bureau team of exterminators to probe into the East Village Section of Manhattan, on the Lower East Side.

A heavy snowstorm hit our county that morning — seven inches — so I wasn't able to get in from the country until midday. The boys had been alerted to my visit and, as they'd called in to the office every half hour to check on my arrival, I had to wait only about fifteen minutes after I'd gotten to 93 Worth Street before Mike Egan had his Chevy-van down at the front entrance.

Schinz wasn't with the crew this time; a tall relaxed young

Negro, Amos Wilson, was in his place. I climbed onto my familiar perch in the back of the truck and we set out toward Chinatown. At its edge we were halted by a funeral, identified as Chinese by placards bearing Oriental characters, attached one to a front window of each car.

"Look at that," Egan marveled, "three open barouches of floral offerings."

"I didn't think Chinese went in for flowers for the dead," said Williams.

"They've become Americanized like everybody else," said Peeples. "They're not a lot different than we are any more. Nobody is. Just like the Spanish is all changing, too; used to be the wife was just home being a mother, and the man was boss supreme, but now she goes out to work just like he does and brings in money too and he's no longer big cock of the walk any more."

Remembering what Castrulli had told me about the difficulty of exterminators' gaining access to Chinese residences, I asked if this were true.

"If you can say something in Chinese," said Wilson, "like 'Health Department' or 'exterminator' — I used to know how, but I've forgot — they will let you in. It's all just if you can communicate just a little bit. After all, they don't know who you are when you come banging on their door yelling something they don't understand." Everyone agreed he had a point there.

"One guy down on Mott Street once, because he couldn't understand me, he put the rat bait in the Frigidaire instead of alongside it or in under like I told him," continued Wilson.

"That may have been where he had rats," offered Peeples without cracking a smile. "You know Chinese aren't the same as we are."

"Man, you got to be kidding," responded Wilson. "Rats don't like no cold at all." Everyone laughed heartily because he'd risen to Peeples' bait.

Peeples then announced that we'd revisit, for my benefit, a particularly atrocious tenement that the crew had treated that morning.

"You won't believe this one," he promised. "It's so bad we're trying to get the Buildings Department to vacate this building, to declare it not habitable."

The place, a five-story brick affair of twenty-four apartments, was near Broome and Norfolk. The street and sidewalk in front of it were much dirtier than any I'd seen in Harlem. Real Dickensian squalor surrounded us. We went immediately down steep narrow wooden stairs off the sidewalk, and through a long dank passage opening onto a small rectangular rubbish-littered areaway. From there we entered the basement, coming directly into the furnace room. Peeples flashed his light around.

"This was a regular grand hotel for bums," he said. "The police cleared them all out only just this morning. Must have been at least twenty by the looks of it."

Filthy old legless couches, grimy lumpy mattresses, and broken-down box springs were spotted about in the gloom. One of these makeshift beds had a satin quilt spread neatly on it. There was a chrome chair with a ratty velvet seat cushion.

"That must be for the super," said Williams. "Sometimes the landlord or the agent hires a wino bum to be super and then he lets his pals slip in at night to sleep where it's warm — maybe charging them a little, maybe not. These kind of supers is paid, not all at once, but a couple of cents a day, or by the bottle."

He swung his flashlight around and picked out one empty bottle after another scattered about on the dirt floor. To read the label I turned one over with the toe of my shoe: *EMBROS Half-and-Half PORT-SHERRY*.

"Now we'll go upstairs and show you some of the luxury apartments," said Peeples. "When I see places like this one I just go blind mad, but I'm too stupid, I guess, to give up trying."

The first quarters we visited were occupied by an aged gray-haired Italian lady. On the wall of her living room, which was about half as big as a single garage, were a large carved-wood cuckoo clock, a framed print of Da Vinci's *The Last Supper*, and her wedding portrait — prettily tinted. Doorframes were so rotted away that they looked like something painted by Ivan Albright in his most morose mood. Without saying a word, the lady moved haltingly about the apartment eloquently pointing out all the rat-holes — at least a dozen in the three small rooms. It was a sort of macabre parody of that famous television tour of the White House made by Jacqueline Kennedy when she was reigning First Lady — as Samuel Beckett might have done it.

"This kind of place gives me the willies," remarked Peeples. "How'd you like for your old mother to be living like this?"

At our next stop, more of the same dreadful deterioration. This apartment's kitchen sported an enamel bathtub; the sink's dish drainboard extended over its one end. Flanking a cabinet jammed with cheap china bric-a-brac there hung a plaque of John F. Kennedy in profile, bearing his famous inaugural words: "Ask not what your country can do for you, but what you can do for your country." (It was the first of many such memorials to our most recently assassinated President that we were to encounter that day, but in all the apartments we visited I saw not one portrait of LBJ, Great White Father of the Great Society.)

Apartment number three was the real nightmare shocker. In a frantic attempt to make the place habitable, the women who occu-pied it — two short, stout Puerto Ricans, mother and grown daughter — had decorated lavishly with five-and-dime-store junk (artifical flowers, all sorts of romantic plaques, framed pictures and mottoes, gaudily colored plaster statuary, religious figurines and chromos, plastic fruit arrangements, and songbirds assembled from do-it-yourself kits. The walls were a veritable jungle of bi-zarre display. A reek of fried onions, garlic, and cheap perfume almost sent me to my knees. Adding to the revulsion was an abnor-mally obese child of about eight — the daughter's son. He was clad only in jockey shorts and his flabby torso was blotched by great angry pink-violet blistery patches. I hope he wasn't contagious. From the little cubicle called a bathroom came the gurgling sound of a constantly flushing toilet. Every once in a while it surged up violently like an angry burbling geyser and overflowed onto the floor. (Why go to Yellowstone when you can have Old Faithful right at home?) The cracked wall-to-wall linoleum of the kitchen, which adjoined the bath, was flooded by a thin squishy film of dirty water. The two females flapped frantically about the rooms —like a pair of crazed, boxed-in parrots—chattering in Spanish and fractured English, pointing out all the ghastly results of neglect and calling attention to the bars and locks they'd had to put on the windows to foil marauders. Evidently they took me to be some higher authority, perhaps because I was white.

"Eighty-five dollars," wailed the elder woman bitterly, "I pay here for rent. Eighty-five dollars. Please, mister, tell to the city to find me new rooms. Mister, please. I go crazy loco here."

Peeples said kindly that he'd do what he could, and we withdrew as gracefully as we could. Out in the hall, he said to me, "I can show you more, but these are typical of them all here. On this job I have to tell myself jokes to laugh at, so's I can go home at night feeling normal."

As we drove off down the street we passed a church sign that said: A CLEAN HEART MAKES A CLEAN MIND.

Next on Peeples' list was a basement-occupancy place, occupied mostly by Italians and Puerto Ricans, although while we were there a few doddering fading Irish trickled through the halls, going in and out with groceries and bottle goods. The crummy apartments here were gems of social iniquity, but not as bad as the ones we'd just left. The television sets were more grandiose—some of them almost as big as sideboards—the artificial flower and fruit displays more lavish, and the holy shrines more tinselly and glittery. One resident, surprisingly, kept a well-groomed and elegantly clipped saucy little white French poodle. One place had a fighting cock confined to the bathroom. In one living room was a life-size plaster head of President Kennedy (painted in what were assumed to be natural colors; the hair was a repulsive shade of brown), and alongside the kitchen garbage can stood a stack of record albums.

On the lintel over the cellar entrance of this building a rusting sign proclaimed that these lower depths once had been the "He-Men's Club."

"Keep your head down," said Peeples. "This is another one of those brain busters. We don't want to bruise you on this detail."

Peeples was especially disgusted by the large vacant lot next to this building. Into it had been tossed all sorts of nonedible junk — bedsprings, baby buggies, broken velocipedes and bicycles, toy wagons and trucks, naked baby dolls, metal hoops, smashed chests of drawers and other furniture, boxes and barrels, you name it. Two small urchins wandered among the rubble, poking at it, with their grimy hands, while sharing a box of Cracker Jack.

"With that lovely Disneyland for rats right next door," Peeples said, "it is a wasted effort to put rat bait in this building. Can you imagine what this is like on a stinking hot night in summer? Is it any wonder that these people get infections?"

In our next building the cellar was soggy with feces overflowing a plugged sewer, and Williams, after making one inadvertent sloshing step, withdrew hastily and then threw into the damp dark chunks of what is known as block bait — rat poison imbedded in rectangular blocks of hard black wax, impervious to water.

We next had a succession of apartments where no one would answer our knocks (there wasn't one bell that worked). There'd be a barely audible click as the shield on the spyhole was lowered; we'd hear someone moving about behind the closed door, but there'd be no response of any sort — not even in Spanish. The supers invariably were unavailable — hiding out. In one place we found a young man cuddled up under a first-floor staircase near a warm radiator.

"Got a drunk here," Peeples called to his crew, then addressed the fellow, "Are you the super? Are you Louie?"

"No, I'm Sam, and I'm not drunk. I'm sleeping."

"Okay, Sam. Go back to sleep."

"Thank you."

All we ever saw of him was a pair of dirty sneakers, his bare ankles, trousers to the knees. The rest was cloaked by the gloom.

All these places had to be marked on the daily report as N.A. — No Access.

Our next calls were in the more turned-on part of the East Village, where we encountered a few minor ripples of the new wave. The real way-out hippies mostly were in their burrows waiting for night to fall. Of all the tenants we contacted in this bailiwick of swingers, the only one who would let us in to inspect the premises as health officers was a willowy light-voiced fellow who was busy at an ironing board amidst an unbelievable clutter of esoteric paperbacks. He didn't want any of our rat poison, and neither did any of the other tenants who bothered to answer our knocks.

"As a general rule," said Peeples to me, "the artistic folk down here keep a pretty clean place. Actually, I believe they've helped the East Village by coming into it like they did. They fix things up a little, as best they can."

The signs here reflected the bellicose spirit of these Lower East Side immigrants of the Psychedelic Sixties. "Bourgeois Elements Must Get Out!" said one. Another proclaimed that "Mayor Lindsay Was a Test Tube Baby." One ordered: STOP COPS. A sign painter advertised himself as a *"Pintor de Letreros Artisticos. Poeta y Declamador."* I saw only one old-fashioned graffito: "Hilburn Injectors," chalked on a door. (Square, man.) A poster in the front window of a crafts shop announced a social event called a "Rock Flow," where one could "laugh, dance, and be beautiful" while observing "wind, astral lighting and sintitalating costumes wearing gorgeous girls."

We made a few more attempts to get down some rat bait among what used to be called the avant-garde (and before that, "bohemians"), then Peeples headed us out of never-never land to make our last stop of the day about two blocks from Bellevue, the municipal hospital known to every true New Yorker.

"Rat bite here," said Peeples as he knocked on an apartment door. We could hear a tapping sound from inside.

"Someone typing," said Peeples.

"Sounds more to me like a dog's claws walking on linoleum," I ventured.

"No that's a typewriter."

"Maybe it's a dog typing," I conceded.

The door finally was opened by a squarely built, short colored woman attired in a yé-yé outfit of quilted oyster-white satin that looked like the stuff they line coffins with. Apparently, the delayed response to our knocks was due to her changing into something respectable enough to greet a representative of City Hall. She had been bitten on the head while sleeping in the bedroom. (From where we stood I could see that one of its walls was covered entirely by a painting on canvas of Christ at Gethsemane.) She didn't want the rat poison because she said it had made her dog sick. Turned out that the mutt, after killing the attacking rat, had eaten a good deal of it. Peeples suggested that may have been the cause of the animal's illness. The lady hadn't thought of that. She launched into a long diatribe against the landlord's agent. He'd flipped into a violent rage after she'd complained about the rat and she'd had to call the cops down on him. To get even with her for this indignity, the man filed a scurrilous report on the woman to his boss, the landlord.

"It's terrible," she said to me, "to take your personal affair and put it in the street for everybody to hear about. You see, this fellow I go with, we're not married and he's your same color—and the agent he put this down in the report he sent downtown. It a terrible thing to humilate a person like that, don't you agree?"

Peeples and I both commiserated with her. Back out on the sidewalk, Peeples waved his arm about and said, "Just look around you. High-class apartment right across the street, one down yonder, and another going up down on that corner. This is a luxury area. Yet still there are rats that bite."

The crew, on their way back downtown, dropped me at Park Avenue South and Twenty-third Street, so that I could take the subway uptown.

"You can go on home now," said Peeples, "and forget all about rats, but we'll be back after them again tomorrow and the day after and the day after that, and next year and next and the next. There's enough rats in this city to keep us all going as long as we live, but we hope we're rid of them before we die."

Forget about the rats, the man said. I'll not be able to forget about rats as long as I live. Rats will gnaw holes in my dreams.

On my way uptown to get my car for the drive back to the country, I stopped off at New York City's fanciest hardware store, Hammacher Schlemmer, on East Fifty-seventh Street, to see what kind of better rat traps they had for sale and who in the world was beating a path to the door to buy them. The clerk smiled sympathetically when I asked for rat traps.

"We haven't stocked them for years," he said, "Why don't you try one of the hardware stores around on Third Avenue or Woolworth's?"

I slunk out of this august establishment in disgrace.

At Woolworth's, in the paint department, I found big sturdy rat traps — the old-fashioned wooden heavy-spring kind. They were called the Victor Four Ways, made by the Animal Trap Company, Lititz, Pennsylvania, which I've never heard of although I am a native of that state.

From this establishment that caters to nonsilver-spooners I went on to the world-famous toy bazaar, F.A.O. Schwarz, on Fifth Avenue facing the Plaza Hotel, New York's most elegant caravansary. I'd heard that Schwarz's was peddling small rats for fifteen dollars a pair. Turned out that these creatures, while members of the order Rodentia, really were not rats, but mice of the same superfamily as that of the rat, Muroidea, and of the family Cricetidae, subfamily Gerbillinae, which contains a number of jumping rodents, some of them quite ratlike. The common name for all the genera of this subfamily is gerbil. These creatures are cousins to the kangaroo rat (family Heteromyidae), which they resemble, and the jerboa (family Dipodoidea), from which they differ in having five hind toes. Gerbils are desert rodents, native to Eastern Europe, Asia, Africa, and southern Russia. They were first brought to the United States in 1955 for medical research purposes, but didn't enter the pet world until about ten years later when they began to travel along the kiddie grapevine by dint of regular television appearances on NBC's popular "Birthday House" and a plug from Barbra Streisand on a CBS telecast. A *Time* magazine story in the spring of 1966 further enhanced the image of the gerbil, by proclaiming its credentials faultless as a replacement for that popular household pet, the hamster, which tends to be neurotic, to eat its young, and to bite the hand that feeds it. "It is clean, odorless, and friendly," said *Time*, in comparing the gerbil to the hamster, "eats little (sunflower seeds, lettuce, corn), excretes less (three drops of urine a day), and never bites. Besides all this, it is happy, playful, loyal, fearless, and curious" — a sort of Boy Scout rat, I gathered. A trustworthy, loyal, helpful, friendly, courteous, kind, obedient, cheerful, thrifty, brave, clean, and reverent cousin to the rat.

Today gerbils are in demand all across the nation. A New York outfit called Creative Playthings claims that it sells "between four and five thousand individual gerbils a year" — through its Manhattan retail outlet at Rockefeller Plaza, its Princeton, New Jersey, headquarters, and through its widely distributed catalogue. F.A.O. Schwarz turns over about three hundred gerbils a year, according to Richard Bendin, sporting goods buyer in whose domain the sexy little creatures fall. This store is hopeful that the gerbil eventually will replace the live bunny as an Easter gift.

The Schwarz gerbils were off in one corner of the third floor. There were only two pairs in evidence that afternoon and a small card attached to the cages said: ALL SOLD.

Leaning against the cages was a sign that read: "Happiness Is a Pair of Gerbils. Four inches of fluffy gray fur, a tufted tail, sparkling black eyes, the tiny cousin of the squirrel, the Gerbil (pronounced Jur-bil) is now the darling of the pet set, a tiny handful of curiosity. Gerbils never bite, are fun to play with, easy to care for and can be taught tricks." Just what those two frantic Puerto Rican ladies downtown need to round out their rich, full-to-overflowing life.

At home that evening I looked up Lititz, Pennsylvania, in the atlas and found that it's in Pennsylvania Dutch country north of Lancaster, has a population of 5,978, and is famous for pretzels and as the burial place, in the Moravian cemetery, of John Sutter, on whose land was discovered the first gold of the California gold rush of '49. I phoned Lititz's Animal Trap Company and learned from a Mr. Tarbox that this trap-maker and its chief competitor, McGill

Metal Products Company of Marengo, Illinois, market more than 1,200,000 rat traps a year in the United States.

New York is not alone in suffering the rat. Every big city around the world has rats running in its cellars and sewers. Officials in West Berlin estimate that there are tens of thousands of them living in that fragmented city's bombed-out ruins, cellars, parks, on rooftops, and especially in the 110-yard-wide zone of no-man's-land along the East Berlin side of the hideous wall that divides the city.

"It is most difficult," one city official lamented, "to reduce the number of unwanted animals. Any plan produced usually ends up with Berliners fighting the authorities."

At the many places in Berlin where the public feeds pigeons, hordes of rats have moved in to eat the leavings. And if the city spreads poison bait for the birds, residents wait in the streets to sweep it up before their feathered *Liebchens* can get to it.

Orientals, who knew the rat long before Europeans, are still greatly bothered by this gnawing nuisance. A news dispatch from Jakarta, Indonesia, tells of a rat roundup in three villages (Srondol, Sendang Guo, and Pedurungan) in which sixty-five thousand rats were killed.

Every once in a while people who know what it is like to have to live with rats get so fed up that they bring the problem to the attention of the general public in an especially forceful way. The Council of Churches of Christ of Greater Cleveland, Ohio, during the Christmas season of 1966, in an effort to stir up interest in welfare problems (the city's per capita welfare payment is next to the lowest of Northern industrial cities) published three full-page newspaper ads dramatizing the plight of the city's poor. The third ad concerned rats. Most of its space was taken up by a large half-tone portrait of a rat and a bold-lettered headline: MERRY CHRIST-MAS, KIDS. Under the photo were five lines of small type: "You were expecting reindeer? In some sections of Cleveland rats are very in, this year. Nearly every kid has one. Sometimes two. In some parts of Cleveland rats actually make out better than people.

At least they eat better." The ads created quite a stir, and Reverend B. Bruce Whittemore, general director of the council, told inquiring news media that forty thousand Cleveland children live in rat-infested homes.

About six years ago in New York City, another newspaper ad concerning rats kicked up a rousing controversy between the Board of Education and a Harlem elementary school principal, Elliott Shapiro, champion of the downtrodden, who is now superintendent of District 3 in the New York City Public School System. The headlines of this ad screamed: HELP! HELP! HELP! HELP US TO GET A NEW SCHOOL TO SAVE OUR CHILDREN GIVE US A BUILDING WITHOUT . . . and then there were listed eleven items that a good school building should not have. Point No. 1 was: "Rats and Roaches on Every Floor." Point 6 was: "Irreparable Plumbing, Resulting In: Backups, Leaks, Flooded Yards and Corridors and Lunchrooms." No. 9 on the list: "Unsanitary Children's Toilets." The ad was signed "The teaching, clerical, and administrative staff of Public School #119 — Manhattan." The startling ad and subsequent rhubarb with the Board of Education made the school famous and had quite a lot to do with the building of a replacement for the dilapidated, oppressive, rat-ridden structure that dated from 1899. Eventually Dr. Shapiro became proud principal of a brand-new school building, P.S. 92, which he helped to design.

"Five years ago the physical conditions were awful," he says in a book written about his good works by Nat Hentoff, *Our Children Are Dying.* "The plaster was falling down. When it rained, there were floods in the halls. And there was no way to get the building clean with all the vermin and cockroaches around. You could run into a rat on any floor. I sent letters and letters to the Board and to the assistant superintendent in charge of this district. No answers. I'd call and be told, 'It's not my department. I'll switch you.' I'd hold on and nothing would happen. Some of the parents went to City Hall to show pictures of water running in the halls. Still nothing happened. We had a number of staff meetings, trying to figure out what to do. Finally, I suggested that we could always advertise in the newspaper. Everybody chipped in, and on May 22, 1961, an ad appeared on the school page of the *World Telegram.*"

It was the first time in the history of the New York Public School System that anything like that had happened. The effect was explosive. Radio, television, newspaper, and newsmagazine reporters descended on the school, saw rats, and reported them. The ad appeared on a Monday; on Friday morning Mr. Shapiro and his school were honored by an unprecedented visit from Mayor Robert Wagner and a small entourage. In the midst of the confrontation a rat appeared, and with cries of "Rat! Rat!" a teacher, several students, and the principal, (armed with the regular rat-chasing broom) gave chase. The mayor was somewhat shaken.

The school superintendent, Dr. John Theobald, hadn't been able to come at that time because he was in Europe on official business making a springtime survey of the school systems of various foreign cities. And when he did return he never would admit that a rat and the mayor had been in the same room together. He charged that the "incident of the rat" had been "a cleverly handled public relations stunt." He told the press that he'd found no one who'd seen hide or hair of a rat on that day, and when Shapiro countered by saying that exterminators had killed forty of them shortly afterward during a fumigating session over the Memorial Day weekend, Theobald, his superior, simply looked stonily at him and said grimly, "Thirty-nine." Hentoff's book is a good one to read if you want a true picture of the struggle against heavy odds for decent education in a slum neighborhood.

Occasionally tenement dwellers will take matters in hand and begin screaming in no uncertain terms about rats. Such an uprising took place in the summer of 1965 up in East Harlem when a residents' organization called the Metro North Citizens' Committee staged a rally, attended by two hundred angry parishioners, to protest against rats, cockroaches, and the general neglect by landlords of four tenement buildings on East 101st Street. A brass band of six young boys tootled a dirge as floral wreaths were placed on the battered front doors of each tenement, indicating that they were dead. "This building is in mourning because of neglect by the city," said a sign held aloft by one of the women tenants. As the small combo swung from Chopin's "Funeral March" into something swingable enough to bring out the twist in the younger mourners, song sheets were distributed and, to the tune of "Goody, Goody," the people began to sing a made-up ditty that started out: "We lie a-wake just hear-ing the rats all night/Oh, how aw-ful . . ."

To get some idea of the bitter struggle of tenant versus landlord versus city administration, I talked to a number of people, both tenants and landlords, about conditions in slums that attract rats. A revealing dialogue developed. Without naming landlords or tenants, I'll set down what I heard from both camps.

LANDLORD: "There's no rat problem; it's a human problem. If people weren't so damned dirty there'd be nothing for the rats to eat and they'd leave. No rat is gonna go for poison when he can get pork chops. These people up here haven't got the vaguest notion of how to keep clean and sanitary."

TENANT: "I ain't had no water up there since last Friday — not even to flush the toilet. All I get I have to carry in a bucket from across the street and then up four flights."

LANDLORD: "Does the landlord make the garbage? Is he the one that throws it from the windows into the courtyard? I have incinerators, but they still would rather throw it out the windows."

TENANT: "There is never enough garbage cans. Eighteen apartments we got here and only six cans for them all."

LANDLORD: "In my building I gave every one of my twenty-eight tenants a brand-new garbage pail and asked them please to keep the garbage sealed in the cans. Do you know in three months there wasn't a half dozen of them left?"

TENANT: "I whangs that junk outa the window because I got nothin' else to do, and I like to watch it fall and hit the roofs and splash in the courtyard."

LANDLORD: "They won't set out the garbage at night, or at the times when the sanitation men do the pickups."

TENANT: "We got no communication with the Sanitary Department. They don't speak to us much or tell us nothin'. And there's no pickups on Sundays, or on holidays when we eats the most. And if it snows nobody comes for the garbage. What we needs is pickups twice a day, seven days a week. Then maybe the rats wouldn't have such easy pickin's."

LANDLORD: "It might be better if people were completely poverty-stricken. Then there'd be no rats, because there'd be no waste food for them to eat."

TENANT: "One morning last winter we had frost on top the television 'cause there only was cardboard in the kitchen window. Even the rats stayed away the night before. It was *cold*, man."

LANDLORD: "If a tenant on the top floor has a party, sixteen windowpanes can be broken by someone on the way down, just to hear the glass tinkle."

TENANT: "Mister, sometime you feel you just gotta break something for psychologic reason."

LANDLORD: "You really should see it up here at night. This is supposed to be a place you can get anything you want up here. Big nice-looking cars from downtown and Jersey come buzzing around, looking for the stuff. You go into an apartment sometimes, and a junkie will be there shooting his arm right in front of you — doesn't care who sees it. Terrible, just awful."

TENANT: "There ain't never a night go by, we don't hear the rats chewin' inside of the walls."

LANDLORD: "To get decertified for rats you've got to practically follow the inspector around with a plasterer right alongside, and when the inspector says there's a hole, you right away throw in some plaster — splat — there's no hole, inspector, sir. Otherwise, it takes you months to get everything just right the way they want it."

TENANT: "Anything what the city does is one step forward and two backward."

LANDLORD: "A responsible landlord has to assume that the poor are people even though sometimes they don't act like it."

TENANT: "I hear that twelve big syndicates owns all the rentals in Harlem, and I half believes it."

LANDLORD: "Did you ever see a refrigerator with hammer marks all over it? I have, in one of my buildings."

TENANT: "I wouldn't say that rats is too much fun, when you get to thinkin' about it."

LANDLORD: "There's so many forms to fill out, if you have violations in your buildings, that any owner will lose six months' rent no matter how fast you work. And if you have only one tenant left in a building the law is you can't close it up without you pay him off — a goodly number of dollars, like this four-hundred-buck check I'm writing out here right now to get a tenant out of a building I want to close up."

TENANT: "If they can keep an apartment vacant for at least two years, they entitled to a 15 percent increase under the rent law."

LANDLORD: "What is needed is a little tenant education."

TENANT: "It's them fly-by-nights out to make a fast buck that's the mostest trouble. They patch up, get a clearance, collect a few thousand in rents and then unload the property or walks away from it. But while they's in charge nothin' gets done and the rats and roaches takes over."

LANDLORD: "We're all of us running too close to the edge. We can't afford to fix up the buildings and still operate profitably."

TENANT: "I pays $75.92 for these four little rooms and most of the time in winter there is hardly any heat. I got to boil up a kettle of water on the gas range to keep warm enough for the babies."

LANDLORD: "My rents run twenty to twenty-five dollars a month without cooking gas or light; they pay that themselves."

TENANT: "If the landlords don't make no money off tenants, how come they don't have to live here like we does and can drive them big fancy limousines?"

LANDLORD: "I'm just hoping for a miracle to be able to get out of this crap. I'm dropping a lot. Five years ago I had a million dollars' equity: now I have a million in debts. The good guy ends up last, gets kicked in the ass. No matter what I try, I'm still a lousy slumlord, a usurer, taking advantage of the poor — and besides I'm a white man. It's a hardship for any poor schnook. It's just like being married to the goddam thing, and you're a criminal if you walk away. You can't sell the property, or even give it away: nobody wants it."

TENANT: "With five kids to feed it costs me a hundred and ninety dollars every two weeks, that's for everything — food, clothing, rent, light, and gas."

LANDLORD: "What no one seems to want to recognize is that with the Negroes we're saddled with a displacement problem. Historically, they are displaced people. They're not a race with a literate heritage. It's hard for them to catch on to books and things like that. What the kids need most in a place like this is athletic things, where they can jump and run — like swimming, dancing and such — to get them unglued from the TV sets."

TENANT: "We got one real big rat comes in the kitchen that my man has been trying to catch now since last Easter when he et up my lily and all my little girl's chocolate bunny basket."

LANDLORD: "These people don't live by the same morality standards that we do. As God is my witness I've tried to understand them and help them. I've had mothers in here with fourteen-year-old daughters pregnant, and nobody gives it a second thought. I used to go to the narcotics clinic — it's just here, on down the block a ways — and talk with the boys, even took some of them out to Long Island with me, let them shoot my guns — but do you know every one ended up stealing from me. I've found out that if I laid down and died for these people it still wouldn't be enough."

TENANT: "If we gets rid of all the rats, then the rent shoot back up again."

LANDLORD: "Down at City Hall once, when I almost broke up a meeting by complaining, they told me, 'Don't get so excited, Maxie, the election will be over next month and things will go back to normal.' Every one of them clucks down there is a political appointee and afraid for his own skin."

TENANT: "The reason they takes out the insides of a tenement and redoes them, leaving the old walls up, is because with a new building it's the law they have to have more air space around it and that would cut down on the number of apartments they could rent."

LANDLORD: "There's some people won't steal unless it's for more'n fifty thousand, and some will do it gladly for five bucks. You want to know what it's like down at City Hall, I'll tell you a story. It's like the guy asking this girl, 'Will you go to bed with that man for five thousand bucks?' She says, 'Sure,' and then he says, 'Will you do it for a buck-fifty?' and she gets sore and says, 'What do you think I am?' and he says, 'We know what you are, we're just trying to establish the price,' and that's the way it is. Everyone has got his price."

TENANT: "Ain't nothin' made easy for the poor."

LANDLORD: "The rat died from the bait they put around and I get a summons for having a dead rat on the premises. I ask you, is that fair?"

TENANT: "And this man come around and he say he sprayed so good this new stuff and he say that if cockroaches comes back he'll eat every one, and I say, mister, I knows you're French, but I think you makin' a powerful strong statement."

LANDLORD: "All these citizens' committees for relocation and rehabilitation are all a lot of hogwash. I can name you women, big leaders now, that was nothing but common drunks before they got hooked up with such uplift societies. And the Puerto Ricans that get involved are in it just for politics. They all got their eye on running for City Council. Up here you can put up Mickey Mouse if you change his name to Miguel Ratacita."

TENANT: "Consultants? Rats don't understand them high-price consultants."

LANDLORD: "People are moving out of these kind of neighborhoods. Nobody wants to run the risk of being robbed, mugged, or raped by some hophead. The decent people are all going away. Even if rent controls went off, I couldn't get any more for my places. Nobody wants to live in these kind of dumps any more."

TENANT: "They lets the building run down on purpose so's the city will make them have to vacate it, then they can close up for a while, remodel, makin' smaller apartments, and open up again chargin' more rent than before for more apartments."

There is no last word. Tenant, landlord, and city: each has its own cross to bear, and each has the hammer and nails ready to pin the other to it. We are all guilty when we overlook social blight. All of us will pay for our willful ignorance. If any onus is to be leveled it should fall on the irresponsible landlord, for there are other ways to make money besides extorting it from the impoverished — just as there are other ways to make a living for the man who purveys narcotics or munitions, or for the men and women who run whorehouses or call-girl syndicates.

There is no easy solution that I can see for the problem of rats in the big city, in what City Hall is fond of calling "Fun City." *New York Is a Fun City.* I'm sure it is — for some people. And, of course, for the rats.

The Pests of War

Here in Paradise, each life moves jointly
from self-propulsion and in multifunctioned
counterbalance
to the tensions and all dancing actions
of each — each other life it touches now.
Here in Paradise, all lives appoint me
partner, singing through the endless junctioned
runs of talents —
changing values, freely feeding fractions,
expanding spherically as strength allows.

Here in Paradise appears a sorrow
dissolving spheres to swell a new dominion:
judgment dealer —
deprivation, subjugation dealer —
suppressor of the morally unfit.
Now, with arrogant eyes, some mind can borrow
worth for metal as exchange for minion.
This revealer
presses, teaches open lives to kneel or
die. Undressed, the innocent submit.

Here, parroting new prayers, all later die,
for famine crawls our damaged globes, and plague
wins, beginning
new quiet cooling Paradise of mold,
both self-propelled and counter-moved. For years
in floating time expanding spherules fly
loose on a drying core, and alter, in vague
elliptic spinnings.
We of past ecology are cold
and scattered, used, once blessed by each other's tears.

9

In Colder Blood: *The Pests of War* In most respects the insects were fortunate the way things turned out, even if it did damage their national image. They hadn't meant to let down the Department of Defense. Can't say they were sorry, because insects may never experience remorse, but anyhow they're fortunate not to be actively involved in man-made warfare.

That the insects blanked out actually was no fault of the DOD strategists. They truly believed that God's smallest creatures would be the best, least expensive, and most unsuspected instruments for carrying biological warfare to the enemy. But insects proved to be not very efficient bearers of bubonic plague, anthrax, malaria, typhus, and such — extremely clumsy, unreliable — so other methods of employing such subtle weapons had to be, and were, devised.

No one could understand the failure of the insects. They had performed gloriously in every other war. Their delinquency lay in the fact that they never seemed to know which side they were on. Otherwise, they did fine. That was the trouble this time too. They couldn't get their allegiances straight. To whom does a secret-agent mosquito report? How does one know that a particular cockroach isn't subversive or even a Communist? (Most of them are, you know.) How do you distinguish chauvinist fleas from non-chauvinist? A louse doesn't know one flag from another. To a bedbug all blood tastes the same.

It was an anxious letter to the editor of the *Calgary Albertan*, a voice calling from the isolation of the Canadian prairie, that finally set me looking into the role of the insect in our government's chemical-biological warfare program.

> Editors, the ALBERTAN:
> There is a vast, multimillion-dollar program for the development of chemical and biological warfare under way in the United States. Why is it that no word of condemnation has come out of Ottawa? Is it not a paradox that Canada's Prime Minister, a Nobel Peace Prize winner, has remained silent on this venture that can only result in suicide? Are our MP's disinterested in the kind of world their children will inherit? Have people become so indifferent that they will sit idly by while insane scientists seek means to devastate the earth with pestilence? Will we allow fellow humans to be cruelly killed by diseases and plagues spread by infected insects directed onto targets selected by the military? . . . The help and care we give to all life around us, the things we do for others are the rent we pay for our room on this planet. The failure of man to pay the rent is going to end in his being turned out.
> — L. CREIGHTON

My quest began in Washington, D.C., at the headquarters of the combined Army-Navy-Air Force top brass. I wasn't prepared for the enormity of the Pentagon. I question that any ordinary citizen-taxpayer ever would be. Actually I was appalled — it's like an American Legion clubhouse gone berserk.

I was surprised to find, at this traffic hub of our armed forces' nerve center, a gigantic shopping complex worthy of the finest suburban development. All it lacks is children. There's an enormous drugstore, a bookstore, a department store and all sorts of other shops and services offering just about anything the military man needs to get through a day behind the lines. An evening gown? Mink coat? Panty girdle? Uplift brassiere? An umbrella? A long-play album for the hi-fi? You can buy it here. A chocolate ice-cream soda with whipped cream and a cherry or an airplane ticket to any place not on the State Department's blacklist. A person of blunted sensitivity toward nature likely could live quite comfortably for some time within the Pentagon. As Brendan Behan once said of the old Penn Station in New York — of which this place reminded me — you could even go to the toilet there.

The armed force I'd arranged to meet was named Lieutenant Colonel Charles W. Burtyk, Jr. He was a press, magazine, and books public-relations liaison officer. I found him — a large, portly, relaxed fellow — sharing one of the smaller offices with another officer, Colonel Gilbert G. Heiman. When I explained my mission (at the Pentagon even a trip to the lavatory is a "mission") to learn about the contribution to science of the insects at the Fort Detrick Research Center, Colonel Burtyk asked blandly, "Are you speaking about biological warfare?"

"Not especially," I replied, exercising my constitutional right to the credibility gap.

"You know that's all classified out there. Doubt any writer could get in there except you apply in writing to the commanding officer."

I hadn't planned to trudge through channels.

He went on casually, "Oh, that's all phased out out there anyhow. No more insects at all. Only place they're doing any experimental work at all with insects is up at Natick, Massachusetts — the Earth-Sciences Division, they call it. They're mapping insect-infested areas to tell the Army what kinds of insects to expect in certain insect-infested areas."

He gave me the name of a Dr. Pratt and the telephone number of the United States Army laboratory at Natick.

"Our boys in the chemical department upstairs," said Colonel Burtyk, "would like to have this whole business opened out, but the State Department says no, now is not the right time."

There didn't seem to be anything more to say, so I thanked him kindly for his help and backed off into the corridor.

At the Pentagon library I learned that Dr. Riley Housewright has been scientific director of the governmental research center at Fort Detrick since 1956, and that he is a graduate of North Texas State College with a B.S. in biology, has an M.A. in bacteriology from the University of Chicago, and has done postgraduate work at the U.S. Department of Agriculture School and at Cambridge University, England.

Also, the primary mission of Fort Detrick was stated: ". . . the investigation of biological agents and weapons and defenses against such weapons. Successful fulfillment of this mission requires a diversified research program in the science and technology of disciplines ranging from aerobiology to zoology. Included are the physical sciences."

Fort Detrick is located about forty miles midway between Washington and Baltimore and just east of the underground Pentagon in the Catoctin mountains and near Camp David, the Presidential refuge. The fort is at the edge of Frederick, Maryland, birthplace of Francis Scott Key and hometown of Barbara Fritchie.

Recently published figures indicate that the research center's staff at the fort numbers 320 people holding a B.S., 110 with an M.S., 120 Ph.D.'s, thirty-four doctors of veterinary medicine, and fourteen M.D.'s — more than forty-five disciplines represented. There are reputed to be more bacteriologists and virologists there than in any United States city except New York and Chicago. The center is said to have a scientific library of 80,000 volumes and to receive regularly more than a thousand technical journals.

I left the Pentagon library and, map in hand, skirmished my way through the labyrinthian corridors. With a little reconnoitering I managed to locate my car in the metallic ranks of the enormous

South Parking Lot and then beat an orderly retreat back to Washington.

From there I phoned Fort Detrick and, to my surprise, got to speak directly with Dr. Housewright. He was extremely genial.

"We do only basic work with insects here at Fort Detrick," Dr. Housewright informed me, "such as testing their endurance and capability—how the valves work on a mosquito, for instance, things like that, or like a treadmill affair we had for mosquitoes, a sort of series of tunnels to keep them flying in a circle to see how far they could go without resting."

I told Dr. Housewright that sounded like the sort of thing I was interested in and asked if I might drive down on the following day to talk about such matters with him and Jim Gilford, an entomologist I'd heard was the big man in the fort's insect division. I'd learned about him from an acquaintance of mine, a member of the Philadelphia-based A Quaker Action Group, a man who'd been keeping an uneasy eye on Detrick for some time.

Dr. Housewright agreed to our meeting—"as long as you understand the ground rules." I didn't say yes, I didn't say no, for I'd no inkling of what the ground rules were. He said not to come too early in the afternoon as he had to be at a Rotary luncheon in Frederick until about two.

In the morning I called upon a local resident who'd been sympathetic to the twenty-two-month Quaker vigil at Fort Detrick that had so irked the townspeople from July 1959 to April 1961. She filled me in on this community of 18,142.

"Ours is a sick county," this woman told me, as she spread on her living-room coffee table a copy of the May 9, 1967, issue of the *Frederick Post* that carried on its front page a story announcing the new biological research laboratory to be built at Fort Detrick, a complex that will house virology, bacteriology, and animal assessment divisions of the work. It is to be 440 by 194 feet, covering 127,058 square feet, and will cost $7,096,000. A second phase, priced at only $6,200,000, is to house a medical-biological lab for the Army's medical unit. (The present establishment, on 1,300 acres of land, is valued at $75 million.) A three-column cut showed the fort's commanding officer, Colonel Peter G. Olenchuck, happily breaking ground for the improvement, flanked by smiling Brigadier General C. F. Vordorbruegge and smiling Colonel Dan Crozier and the fort's smiling public-relations officer, Colonel Oliver J. Cejka.

"Everybody out there wants to be acceptable," my informant said. "They want to be loved. Part of the problem here is that a good many of the people are either German Lutherans or Methodists. Both of them are grim. They take what's dished out and question nothing. They don't ever take a stand in their churches on political matters. This is a county with a badly split personality. They're guilt-ridden, but won't admit it. They know in their hearts that what's going on out there is morally wrong, but they say it's none of their doing; they're just taking orders and have to live same as anybody else.

"To give you some idea of how church people here regard biological warfare," continued my newfound friend, "at a mother-daughter banquet held recently at one of the Lutheran churches they had a little entertainment program, and the joke that got the biggest rise out of the audience was when one little girl asked another, 'How do you feel about germ warfare?' The reply was, 'I don't know; I'm not a germ, so I can't say about their warfare.'"

Typical of the attitude of townspeople working at the base, I was told, was the remark of one worker who said, "I'm in the middle. I'm a church member and I believe in peace. But I make twice as much now as I ever did, and even if it is blood money it's paying for my house, it's sending my son through college, and I give generously to good causes, especially my church."

However, there were others less confused, such as the woman who declared vehemently, "I'd support my country no matter what. I'd kill ten thousand enemies to save ten American lives."

But all the citizens of Frederick are not so socially irresponsible. One churchwoman is reported to have stated, "I would rather my own son be killed in a war than have such a wicked thing as the atomic bomb on Japan happen again to defenseless people."

At the checkpoint gate to Fort Detrick, which is just at the edge of town, a brisk, spit-and-polish, well-scrubbed, very young, slim,

stern, and serious MP stopped my car while he made a phone call
in to Dr. Housewright to okay my entrance. A large sign at roadside announced that all vehicles entering the compound were subject to search at any time, any place. I had some qualms about my
morning's notes stuffed in my bag locked in the turtleback. Kafka
began choking up in me.

The place didn't look sinister, any more so than any Army base,
yet it gave me a creepy feeling to cross the invisible line into it. Dr.
Housewright received me most pleasantly, and reminded me that
implicit to our meeting was an understanding of what he continued to refer to as "the ground rules," as though we were teaming
up for a game of softball.

Aware of the secret aspects of Fort Detrick, I certainly didn't
intend to disclose anything that would get me tied blindfolded to
a post being granted a last puff on a last cigarette.

I'd prepared some questions intended for Dr. Housewright and
Mr. Gilford — not too long a list, but the queries were significant
ones. I wanted to know what specific outstanding beneficial ad-
vances had been accomplished by Fort Detrick's entomologists. I
wanted to learn of other such fascinating insect projects as the
mosquito wind tunnel, and was curious to know if disease-carrying
insects were being used, or if the Department of Defense planned
their use as vectors in Vietnam, and if so were such disease-spreading experiments being carried on with a large-scale Asiatic war in
mind — say, for instance, with China? I wanted to learn if the transmission of diseases by arthropod vectors is considered practical, and
what we were doing to protect our fighting men in Vietnam against
diseases carried by insects; and if disease viruses ordinarily transmitted by insects can be created in the lab and distributed by man-
made devices. Do the Russians have a project paralleling that at
Fort Detrick? Was the current bubonic plague outbreak in Vietnam caused by our rat fleas or by native unaffiliated ones? Are the
lethal-disease vaccines that are being discovered and manufactured
at Fort Detrick being made available to the world community, or
are they being kept exclusively for us, to be used as countermeas-
ure in the case of biological warfare attack by an enemy?

Dr. Housewright and his confrere, Mr. Gilford, smilingly, politely, and adroitly dodged all my pitches. I got no firm answers. After long deliberation, young Gilford could come up with only two Fort Detrick projects involving insects that had been directly beneficial to mankind, and to me they seemed insignificant.

It all finally boiled down pretty much to nothing. The game ended: no hits, no runs, no errors. Nothing of importance regarding insects as warriors was disclosed, although I did learn what is no secret to any scientist: that disease microbes can readily be cultivated in the laboratory, and Dr. Housewright, in reply to one prudently worded query, stated that an enemy conceivably could disseminate disease germs against us. "Then," I suggested warily, "it is possible also for us to do the same against them." He said yes, it was possible.

"What about defoliation and crop destruction by insects?" I asked. "How about that woman scientist here, Dorothy Latterall, who got the distinguished civilian service medal, or some such, for a blight she developed that destroys rice?"

"Not *Dorothy*," said Dr. Housewright coolly, "it's Frances Latterall, and that had nothing to do with insects. That was a *fungus* — a rice blast." (If Typhoid Mary were living today she'd likely be a proper candidate for a distinguished service medal and might even stand a good chance of becoming our Army's first female general.)

"But, to distribute disease germs," I asked, "isn't that a bit like playing God?"

"Isn't pointing a gun at someone also playing God?" Dr. Housewright countered a trifle testily, then added plaintively, "I *wish* we didn't have war, but can we believe *they're* not going to use such biological weapons against us? We must be prepared." He didn't identify who he meant by "they."

When I probed further into the recruitment of insects as wartime disease vectors, Dr. Housewright made only this carefully considered response: "All that I can say about insects here at Fort Detrick is that they are *not* being used for offense. As to defense, that is another matter. And that's about as far as I'd care to go."

He smiled benignly and hitched up one of his ankle-length socks that had begun to sag. (As long ago as June 1959 Brigadier General J. H. Rothschild, U.S. Army Retired, but once commanding general of the Chemical Corps Research and Development Command said, in an article in *Harper's* magazine: "But surely everyone who thinks about it must realize that we are working on offensive weapons as well as defense against them; the Department of Defense would be impossibly incompetent if it weren't.")

Dr. Housewright then proceeded to complain about the bad press Fort Detrick had been getting because of its biological warfare activities.

"I deplore reporters coming here and going away with the wrong impression of us," Dr. Housewright deplored. "They make us out to be some sort of monsters out here. We're not. We're just ordinary human beings like everyone else. They ask the wrong questions of the wrong people and get wrong information. Elinor Langer — she was very unfair to us when she wrote those two articles in *Science* magazine. Why, she hadn't even been out here to talk to us. There were many things she got wrong that we could have corrected if she'd only gotten in touch with us, sat down with us here, and given us the chance."

At this my ears perked up. I hadn't heard of Miss Langer and her articles, but felt that in the interest of accurate reporting, which Dr. Housewright was espousing, I should look her up and read the pieces.

When I got back to Washington I found *Science* magazine listed in the phone book, put in a call, and got Miss Langer. She said she'd be delighted to see me; we made a date for lunch on the following day.

Elinor Langer turned out to be quite a bit younger than I'd expected a science authority to be, pretty and lively, and she answered all my questions frankly. After lunch we went back to her cluttered office in an imposing stone building on Massachusetts Avenue, headquarters of the American Association for the Advancement of Science, publishers of *Science* magazine. There I read the two issues mentioned by Dr. Housewright, those of the thirteenth and twentieth of January 1967, Volume 155, numbers 3759 and 3760. The articles are entitled: "Chemical and Biological Warfare (I), The Research Program"; and "(II), The Weapons and the Policies."

Miss Langer said she didn't know what I'd find in them about the insects' role in biological warfare ("they've now got much better ways to carry viruses"), but added that I was welcome to paw through the dozen or so large cardboard cartons of research material that she'd amassed in preparation for her magazine articles.

I spent the next four days doing that. Naturally, there was a great deal of material not directly related to insects. I was astonished by much of this. There was some hair-raising stuff tucked in those cartons. One of the truly terrifying weapons of biological warfare that I learned about is a nerve gas called Sarin, known as GB. It qualifies for mention in this work because it is a poison that acts like a superinsecticide on humans. In this case we are the insects. Like DDT, the lethal effect of GB is widespread and practically instantaneous. It strikes at the most mysterious and vital substance in the human body, an agent called by its discoverers, cholinesterase, which enables nerve signals to be transmitted to the body's muscles — for example, the nerve impulse to the muscle that gives the heart its rhythmic beat. This stuff called GB attacks cholinesterase and the sudden impairment of that substance blocks almost every bodily function — blood circulation, peristalsis, digestion, cell reproduction, utilization of oxygen, temperature control, heartbeat, sexual impulses. GB is said to be four times as toxic as Tabun (known as GA), a German gas. A plant for manufacturing it was confiscated by the Russians at the close of World War II and removed intact to the U.S.S.R., where it is said to be operating as efficiently as ever. The United States gas, GB, is purported to be thirty times as toxic as the previously favored lethal gaseous agent, phosgene. Sarin is colorless, odorless, and poisonous in minute quantities. According to the Army technical manual, *TM 3–215 Military Chemistry and Chemical Agents*, its effects are, in order of appearance: ". . . running nose; tightness of chest; dimness of vision and pinpointing of the eye pupils; difficulty in breathing;

drooling and excessive sweating; nausea, vomiting, cramps and involuntary defecation and urination; twitching, jerking and staggering; and headache, confusion, drowsiness, coma and convulsion. These symptoms are followed by cessation of breathing and death. . . . Although skin absorption great enough to cause death may occur in 1 or 2 minutes, death may be delayed for 1 or 2 hours. Respiratory lethal doses kill in 1 to 10 minutes, and liquid in the eye kills nearly as rapidly."

Some authorities say that a liquid droplet the size of a pencil point dot on the skin will penetrate the surface tissue and kill within ten to fifteen minutes.

I almost didn't have the nerve to go on, but I did and managed to learn much about conscripted insects. One of the first insect items to catch my eye was an article by Walter Schneir in the *Reporter* magazine of October 1, 1959. This report indicated that then, eight years ago, insects were being seriously considered as potential spreaders of pathogens — no matter how "phased out" they may be today. The article states: "According to a new limited-circulation Army publication (*U.S. Army Capability in the Space Age*), the Chemical Corps has pioneered in the mass rearing of insects for biological warfare. Research centers are located at Dugway, Utah, eighty miles southwest of Salt Lake City, a Joint Chiefs of Staff top-secret facility the size of Rhode Island that employs about thirteen hundred persons, and at Fort Detrick, in Barbara Fritchie's home town of Frederick, Maryland.

"I was told that infected insects are kept constantly available at the Fort Detrick installations. The inventory includes mosquitoes infected with yellow fever, malaria and dengue; fleas infected with plague; ticks with tularemia, relapsing fever and Colorado fever; houseflies with cholera, anthrax and dysentery. The facilities at Fort Detrick include laboratories for mass breeding of pathogenic microorganisms and greenhouses for investigating crop pathogens and various chemicals that harm or destroy plants. Studies are in progress on the most effective means of spreading plant diseases that attack wheat, barley, oats, rye, rice and cotton.

"In addition to the use of insects as disease carriers, methods of spreading various bacilli, viruses, and toxin in the form of aerosols have been successfully developed. Last year (1958) a Fort Detrick physician, Dr. LeRoy D. Fothergill, reported at a meeting of the American Medical Association in San Francisco: 'I should like to say at this point that many of these aerobiological instruments and techniques have been developed to a remarkable state of technical perfection.'"

A little farther on in the article was this: ". . . the Chemical Corps . . . is convinced from various harmless field trials that germs could be an extremely potent weapon. For example, a few years ago the Chemical Corps had two hundred thousand mosquitoes in special containers dropped near a Florida airbase, located in a relatively mosquito-free area. Within a few days, a high percentage of the people living on and around the base had been bitten many times. Had the mosquitoes been carrying a disease such as yellow fever, the Chemical Corps believes most of the local inhabitants would have been infected."

That was followed immediately by an account of the results of some United States war games in the Far East in which a simulated attack with biological weapons was ordered on simulated Chinese troops, who for the purposes of the problem had penetrated far into a simulated South Vietnam and supposedly were heading toward the capital of Cambodia, Pnompenh. When Chemical Corps experts calculated the results of this dummy attack, the State Department became so alarmed by them that it made a vain effort to suppress the information. For, along with the 75 percent of enemy troops assumed to have been killed or incapacitated, there were some six hundred thousand casualties among friendly or neutral civilians.

Delving deeper, I understood why the chemical and biological weapons program is considered one of the most secret of all United States military endeavors. It is not the most important of our nation's military research and development activities, but the Pentagon believes it to be the most easily misunderstood and most provocative of emotional distress and moral turbulence. Even people who have no compunction about bludgeoning, bombing, or shooting enemies have a revulsion against poisoning fellow human beings.

A pamphlet published by the U.S. Department of Health, Education and Welfare, July 1959, describes biological warfare as the intentional use of living organisms or their toxic products to cause death, disability or damage in man, animals or plants. "The target is man, either by causing his sickness or death, or through limitation of his food supplies or other agricultural resources. Man must wage a continuous fight to maintain and defend himself, his animals and his plants in competition with insects and microorganisms. The object of BW is to overcome these efforts by deliberately distributing large numbers of organisms of native or foreign origin, or their toxic products, taking full advantage of the ability to utilize more effective methods of dissemination and unusual portals of entry. BW has been aptly described as public health in reverse."

Often biological warfare is justified by its proponents on the dual grounds that first, the godless Russians are working on it (and possibly the heathen Chinese as well); secondly, that since Communists obviously have no morals, we cannot afford to have any either. It might be comforting to know for sure that those exotic unpredictable peoples are not involved with BW, but it would be more satisfactory all around if we could regard them as human beings much like ourselves.

Biological warfare is not new. The poisoning of wells is as old as recorded history, and Tartars in the Crimea hurled bodies of plague victims over the walls of Italian forts. The Italians, in turn, in the sixteenth century, developed an artillery shell that could deliver disease to the enemy. In pre-Revolutionary America unscrupulous European traders gave blankets infected with smallpox germs to Indians in order to impair their fighting strength.

The step leading toward modern biological warfare was made by a German named Fritz Haber, who dreamed up the idea of using poisonous gas during the First World War. The first use of the gas routed French Colonial troops at Ypres on April 22, 1915, and temporarily placed *Deutschland über Alles*. Many species of insects attack their enemies with self-generated gases, but until then man had never done so.

Some members of the scientific community are ready to believe that every time someone in Vietnam sneezes it is because the United States interlopers there are distributing germs. However, in the defense establishment the chemical-biological warfare program is represented as being a sort of cross between defensive preparations and peaceful by-products in preventive medicine. Actually, defensive preparations are only one part of the program; the United States government definitely is developing chemical and biological weapons and learning how to use them effectively, while quietly probing the public's reaction to their use.

Chemical-biological weapons, designed to meet the requirements of all services, are produced in a variety of forms which include the Honest John and Little John rockets, chemical land mines, the M–91 rocket launchers which can fire a rapid salvo of forty-five chemical rockets to targets twelve thousand yards away, and the Sergeant missile, which is capable of delivering 600-kg. chemical or biological warheads to a target one hundred miles distant. Detailed information on delivery systems for chemical-biological agents is classified, but unclassified manuals suggest that biological warheads are available for missile systems (for large-area attacks) and that biological material can be distributed by cluster bombs, from spray tanks and dispensers mounted on aircraft, and by what are called bomblets — little bombs that have outside vanes causing them to rotate in flight, thereby achieving lateral dispersion of their biological contents during free fall and resulting in random distribution over the target area.

Although studies of their inimitable chemical poisons are not being neglected, it is doubtful that insects are still being seriously considered as direct disease vectors. The newest method of distributing disease germs is by aerosol sprays. Detrick is widely recognized as the American home of the science of aerobiology — the study of airborne infections, both their causes and cures.

On the two or three occasions that Detrick has emerged from

behind its secretive cloak to participate in a conventional way in the affairs of the scientific community, there have been indications that extensive studies are in progress at the fort's research center regarding airborne infection. The first national conference on that subject, held in Miami Beach in December 1960, was supported jointly by Detrick and the National Institute of Allergy and Infectious Diseases, and sponsored by the National Academy of Sciences. Detrick papers there included: "Viability and Infectivity of Microorganisms in Experimental Airborne Infection," "Techniques of Aerosol Formation," and "Airborne Q-Fever." At subsequent aerobiological conferences Detrick researchers presented papers covering many other phases of viral aerosols.

It is possible to surmise a great deal about the Detrick research program from reports which its scientists have made in open literature on such subjects as instances of laboratory-induced or accidentally acquired infection, immunization, therapy, routes of infection in man and animals, various experimental techniques, and meteorological studies. Diseases that are at least the objects of considerable probing and that appear to be among those regarded as potential biological warfare agents include: bacterial diseases — anthrax, dysentery, brucellosis, glanders, plague and tularemia; rickettsial diseases — Q-fever, and Rocky Mountain spotted fever; viral diseases — dengue fever, several types of encephalitis, psittacosis and yellow fever; a fungal disease, coccidioidomycosis. There appears to be some interest in botulinus toxin. Five or six ounces of it would be enough to kill every person in the entire world, were it possible to achieve anything like total distribution.

An article in the British publication, *Science Journal*, written by its editor, Robin Clarke, states that a one-inch cube of botulinus toxin would be sufficient to kill every living creature in the United States and Canada combined (and possibly a few thousand Mexicans thrown in for good measure — why not?). It is a natural protein product of the bacterium *Clostridium botulinum*. According to Mr. Clarke, during World War II, methods of isolating the toxin in six pure forms were developed at Fort Detrick — the two most toxic types being A and B. The lethal dose of Type A is estimated to be about 0.12 micrograms; less than five hundred grams of this type might suffice to wipe out the population of the entire world. So, who needs the H-bomb? Very old-fashioned. In fine powdered form this toxin can be spread over considerable distances with very little breeze. Within six hours it fatally poisons the central nervous system, and within twelve hours it has oxidized and disappeared completely so that it does not contaminate the ground, a quality that endears it to those who treasure material things above animal life. There is no known defense for this killer. Unfortunately, it is an extremely painful poison, but then one mustn't be too fussy.

James N. Marsden, an advanced design engineer of the Aircraft Missile Division of Fairchild Stratos Corporation, in a talk before the Torch Club of Hagerstown, Maryland, very likely was alluding to this biological agent when he announced that our weapons arsenal contained "at least one biological agent so potent that the entire human population of the earth could theoretically be killed by one ounce of a harmless-looking liquid."

In order for biological agents to evolve from naturally occurring organisms into effective weapons, they need to possess certain characteristics. They must be: highly infectious; able to maintain viability and virulence during production, storage, transportation, and dissemination; be sturdy enough to withstand injury during distribution; have a slow rate of decay; be capable of being produced on a militarily significant scale. By evaluating what information has publicly surfaced it would seem that a substantial portion of fundamental research at Detrick has been devoted to development of these qualities in the organisms that produce the diseases just listed.

Some research done at Fort Detrick is neutral — not readily adaptable, that is, to use by a weapons program, but much of the work there inescapably has a special character, an inverted quality that Miss Langer in her articles aptly described as "medicine turned inside out." For example, efforts are being made to breed into pathogenic organisms precisely the characteristics — such as resistance to antibiotics — that most medical researchers would like to see eradicated. In the context of biological warfare even lifesaving techniques, such as immunization, take on a strange aspect: immunity among one's own civilian population and troops is a prerequisite to the initiation of a disease by our own forces, as well as a precaution against its initiation by others. Some diseases now are excluded from active consideration as BW agents chiefly because no vaccines against them have yet been developed.

Many of Detrick's aerobiological and meteorological projects are let out on contract to various private corporations, research establishments, and institutions of higher education. One such investigation, undertaken by the Travelers Research Center of Hartford, Connecticut, was described in a company promotion brochure thusly: "In another study for the Army, TRC began comprehensive research on dosage prediction techniques to provide up-to-date knowledge of dispersion processes in the lower atmosphere, and with a critical evaluation of the capabilities and limitations of present quantitative techniques for predicting the behavior of atmospheric contaminants. This study is similar in many respects to those being conducted on urban and regional air pollution." Quite a many-syllabled mouthful to justify what must have been a rather large dip into the taxpayers' pockets.

At Senate hearings it has been disclosed that despite precautions there have been almost 350 cases of illness at Fort Detrick due to accidental exposure to biological materials: 304 such cases had occurred from Detrick's beginning in 1943 to 1960, and 41 during the period between then and 1966. (A Detrick spokesman claimed that some of those 41 cases are duplicate reports of ones listed in the earlier period.) Three of every four reported cases required hospitalization, according to Dr. Arnold G. Wedum, the post safety officer. He contended that the Detrick disabling-illness rate was about one-half of one percent per million man hours, as compared to "much higher rates in other industries."

Some of the Detrick diseases, culled from various reputable medical sources (including the *American Medical Society Archives of National Medicine*, the *Medical Journal of the American Medical Association* and that of the *American Trudeau Society*) were: 60

cases of acute brucellosis, 62 of tularemia, 12 of psittacosis, 27 of Q-fever, 14 of Venezulian equine encephalitis, 6 of human glanders, 25 of anthrax and 6 of shigellosis (bacillary dysentery).

Despite the risks involved in preparing them, militarists are delighted with chemical and biological agents because they can penetrate structures, cover large areas, and produce a range of effects for varying periods — severe illness for a brief time or less severe for a long time, tears or hallucinations, paralysis or death. A most useful quality of biological weapons, according to the unclassified military field manual FM 3–10 (*Employment of Chemical and Biological Agents*) is their ability to "accomplish their effects . . . with little or no physical destruction. This constitutes an advantage both in combat operations . . . and — from a longer range viewpoint — in postwar rehabilitation, where overall rebuilding requirements would be reduced." In other words, the new boards of directors can assemble around undamaged long mahogany tables and get on with the fascinating business of acquisition.

The ideal biological warfare agent is a disease for which no widely known treatment exists. Melioidosis is a likely candidate — only about one hundred cases have ever been recorded, all of them fatal.

There have been rumors of the use of biological weapons on the field of modern battle but thus far no authenticated instances. During World War II, the Japanese were thought to have instituted plague outbreaks in China by dropping grain and fleas on three cities, according to Dr. Robert Pollitzer, author of the outstanding contemporary medical work on plague. He claimed that the grain attracted city rats, and the infective fleas, using them as hosts, set off epidemics. Chinese allegations that the United States used biological weapons in the Korean war were never substantiated, despite an impressive seven-hundred page report that included photographic documentation made by an international committee of investigators. The report cited our use of cholera-infected clams, anthrax-infected feathers, and plague induced by infected rat fleas. The source of reports that chemical agents had been employed in the Korean combat may have been our use of riot control gases against North Korean prisoners of war during outbreaks in the POW compounds.

Although disease-creating and food-poisoning powers of chemical-biological weaponry have not yet been unleashed there is great danger that they will be. We cannot be absolutely certain that the unthinkable will not suddenly become perfectly acceptable national policy. Frustration and futility such as is being experienced in Vietnam may drive our militarists to embrace the most bizarre methods of achieving political victory.

In an essay entitled, "The Unit of Survival Is the Human Race," Hudson Hoagland, Ph.D., Sc.D., executive director of the Worcester Foundation for Experimental Biology, made this provocative statement: "It has been said, probably incorrectly, that the dinosaurs became extinct because their brains were too small. We may become extinct because our recently evolved cerebral cortex may be too large — a sort of phylogenetic tumor that can produce absolute weapons but is unable to control our 100-million-year-old hypothalamic and limbic centers to mediate hates and aggressions. While aggressive behavior is with us to stay, a major question is whether we can find alternative ways of expressing it in the resolution of international conflicts. Can lawless sovereignty be controlled or abolished before it abolishes us?"

Our government's policymakers do not recognize any international prohibition on the use of biological means of warfare, an attitude that is reflected in a United States Army field manual, *The Law of Land Warfare*, which states that "the U.S. isn't a party to any treaty now in force that prohibits or restricts the use in warfare of toxic or nontoxic gases, or smoke or incendiary materials or bacteriological warfare."

The United States never ratified the Hague Convention of 1899 nor the Geneva Protocol of 1925, both of which ban the use of such weapons. According to another unclassified Army field manual, "the decision to employ lethal or incapacitating chemical or biological agents is a matter of national policy."

The Johnson administration maintains that its operations in Vietnam do not include chemical and biological warfare. Officials at the Pentagon and State Department deny that we are setting a precedent in biological warfare or that there is risk of escalation in that respect. On historical grounds alone their position is weak.

Biological warfare is not the most expensive of our nation's military endeavors, but its cost is considerable and has mounted steadily during the past eight years. In 1959, the Chemical Corps budget for biological warfare research and development was $18.9 million. By 1964 it had climbed to $158 million, a startling increase due largely to a gigantic public relations effort known as "Operation Blue Skies," conducted by the United States Army Chemical Corps, aided and abetted by the House Committee on Science and Astronautics and a variety of outsiders, including the American Chemical Society. The campaign boosted the possibilities of "incapacitating weapons," less flesh-tearing and bone-shattering than the usual tools of war. The attractive idea of a "war without death" was widely and ruthlessly promoted by the Army Chemical Corps in carefully placed magazine articles and by newspaper releases, speeches, lectures, symposia, Congressional appearances, and planned leaks.

An Associated Press sum-up story on germ warfare, published in early April 1967, stated that the Department of Defense was now spending $230 million on its chemical and biological warfare program, embracing six military bases as research centers, government-sponsored research and development projects on about a half hundred college and university campuses, and the involvement in government contracts of scores of private firms, ranging from such industrial giants as General Mills, Westinghouse Electric Corporation, General Electric and Du Pont to small engineering companies and research consultants. The Associated Press article reported the 1967 estimated budget of Fort Detrick alone to be $38 million; the actual figure is a classified secret.

Researchers on these United States government-assigned biological warfare projects sometimes are unaware they are working for a military organization. One such group was at the Field Mice Research Institute of the Sapporo Forestry Experimental Station at Noboro, a village of Ebetsu, Japan. There, studies were being made of the *Rickettsia* virus, cause of Yezo fever, a sickness that produces high fever and often is deadly. It is transmitted by field mice, which are plentiful in the Noboro and Maruyama forest areas outside the city of Sapporo. The request to undertake this work was made by the Japanese government's National Institute of Health to the Hokkaido Prefectural Health Institute and to the Forestry Experimental Station. A previous request for such research directly from the United States military authorities to the University of Tokyo and its Institute for Research in Infectious Diseases had been turned down on the basis that no research commission from a foreign government could be accepted. The Hokkaido Committee of Peace unearthed the facts, and the workers in the Field Mice Research Institute then refused to continue the research, due to its being a military project.

Spreading diseases is not a new function of military forces. History shows that armies have always brought pestilence in their wake. Insects and rodents have always gone to war. Of all recruits they are the most eager to get on with the carnage, for bloodshed of battle and its chaotic aftermath affords them the most delectable viands. Happy days are here again.

Hans Zinsser, in his classic biography of a bacillus, *Rats, Lice and History*, contends that soldiers rarely have won wars; more often, they simply mop up after the barrage of epidemics. Mr. Zinsser also wrote that typhus, with its brothers and sisters — plague, cholera, typhoid, and dysentery — has decided more campaigns than did Caesar, Hannibal, Napoleon, and all the inspector generals of history. "The epidemics get the blame for defeat," he says, "the generals the credit for victory."

The greatest of all war-caused epidemics that helped undermine ancient civilization was the plague of Justinian, Byzantine Emperor during the sixth century, a period of calamity unequaled in history. Earthquake, volcanic eruptions, floods, fires, and famines spread destruction throughout Europe, the Near East, and Asia for over sixty years. The attendant agricultural disorganization, population displacement, and impoverishment of these catastrophes contributed greatly to the origin and spread of pestilence.

For four months, plague, which began in Egypt near Pelusium, remained in Byzantium, eventually taking ten thousand lives a day. When a scarcity of gravediggers developed roofs were taken off forts, their interiors filled with corpses, and the roofs replaced. Dead bodies were placed on ships that then were abandoned to the sea. The Justinian pestilence exerted profound influence upon the decline of the Eastern empire, for in the course of sixty to seventy years that disease devastated much of the known world, and the entire Roman domain was thrown into confusion. Gibbon, the historian, states that during three months ten thousand people died each day at Constantinople, that many cities of the East were abandoned, that in Italy the harvest and vintage withered on the ground. "The triple scourges of war, pestilence and famine," said Gibbon, "afflicted the subjects of Justinian; and his reign is disgraced by a visible decrease of the human species which has never been regained in some of the fairest countries of the globe."

Hans Zinsser, in commenting upon destruction during the reign of Justinian, states: "It is a reasonable conjecture that it may have been only our relative ability to control pestilence which has preserved the modern world, for a time, from breaking up as did the empire of Justinian. In studying, through the eyes of Procopius, the reign of Justinian, one obtains an extraordinary vivid picture of the manner in which the three major agencies — war, political corruption and pestilence — cooperated to bring the empire to its knees. Justinian was making a final effort to restore the imperial world power. Wars with Persia, wars against the Vandals in Africa and against the Goths in Italy, and armies to maintain on all fronts, in widely separated parts of the world, strained the resources of the government to their utmost. Everywhere the ring of defense was being pushed back by ever-increasing hordes of barbarians, who had by this time learned much of the art of war and organization from their former overlords. Internal insurrections, as at Byzantium in 532, threatened the rear. Treachery and graft weakened the administrative power at court. And superimposed upon these almost, perhaps entirely insuperable difficulties was the pestilence — sweeping from east to west, north to south, again and again, for almost sixty years — killing, terrifying, and disorganizing."

The Justinian plague lasted until A.D. 590. The power, grace, administrative logic, and glory that once were Rome died between 568 and 570 when most of Italy was conquered by the Lombards, barbarians said to resemble "in figure and in smell the mares of the Sarmatian plains."

War and lice, harbingers of typhus, seem always to have gone together. There is in existence a clay tablet from 2500 B.C. on which a Sumerian army doctor prescribed sulphur to relieve the itch of crab lice. The "cooties" of the trenches in the First World War were body lice. In World War II they were called "motorized dandruff." At many United States Armed Forces' installations during that war three out of five enlisted men's toilets were designated, "For Those with Crabs."

The crab, or pubic, louse (*Phthirus pubis*) is one of three kinds of lice that attack man. The others are the body louse (*Pediculus humanus corporis*) and the head louse (*P. humanus capitis*). The true louse is a wingless insect, parasitic upon birds and mammals, and belonging to the order of Anoplura.

Not every creature called a louse is a true one. The plant louse is an aphid, the bee louse a fly, the bark louse a scale insect. The wood louse is not even an insect, but a sow or pill bug. Neither are fish or book lice bona fide members of the louse family.

The eggs of female lice (called nits) are laid ten a day for thirty days. Lice have strong claws (as anyone who has dealt with crab lice can attest) and piercing-sucking mouth parts. The beak, when not in use, is completely withdrawn into the head, leaving only a fringe of minute teeth to be seen at the foremost part.

Body lice and occasionally head lice carry diseases, the most serious being epidemic typhus. Typhus was brought by lice to Naples, Italy, during the last world war, in July 1943. The first cases were three soldiers who'd returned from the Russian front and the proprietor of a bathhouse and one of its clients. By August, there were three additional cases, and by December, 341. In January, the total had grown alarmingly to 913 cases. Then the United States Army began mass spraying of DDT, and by February the number of cases had been reduced to only 174. (The final chapter of this book recounts that battle.) Typhus broke out elsewhere in Europe during that war: in March 1945 at Aachen, Germany, and later at München-Gladbach. The source was a Gestapo prison that had released conscripted laborers into nearby communities.

Crab lice are not known to transmit disease but they are a devilish nuisance. Their crablike shape accounts for their name; it does not allude to a grumpy disposition. In Italy there is a superstition that if a crab louse crawls up your nose, you die. A friend who once lived there told me that he was summarily thrown to the floor by his housemaid upon her discovery of a crab louse entangled in the hairs of his chest and then had his chest and underarms forcibly shaved by her.

Flies seem to have been a particularly persistent military pest. As long ago as 2000 B.C., Sinhue, a physician to one of the early pharaohs of Egypt, recorded this about flies (and in so doing also commented on the time-honored relationship between common soldiers and generals): "When all were paraded, Horembeb stepped out from the dirty hut with his golden whip in his hand, and a servant held an umbrella over his head and kept the flies off him with a fly whisk while he addressed the soldiers . . . Their eyes were sore from flies, and I reflected that soldiers in every country were alike. They rave in their cups like wild beasts, their sleeping dens stink and they are verminous."

Flies still were a major pest in World War II. In some military messes in North Africa it was impossible to eat without getting a mouthful of filthy flies that competed with vultures for garbage, sewage, and carrion. In the conquest aftermath of the Sicilian invasion of July 1943 (during which 31,158 men were killed in two days and only eight thousand were able to make it to shore) an especially nasty sandfly added to the fearful occasion by bringing pappataci fever. On most of that war's invasion beaches in the Pacific, dog flies, most horrible of all bloodsuckers, bred in the seaweed. Even in the Arctic flies spread their miseries to the military — black flies, horse and deer flies, snipe and filth flies, and biting midges (nasty little bloodsuckers known also as punkies, moose-flies, and no-see-ums). Regarding filth flies, an Army directive states: "The practice of urinating or defecating in the snow near quarters during winter may be convenient but will produce swarms of flies in spring."

The mosquito, too, is one of the more evil insect demons of war. Yellow fever is caused by a mosquito, the *Aedes aegypti*, first suspected as a carrier of that disease by Charles John (Carlos Juan) Finlay in 1881; he specified the genus *Stegomyia*. In the following year a series of experiments was begun by Major Walter Reed, of the United States Army Medical Corps, that proved beyond a doubt the correctness of Dr. Finlay in suspecting the mosquito as the villain behind the epidemics of yellow fever that plagued the tropics of the Western Hemisphere. The disease subsequently was eradicated in the Panama Canal Zone through the efforts of our government's mosquito-control campaign. But in 1930 yellow fever again broke out in the Western Hemisphere, this time in Brazil, and the culprit was identified as another type of mosquito, *Aedes triseriatus*. Sanitation crews soon were able to establish control measures that curbed this new threat.

Yellow fever struck the United States ninety-five times between the years 1693 and 1901: 500,000 casualties, 100,000 of them dead (41,000 in New Orleans; 8,000, Memphis; 5,000, Charleston; 10,000, Philadelphia).

The most dire disease brought by the mosquito is malaria. Twenty-odd species of the anopheline group of mosquitoes are known to be vectors of that peril, which affects millions of people annually — many of them in the Far East, especially India, where nearly one hundred million people suffer this affliction. Malaria is expected to strike 150 million people in 1967, kill at least a million and disable the rest for long periods, according to the World Health Organization. At least half the dead will be Africans, most of them children of poor highland people. On an average night in one African hut usually there will be two thousand female *Anopheles* mosquitoes which transmit the malaria parasites. There is virtually no chance that an occupant of such a hut can escape getting one new infection each night if he or she remains at home. Mosquitoes in Africa never hibernate as they do in cooler climates, so transmission of the infection goes on year round. Control units never get a chance to get one jump ahead of their enemy.

No disease is more debilitating, more dulling, or more depressing than chronic malaria. Children particularly are retarded and enfeebled by it. M. A. Sinton, a British malariologist noted for his work in India, has said: "There is no aspect of life in a malarial country that is not affected, either directly or indirectly, by this disease. It constitutes one of the most important causes of economic misfortune, engendering poverty, diminishing the quantity and the quality of the food supply, lowering the physical and intellectual standard of the nation, and hampering increased prosperity and economic progress in every other way."

According to Martin D. Young, a leading American malariologist and member of the World Health Organization's panel of experts on malaria, it is responsible for more deaths per year than any other transmittable disease. Marcolino G. Candau, director-general of WHO, declared in 1965 that malaria holds the most prominent place among communicable diseases.

Malaria is one of mankind's oldest diseases, recognized as early as the fifth pre-Christian century. The Book of Leviticus, written about that time, contains in one of the several truculent outbursts of the Lord, an allusion to malaria: "I will even appoint over you terror, consumption, and the burning ague." Hippocrates wrote of malaria, as also did many Roman scholars of the first pre-Christian century: notably, Aulus Cornelius Celsus and Marcus Terentius Varro. A century later a Hispano-Roman writer on agricultural subjects stumbled upon the notion that malaria somehow came from "a marsh which breeds animals with mischievous stings which fly upon us in exceeding thick swarms . . . whereby hidden diseases are often contracted." With the fall of the Roman Empire this implication of the mosquito in the cause of malaria disappeared from the European mind — lost, along with most of the rational arts and sciences of Greco-Roman culture.

During the Middle Ages, malaria was attributed to the malicious visitations of supernatural fiends and chants were devised to disperse them. One such: "Tremble and go!/ First day, shiver and burn/ Second day, shiver and learn/ Tremble and die!/ Third day, never return." The only surviving remnant of the belief that insects were the instigators of malaria was a vague distrust of marshy places. From that fear is derived the name *malaria* — coming from the Italian *mala* (bad) and *aria* (air). Horace Walpole introduced the term into the English language in 1740 in a letter to a friend, which told of a "horrid thing called *mal'aria*, that comes to Rome every summer and kills one."

Malaria was most prevalent in the mid-nineteenth century, when it was endemic in almost every part of Asia, Africa, and Latin America. It was prevalent in the Mediterranean countries (Byron died of malaria at Missolonghi in 1824) and in much of Russia, Germany, Holland, and England, where malaria was responsible for five or six of every one hundred patients treated at St. Thomas's Hospital in London between 1850 and 1860. There was much malaria throughout the United States until about the end of the nineteenth century when the disease was confined mostly to the Deep South. There, malaria raged wholly unimpeded until shortly after the Second World War. As recently as 1940, some 150,000 cases of malaria were reported in the United States, most of them from Southern states. By 1965 there were fewer than two hundred cases.

The World Health Organization of the United Nations launched its malaria eradication program in 1949, and today the disease has been uprooted in much of South America, in most of the western Mediterranean countries (including that notorious hotbed of pestilence, the island of Sardinia), and even in parts of India and Pakistan. The WHO estimate of malaria cases throughout the world (exclusive of China, Vietnam, and North Korea) in 1955 was 350 million — 3.5 million of them fatal. In 1965, the total for the same area was down to one hundred million cases, with about a million deaths. Malaria thus appears to be on the way out, unless the mad dogs of war succeed in upsetting the balance of control by opening a Pandora's box of manufactured germs.

In the South Pacific war arena malaria caused five times the casualties of enemy action. Of all United States Army personnel fighting Japanese, 246,166 combat and service soldiers, in the duration of the war, were rendered ineffective by malaria, each for an average period of two weeks repeatedly during the season. Time lost in the Pacific by United States Army combat troops amounted to a total of 10,140,872 man days. The rate among land-based Navy also was high with 11,272 cases; the Marine Corps was heaviest hit.

Although the first Pacific landings, in the Solomon Islands, were made in the first week of August 1942, suppressive atabrine was not inaugurated until September 10. In October, 1,960 men of the 1st Marine Division were hospitalized from malaria. Up to December 1942, of 10,635 casualties in that division only 1,472 were from gunshot wounds; there were 5,749 malaria cases. In November alone 3,283 cases occurred. (All figures are from *The History of Entomology in World War II*, by Emory C. Cushing, Colonel, U.S. Army Retired, published by the Smithsonian Institution, 1957.)

The Army was caught almost completely unprepared for this onslaught by mosquitoes. No malaria control personnel were permitted on Guadalcanal until mid-November. Little had been done to check mosquito breeding; malaria prevention was lax in all units. By January 14, 1943, only 75 percent of the 2nd Battalion was fit for duty; the rest had malaria.

Malaria hastened the fall of the Philippines by thirty days. It grievously hurt Stilwell's campaign in Burma. Not since Teddy Roosevelt's day, when dysentery-drained troops slogged up San Juan Hill, had American soldiers been compelled to fight under such debilitating conditions as those encountered by the first men ashore in the Pacific islands. (For further details, read *G. I. Jungles*, by E. J. Kahn.)

Back home, to protect soldiers at military bases, mosquito control operations finally were instituted in 317 counties of twenty-one states, the District of Columbia and Puerto Rico. These operations, carried out in the vicinities of two thousand Army, Navy and war-oriented establishments, included 1,274 miles of ditching, the clearing of 12,940 acres, 60,000 cubic yards of filling, the cleaning of 4,319 miles of drainage ditches, the creation of 4,319 miles of drainage lines, and the use of 448,000 pounds of blasting dynamite.

DDT as a mosquito battler was not available in combat areas until 1944, and it had its limitations, as did all such chemical repellents. They fogged crystals of watches worn by soldiers, made their rifle stocks sticky, stung the eyes and had an odor detectable to the enemy.

The majority of the first antimalaria units were not activated until January 25, 1943, when six survey and fifteen control units embarked from the port of New Orleans for the Pacific. By the end of February, ten more survey and control units had been authorized. The Navy assigned one malariologist to the island of Efate in the New Hebrides in April 1942. By September of that year the Navy had malaria units on one other military base in the South Pacific, on the island of Espiritu Santo, and by mid-November on Guadalcanal. By May 1944, there were 4,407 persons engaged in malaria control in the South Pacific, a joint operation of Army and Navy. This group included 350 officers and 2,500 enlisted men.

During the final three years of World War II nearly a half million of our soldiers were stricken by malaria. Among those stationed within the continental United States there were 92,649 cases.

Most of the 517 cases of malaria imported to the United States last year came from Vietnam, according to a United States Navy research team reporting to a national conference of scientists, farm officials, and technicians that was sponsored by the California and American Mosquito Control Association. According to *Military Medicine* (September 1966 Supplement), during 1965 the number of soldiers evacuated from Vietnam because of wounds and the number evacuated due to malaria were equal. Practically all cases came from infantry companies engaged in actual combat. What the military calls "malaria discipline" (keeping arms, legs, and torsos covered and adhering to the medical preventive program) is likely to be pretty much ignored under the stress conditions of battle. The number of malaria cases in the United States increased by 418 in 1966, the biggest jump—147 cases to 565—since 1935, according to federal health officials. The sharp rise was attributed by the National Communicable Disease Center in Atlanta, Georgia, to the increasing number of servicemen returning from Vietnam. Incidence of leprosy in the United States also set a record, with 109 cases reported. The leprosy rate had been on the decline since 1963.

For years, the only recognized weapon against malaria was quinine, a complicated alkaloidal compound ($C_{20}H_{24}N_2O_2$), originally derived from the bark of the cinchona tree, a South American evergreen indigenous to Peru. A Jesuit missionary, Juan López, was the first European to experience the healing effects of an infusion of cinchona bark when a Peruvian Indian gave him a draught of it in 1600. The bark was introduced to Europe in 1632 by another Jesuit missionary, Alonso Mesias Venegas. A succession of ailing Jesuits soon heartily endorsed the curative powers of this Latin-American remedy, which came to be known as Jesuit's bark, but it was widely rejected by orthodox practitioners of seventeenth century medicine. They could not reconcile its action to the humoral theory of pathology then in vogue, which contended that disease was the result of an imbalance of the body's constituent fluids (generally considered then to be blood, phlegm, yellow and black bile), and that a restoration of balance could be achieved only by seeking out harmful substances, neutralizing them, and finally causing their elimination by means of violent purgatives that would induce vomiting, sweating, salivation, urination, and hemorrhage. Calomel was the favorite purge for malaria. The renowned seventeenth century Protestant Oliver Cromwell was an especially adamant opponent of the so-called Jesuit bark; he died of malaria in 1658, stubbornly sectarian to the end.

The curative Peruvian bark was supplanted in 1820 when two French pharmacologists, Pierre Joseph Pelletier and Joseph Bien-aime Caventou, isolated an essence of the bark, which they called quinine and found it to be a more potent, more potable remedy for malaria. Within three years of that discovery, quinine became available almost everywhere in the world wherever it was needed. Today, modern chemistry has produced a synthetic quinine and a host of other remedies for malaria. The most esteemed among them are chloroquine, amodiaquine, and primaquine. The first two substitute for quinine; the third is a supplement, lethal to the liver-dwelling plasmodia, and also it kills or sterilizes sexually mature products of the red-cell stage — the organisms whose ingestion by an *Anopheles* mosquito perpetuates the disease. A radical, or total cure of malaria can be brought about by eight to ten days' ingestion of quinine (or three days of one of its companion drugs), followed by fourteen days of primaquine.

In 1966, the United States military began using, against a strain of Vietnamese malaria that is resistant to standard medication, a drug used originally to combat leprosy. This drug is sulfonyldianiline or DDS; the especially troublesome strain of malaria is *Plasmodium falciparum*, which was first brought to the attention of military medical authorities as far back as 1946, when it was discovered at Aitaipe-Wewak during World War II. At that time the military poobahs considered it not very significant. Almost twenty years passed before they did anything concrete about prevention of that new malaria strain, and then only after four thousand American soldiers, the equivalent of a light infantry brigade, had been made victims of it. Santayana once said, "Those who cannot remember the past are condemned to repeat it." This type of malaria is especially dangerous because of its potentially lethal complications: black water fever, which inhibits normal kidney functions, and cerebral malaria, which can clog the smaller blood vessels of the brain and prevent blood circulation.

During World War II, the total home and overseas hospital admissions of United States troops from 1940 to 1945 and their causes were: diarrhea and dysentery, 743,812; malaria, 647,763; dengue fever, 107,941 (on Saipan, Tinian, Tarawa, and Makin Atoll); scabies, 21,286; typhus, 7,352; filariasis, 1,653; sandfly fever, 12,438 (also called pappataci fever). There were sixty-one cases of Rocky Mountain spotted fever, fifty-seven of Colorado tick fever and one of trypanosomiasis (sleeping sickness — contracted by an Air Force officer while sport-hunting in the bush fifty miles from Maidur Maiduguri, Nigeria). There were some amputations as the result of stings by the giant scorpions of New Georgia. Soldiers suffered from visceral leishmaniasis and cutaneous leishmaniasis picked up from the small desert rodent known as the gerbil (all but a few of these fifteen hundred cases were in the Persian Gulf command). Trombiculid mites caused tsutsugamushi fever, a scrub typhus.

A disease called akamushi, thought to be spread by rats, was particularly devilish. There were two thousand cases of it among the 6th and 41st Divisions during their first two months at Sansapore and on Owi and Biak islands. The 6th Army lost 150,000 man days due to this disease. In one regiment 403 men, including twenty-eight key officers, were cut down by it. In Ceylon during jungle exercises, 756 men of one division were affected. There were 6,861 cases in the United States forces stationed in India, Burma, and the Philippines, and 6,730 in the British and Indian armies there. The United States Navy had 613 cases on its hands, and 176 of Merrill's Marauders went down with it. In some units, after two weeks' exposure to the disease, the rate of afflicted was nine hundred per thousand.

For up-to-date warriors, all sorts of diseases are readily available in Vietnam: smallpox, infectious hepatitis, dengue fever, hemorrhagic fevers, eye infections including trachoma, leishmaniasis, trematode infections (from eating raw fish and water chestnuts), leptospirosis (Weil's disease), typhus (murine, epidemic, and scrub), tick-bite fever, relapsing and Q-fever, scabies and other ugly skin infections, poliomyelitis, encephalitis, filariasis (elephantiasis is its manifestation), rabies, anthrax, melioidosis, bacillary and amoebic dysentery, cholera, venereal diseases (gonorrhea, syphilis, chancroid, granuloma inguinale), intestinal parasites and plague.

There are three kinds of plague and Vietnam has them all. In pneumonic plague, the infection comes from plague germs in the atmosphere. Septicemic plague infection is received directly into the blood stream. Bubonic plague is acquired by the bite of the flea, Xenopsylla cheopis, of the black rat.

Oddly, in Vietnam there is no yellow fever, although its vector, the Aedes aegypti mosquito, is present among that land's plethora of disease-bearing insects and rodents. There are forty species and subspecies of *Anopheles* mosquito (seven of them vectors of malaria); horse, blow, deer, sand, and ordinary house flies; fleas, ticks and mites galore; spiders and scorpions; ants, termites, bedbugs, and cockroaches; a great number of rats — black, brown, and bamboo; voles, squirrels, and other rodents; and lice of all kinds.

In Vietnam three of every four hospitalized United States soldiers are sick rather than injured. Despite the efficiency of American battlefield medical care, the illness rate is high because our young men haven't yet developed immunity to the indigenous scourges of Vietnam's tropics. Adding to the problem of good health in that invaded country are occasional diseases that United States-trained doctors have never before seen. Melioidosis is one such. It is caused by bacteria of the Pseudomonas family and enters the system through open wounds, the mouth, or the nose, and lies dormant for as long as six years. Soldiers call it the Vietnamese time bomb. Treatment by the drug Chloromycetin poses the risk of dangerous side effects, including possible fatal anemia.

Despite all the dreadful diseases present in Vietnam, plague scares our imported soldiers the most. Plague sounds like something of the unenlightened time of Genghis Khan or Charlemagne, a repellent horror that only inferior, heathen foreigners are supposed to get — not clean-living, upright, apple-pie Americans. It is the bogey of our present military adventure, the "in" disease of Southeast Asia.

Thus far, only one case of plague among United States soldiers has been officially reported (March 1963). Evidently it was picked up at Nha Trang in Khanh Hoa Province. Army doctors at first diagnosed the case as a venereal infection.

There wasn't much plague in World War II, except for a breakout of bubonic plague at Dakar, Africa, in April 1944, which hung around until November of that year affecting 566 civilians, but no military people. The disease spread to Oran, Algeria, by December 1944 and turned up in Casablanca in 1945 (three cases).

In Vietnam now, plague is widespread, occurring especially in many parts of Saigon — 256 confirmed cases in 1965. The plague problem in Vietnam is aggravated by reliance of the people on unlicensed healers, mystic sorcerers, and self-appointed pharmacologists, due to a scarcity of genuine doctors (only about three hundred serve the nation's sixteen million citizens). Many of the amateur medical practitioners travel from village to village — a bit like old-time American medicine shows — with drummers, flute players, clowns, acrobats, and trick monkeys. They dispense ancient remedies beefed up with modern antibiotics obtained on the black market. The effect of using such nostrums on plague is to create new strains of the plague bacillus that are resistant to antibiotics. In Vietnam last year 20 percent of the strains of plague bacillus tested were found to be resistant to streptomycin, the chief drug used against plague. So far, no resistance has been observed to two other antibiotics effective against plague, Aureomycin and chloramphenicol.

A Vietnamese coastal town, Nha Trang, once was the home of the discoverer of plague germs — a Russian named Alexander Yersin. A local street still honors his name.

The Vietnamese plague evolved from one begun in the 1850's during a civil war in the province of Yünnan in southwest China. It still continues throughout the Orient, and thus far has taken thirteen million lives. This particular plague reached Saigon from Hong Kong and Canton in 1906. In its peak year, 1910, a thousand cases were reported by authorities. Undoubtedly there were many more as Vietnamese medical statistics are inclined to be minimal estimates rather than strictly factual, because revelation of plague cases has a tendency to harm commerce and to create unease among the populace.

After the 1920's, plague in Vietnam declined somewhat, occurring in only a few endemic places, such as Tay Ninh, Phan Thiet, and the Central Market of Saigon. Subsequently, there were only a few cases each year, even during the most severe phases of the war with the French. From 1954 through 1962 there were fewer than forty cases of plague in South Vietnam. The appearance of fifty-six cases in 1956 was considered so unusual that Professor Nguyen Van Ai, of Saigon's Institut Pasteur, wrote a paper about it for a Parisian medical journal. (In 1959, the World Health Organization reported fewer than three hundred cases of plague in the entire world.)

In Vietnam in 1960 there were only fourteen cases in Phuoc Tuy, in 1961 eight in the adjoining province of Long Khanh. In 1962, still nothing to get excited about — thirty-two cases. Then in 1963 the pattern of plague altered dramatically. The disease broke out in nine provinces and in the cities of Saigon and Dalat — 111 cases. When the American troop buildup began in earnest in 1965, along with defoliation, crop destruction, and the blighting, bombing, and napalming of villages in the southern countryside, plague flared up in thirteen provinces, and during an eight-month period 3,443 cases were confirmed — with doubtless many more going unreported.

In 1966, Vietnamese officials reported to the World Health Organization 351 cases with 26 deaths. In addition, 2,404 cases of suspected plague with 119 deaths were listed. Throughout the world in that year almost 1,300 confirmed cases of plague were reported with 134 deaths.

South Vietnamese government statistics indicate that plague has lately infected twenty-two of the nation's twenty-nine provinces; in 1961, plague had been reported from but one province, Long Khanh. The Reverend Do Van Quy, chief of the ministry of health's plague laboratory, has said, as quoted by the *New York Times*, "The main reason for the spread of plague seems to be the movement of troops and refugees. I predict that this problem will not be solved until the war is ended."

We in America are not smugly safe from plague. There is some danger of bubonic plague being introduced here, since precautionary measures taken on the Saigon waterfront are said to be not stringent enough to prevent rats from boarding American, Korean, and South Vietnamese ships tied up along the Ben Bach Dang esplanade. It has been reported by the *New York Times* that few hawsers there are outfitted with rat guards, the metallic cones recommended by health authorities to prevent rats from boarding ships. Also, to cover the entire port and airport areas of Saigon there are only four quarantine inspectors.

The ultimate source of plague infection lies elsewhere than in rodents. It may be obscure. During a bubonic plague rats die first. The rat flea takes in the plague bacillus with the blood of a sick rat. The bacillus multiplies within the flea, blocking the entrance to its stomach. Though ravenous, the flea now cannot eat. When such a starving flea bites, the blood it extracts from the bitten animal cannot be swallowed. It comes up against the block and then recirculates into the wound, carrying plague organisms along with it, producing infection. As the rats die, their fleas seek new hosts upon which to feed. When the supply of live rats runs out, the host is likely to be man.

Plague is not something found only in the tropics. There have been over 950 plague cases (more than seven hundred deaths) in the United States since 1900 — more than eight hundred of them occurring in California and Hawaii. San Francisco has accounted for 288 cases of plague and 207 deaths from it in two epidemics (1901 to 1904; 1907 to 1908). Small epidemics occurred prior to 1925 in New Orleans, Galveston, Beaumont, Seattle, Los Angeles, and Pensacola — all port cities. Almost certainly those outbreaks came from infected rats imported from plague regions abroad. There have been no human plague cases stemming from domestic rat infection in our cities since 1925. Whatever plague cases we have had in the past four decades came either from wild rodents — prairie dogs, wood rats, ground squirrels, chipmunks, marmots, field mice, kangaroo rats, and rabbits — or were brought in from overseas by an infected person, or were contacted in a bacteriological laboratory. However, occasionally plague-infected rats and their fleas still are found in cities here: in Tacoma in 1942, 1944, and 1954; in San Francisco in 1949 and 1963.

The transfer of plague from field mice to urban rats has been observed in the San Francisco area. The fact that such a transfer actually can take place under conditions of modern sanitation indicates the thin protection now afforded humans in certain areas. Experts in such matters have stated that it would take only a slight breakdown in present conditions to allow an increase of plague to spread to domestic rats. Under disaster or emergency conditions such a spread could be explosive. The normal sanitary barriers could conceivably be severed in times of natural disasters such as floods, earthquakes, and great fires, and also especially in cases of devastation due to war. We are by no means safely out of the combat zone. As long as the flames of war are fanned we will live under the threat of deadly plague.

Someday I must go back to Fort Detrick and ask for a copy of the ground rules. Also, I'd like to leave at each of the many churches of Frederick County a copy of this prayer written a long time ago by Mark Twain:

> O Lord, our Father, our young patriots, idols of our hearts, go forth to battle — be Thou near them! With them — in spirit — we also go forth from the sweet peace of our beloved firesides to smite the foe. O Lord, our God, help us to tear their soldiers to bloody shreds with our shells; help us to cover their smiling fields with the pale forms of their patriot dead; help us to drown the thunder of the guns with the shrieks of their wounded, writhing in pain; help us to lay waste their humble homes with a hurricane of fire; help us to wring the hearts of their unoffending widows with unavailing grief; help us to turn them out roofless with their little children to wander unfriended the wastes of the desolated land in rags and hunger and thirst, sports of the sun-flames of summer and the icy winds of winter, broken in spirit, worn with travail, imploring Thee for the refuge of the grave and denied it — for our sakes who adore Thee, Lord, blast their hopes, blight their lives, protect their bitter pilgrimage, make heavy their steps, water their way with their tears, stain the white snow with the blood of their wounded feet! We ask it, in the spirit of love, of Him who is the Source of Love, and Who is the ever-faithful refuge and friend of all that are sore beset and seek His aid with Humble and contrite hearts. Amen.

The Pesticides

You
rake the dark —
shake your antennae out
in quick nerved work and lissome stirring.
You shamelessly move,
feeling in the black new space
(abyss or weaving passages)
and measure floor and ceiling,
always leaving
your own mixed pattern on the path you take.

You
go and shift —
open in altered air —
answer change in flow you soak in —
miscegenate, fly,
mutate — rearrange each line
of force in metaphase — survive
to reach: one bright blue pool,
oblivion's tool
of formal single-purpose bits in glowing rows.

10

Have You Read Your Label?: *The Pesticides* In the preceding chapter it was indicated that certain American entomologists, biologists, and chemists seem possessed of a warped understanding of social responsibility in the world community — if indeed they recognize such a concept. Apparently they have sold out to chauvinism, or perhaps it is just that they will do anything for money, though it pays for human anguish and may be blood-spattered. What matter? United States currency is so well made it can easily be washed. Just pop it into the automatic spinner and add a twist of the magic tornado or a charge of that whiter-than-white knight on horseback — and *voilà!*

Cold-hearted opportunists once again have clambered willingly onto the ageless rumbling juggernaut of Mars. On its turrets they go down on all fours in obeisance to the god of war. His naked thighs press against their willing buttocks to gratify again and again his brutish stabbing shaft; the lust never cools. Cloaked in star-spangled nationalism, the perversion and immorality are condoned. When the cape is opened to reveal the filthy pictures, these people look away discreetly or purse their lips and swivel their heads in denial of the exposure. To them, nothing is there but the rosy silken lining reflecting their own self-righteous faces. Thomas Jefferson put it rather well a long time ago when he said, "Indeed I tremble for my country when I reflect that God is just."

Lest men of goodwill despair in this shameful time of our nation's history, let them be reminded that these compatriots afflicted with bestial astigmatism are a minority albeit an influential one. Most thinking people — those that trust their instincts — are aware that when we make inhumane action respectable, we gamble recklessly with the future.

Among all men, regardless of how or where they live, reasonableness must prevail if the human race is to survive unmutilated, uncharred. People must tolerate political differences, stop polishing The Bomb, put away cherished lethal toys forever, and settle down to peaceable activities of trading together, exchanging ideas, sharing aspirations, doubts, and discoveries, and learning to understand one another despite all barriers. Is it naïve — as the hate-peddling warmongers scornfully would have us believe — to hope for such a change in the deep-seated aggressive nature of man? I think not. Nor does the generation now coming into flower.

Youth is trying to tell us in which direction to go, but sit we on our tails so smugly, so high on our stools that we don't dig the message — it's not getting through. Each of us — young, middle-aged, or old, living here, living there — must come to realize that the world is big enough for each to reproduce his own kind within his own brand of freedom. It is the exchange and mixing of all varieties, without malice or envy, without shakedown or putdown, that makes life exciting, absorbing, gloriously satisfying and worth living.

Come then, for the final attraction in this Sideshow of Insect-dom — the creation of an insecticide — to Switzerland, where rationality and tolerance have endured for centuries, where it is taken for granted that man is a reasonable being responsible to Creation. In this nation, insect-sized among the world's behemoths but no longer challenged by them militarily, no young man is haunted by the fear that at the first awesome surgings of his creative potential he will be forced to abandon his budding loves for a life of warfare. Except to defend his native land against invasion, he will not be commanded to shoulder a gun, to load a cannon's muzzle. He will not be taught to push buttons high in the sky with intent to maim and murder fellow creatures, who are strangers and terrifying only because their eyes have not yet been met, their own voices not heard, their embraces not yet felt.

In this compact nation no one even dreams of poisoning crops or plans, secretly or openly, to spray enemies, designated or otherwise, with disease germs, poisonous gases and searing flame, or to set upon them disease-bearing insects. The Swiss long ago learned to respect the inherent dignity of man. They comprehend truths of nature and the nature of truth. There is no credibility gap. In Switzerland, a man and his countrymen are the state, the governors truly are the governed, and dishonesty among them is not easily tolerated.

Switzerland has no iron, oil or coal, and so, fighting at times for the bare necessities of life, has had to create its livelihood from other sources less natural and by utilizing its brain power to the utmost. The textiles industry was mother to most of Switzerland's other industries. From it was developed engineering (for machinery) and chemistry (for dyestuffs). Today the chemical industry is Switzerland's second largest in export trade, superseded only by the manufacture of machinery and electrical equipment.

In the early 1930's Switzerland's pesticide business emerged from chemistry's burbling retorts and flasks. Center of chemical manufacturing is Basel, the nation's second largest city (population, 220,000), with four of the world's biggest and most important chemical concerns located there (Ciba, Geigy, Hoffmann-La Roche, and Sandoz), plus a handful of smaller ones. To Americans, the best-known firm is that of Geigy — officially, J. R. Geigy, A.G. (*Aktien Gesellschaft*) or S.A. (*Société Anonyme*). Geigy has had ties to the United States since 1870, and Geigy scientists during World War II discovered and developed the insecticidal properties of DDT that prevented much suffering among Allied troops and civilians, especially in Burma and the Pacific. The achievements of DDT during the Italian campaigns prompted Sir Winston Churchill to say (in *War Review*, September 28, 1944): "The excellent DDT powder, which has been fully experimented with and found to yield astonishing results, will henceforth be used on a great scale . . . and will be a help to all the Allies. . . . The eradication of lice in Naples by the strict hygienic measures taken may be held to have averted a very grievous typhus epidemic in that city and neighbourhood when we occupied it."

Begun thirty years before the American Declaration of Independence, in the age of Voltaire, Rousseau and Frederick the Great, Geigy is the oldest chemical firm in Basel and likely the world's most venerated, with a continuous record of progress in the chemical field.

In early April 1967 I stood on the roof of the Geigy administration building (fourteen stories tall, with two more below ground), highest of several severely designed creations of concrete, brick, and glass. The pesticide work force of Geigy is the equivalent of a university staff actively engaged in such scientific fields as entomology, plant physiology, nematology, organic chemistry, genetics, toxicology, enzymology, biochemistry, physical and analytical chemistry, plant pathology, and microbiology. Nowhere, except perhaps in the pharmaceutical industry, is there such melding and teamwork of physical and biological sciences as there is in the pesticide industry.

The term pesticide broadly includes compounds intended for a variety of purposes: to control insects, mites, ticks, fungi, nematodes, rodents, pest birds, predatory animals, rough fish, plant diseases, and weeds, and also to act as plant growth regulators, defoliants, and desiccants. The pesticides used in the greatest tonnage in this country are the cholorinated hydrocarbons — those that contain carbon, hydrogen, and chlorine. Most familiar of them are

DDT, dieldrin, aldrin, endrin, lindane, methoxychlor, chlordane, and heptachlor.

The first mention of a pesticide was made one millennium before the coming of Christ by Homer when he spoke of a "pest-averting sulfur." In 470 B.C., the Greek philosopher Democritus recommended a blight cure made of olives. Pliny, the Roman, in 60 B.C. suggested soaking wheat seed in wine to prevent mildew. A bowstring of Ulysses was gnawed through by moths. Another early pesticide was Paris green (arsenic trioxide and acetate of copper), a paint pigment used in 1867 against the Colorado beetle, a pest of potatoes. Bordeaux mixture (copper sulphate, lime, and water) was an old-reliable spray for grapes.

The development of a pesticide has been likened to an obstacle race in which runners have to undergo various tests and ordeals. Many falter and fall. Only the most fit finish the course. I was astonished to learn from Geigy officials of the high cost of developing a new pesticide and bringing it to the international market. It can amount to as much as eight to ten million Swiss francs, or about $2 million to $2.5 million. Elapsed time from its beginning within the brain of a chemical researcher to the consumer market can be from six to ten years (however, if no crops are involved, it may take only four years). That somewhat explains why good pesticides are not cheap. Even after a new pesticide has been approved for sale it needs additional time and an outlay of more money to get it to the ultimate customer.

Worldwide head of Geigy's pesticide operation (called in German *Schädlingsbekämpfung*, meaning pest fighting) is Dr. Hans Gysin, a native of Liestal, capital of the half-Canton Basel-Land (country), and a graduate of the University of Basel with a Ph.D. in chemistry. He has been associated with pesticide research since 1949, was the first man to synthesize carbamates as pesticides, and is noted as the inventor of diazinon, Geigy's most renowned all-purpose insecticide. Upon meeting Dr. Gysin in his office in the Research Building at Rosenthal, I asked about the difficulty of producing a new pesticide.

"It is not really so difficult these days," he commented, "for the synthetic chemist to come up with a new patentable and highly active molecule. The difficulty is in finding one with superior performance, one that is more economical than those already in existence and also devoid of undesirable side effects."

Since my chemical experience has been limited to boyhood attempts to blow up the family kitchen with an A. C. Gilbert Elementary Chemistry Set and to a smattering of Bunsen burner and test tube piddling in high school (all I remember is how to create a fine rotten-egg stink), rudimentary information on which the pesticide chemist bases his work had to be ground into me one morning at Geigy by a very accommodating scientist, the group leader in Biochemistry, Dr. Pierre H. Payot, Ph.D. and M.D., late of the University of California at Berkeley and the University of Washington at Seattle back in the States. He was delighted to be able to return momentarily to the academic milieu, and I in turn was pleased to have the complexities of pesticide chemistry so thoroughly and clearly explained to me on a blackboard as I sat back and kept my powers of absorption primed with sip upon sip of mineral water (Meltinger Automaten Füllung, 1450) poured from a wire-glass-rubber-stoppered bottle like we used when we made root beer back home when I was a kid. (This bubbly water is a favorite stimulant of the research chemists, along with a specially made Geigy tea that looks like pink soda pop and is served cold and unsweetened—a delightful beverage; a chemical flask of it stands on the desk in most every chemist's office.)

In this cram course I learned about aliphatic hydrocarbons, branched aliphatic hydrocarbons, cyclic hydrocarbons and aromatic hydrocarbons (so-called because of double bonds, or dashes, alternating with single ones in a cyclic hydrocarbon, and not allied to odor in any way). I was introduced to substituted aromatic hydrocarbons and heterocyclic compounds. I cannot readily explain any of these terms without resorting to a blackboard, piece of chalk, and my scribbled notes, but I don't believe your life will be blighted by being deprived here of this knowledge. The formation by a chemist of these cryptic diagrams of letters, dashes, and numbers is fascinating and seemed to me like some higher form of dominoes — an esoteric game only for the initiated.

While all this may seem pretty far out to the average insect avenger, it is vital to a chemist making a synthesis of a compound in an attempt to learn whether the material in question will have the expected effect or not. After a compound is decided upon it is made up in small quantities of from ten to twenty grams and sent to the biological laboratories for testing. The biologist informs the chemist whether his selected compound has activity or not, and to what degree. If the compound looks promising it is then sent on to the biochemical laboratory for study of its chemical reactions and behavior in living organisms (laboratory animals, plants, insects, and microorganisms).

It must be decided now just how the compound is to be distributed. Perhaps one-half or even only one-tenth of a gram of the chemical per square meter is all that is needed to be effective. How can such a small amount be equitably spread? Will it best be in emulsion, or fine suspension in a liquid, as a wettable powder, a dust, granules, or by some other method? Will it be used as a contact poison, one to be ingested, or one to be distributed as a gas or fine mist?

Problems likely to be encountered in transportation of the finished pesticide must be considered at this time. Much of the Geigy shipping is done by air since customers of this firm are scattered all over the globe.

"It is colder than hell up there," said Dr. Payot, in jest. "No, not hell — the opposite place. Emulsions settle. But then too there often is heat to consider. A compound that is stable in Basel might in Iraq or Mozambique be exposed to burning sun and your compound will just fall apart. Sometimes we must pack in white-painted drums to reflect the sun, instead of in dark-colored ones that absorb heat. And we must know how light will affect a pesticide, and also of its persistence — in rain, for instance."

I was shown how the melting point of an organic chemical is determined so that purity can be established. The science of chromatography was briefly explained — another check on purity.

The chemists know, from previous experience in working with biologists and from observations made on small lab animals, something of the toxicity of the new material, but now it must be processed on a more advanced scale through the toxicology department to learn more exactly about harmful properties.

A new compound must be tested in its relation to plants and fruit. What do these growing things do with the chemical? Do they break it down into compounds similar to their own constituents? Do they burn it? What amount is washed away or evaporated? What fraction is absorbed? All this must be determined at an early stage of the game, for in consideration of public health it is most important to know what residues must be dealt with, what possible harmful side effects are present.

In this department tests are made also on animals, beginning with mice and progressing through rats, rabbits, to monkeys, pigs or dogs. (The U.S. Pure Food and Drug Act requires tests to be made on three species of animal, one of them not a rodent.) With Dr. Payot I visited one of these clinical chemical labs at Geigy, where Dr. Edgar Peheim, a native of Germany and veterinarian as well as toxicologist, was in charge of the technicians.

"A toxicologist is a criminologist," explained Dr. Payot. "We are like detectives looking for something to change, but first we must know what is normal. We are here to test and if possible give either the red or green light to the compound for its use in connection with a human being."

The U.S. Food and Drug Administration requires the determination of toxicity ranges with animals in order to establish a safety factor in regard to human ingestion of a pesticide compound. On the basis of the tests made in the lab on animals, the FDA decides whether the compound is dangerous to man and human tolerance to it. It will be found, for instance, that a man eating so much cabbage, tomatoes, strawberries or whatever, can ingest only so much of the pesticide that has been sprayed on the food in its raw state without impairment to health. In some cases, tests are run on human volunteers — such as men in prison.

"We have to make sure," Dr. Payot told me, "that we have foreseen just about everything that possibly can happen regarding the pesticide. There are strict government regulations that we must abide by, but we would do that anyway without such controls."

Before the development of a pesticide gets too far along, the entire field of pesticide products must be combed to determine whether there is anything identical to or approaching the new formulation that would prevent its being protected by patent. The patent situation can be extremely exasperating. It is a complicated procedure, at variance all over the world, and rough on the chemists who must handle this facet of a pesticide. They have had to become lawyers without shingle. In Italy, an infringer of a patent is protected by being permitted to sell his pilfered product all the while the lawsuit filed against him by the original patentee is pending; eventually, the infringer must pay up, but the penalty of damages never equals the loss incurred by the product's originator in bucking the competition. Certain countries can only protect manufacturing processes or use of the compounds. In others a product must be manufactured locally. India is trying to introduce compulsory licensing of pesticides and wants to shorten the protection time to a period below ten years, which is just about how long it takes a pesticide to begin getting a return on its large investment. The duration of patent protection in Switzerland and Germany is eighteen years from filing date. It is twenty in France, seventeen in Canada, sixteen in Great Britain, and fifteen in both Russia and Japan. However, in that last-named country protection begins from the date of "laying out for public inspection."

A new compound is extensively tested on insects that it expects to control. For this purpose fifty species of insects are bred in sixteen Geigy insectaria, deep in an underground level of the Research Building. Temperature and humidity of each of the insect-housing rooms is controlled — with a complete change of air four times an hour — in accordance to the natural climatic conditions of its particular inhabitants, whether they be cockroaches, beetles, aphids, stable flies, spider mites, water snails, or *bettwanyens* (bedbugs).

Some of the insects are fed on host animals — hamsters, rabbits, guinea pigs — each one of which works only one day each week. Mosquitoes, for instance, are fed on rabbits, their heads held in a boxlike affair resembling a Pilgrim stocks (not so much to protect the animal's face from the biting insects — which it does — but to keep the rabbit from hunting down the pesky mosquitoes in the fur).

I made the tour of the insectaria with Dr. Rudolf Gasser, who heads the Geigy biological department.

"At one time," he told me, "all of us researchers in the department fed body lice carried in a special case strapped to our wrists like a watch. I soon got accustomed to it; my wife never did. She didn't like it too much — especially if I wore the case to bed. She'd make me take it off and put it on the bedside table. For a long time after the test still I was impelled to scratch even though there were no lice."

When I asked Dr. Gasser if there was any one particular pest that bothered him personally, he said, "Yes, the cork moth. It disturbs the corks in my wine cellar."

The Geigy insecticide labs require about ten thousand flies a week, four to six days old, both a normally sensitive strain (DDT knockdown in forty-five minutes) and resistant flies. The fly larvae are developed in dishpan-like metal containers holding a mixture of alfalfa, sugar, meal, yeast, and milk. It looks like tanbark and to me it had the aroma of a beer hall, but Dr. Gasser assured me that a fly cannot get high on it as this fly food is sterilized at a temperature of from 70 to 80 degrees Centigrade to eliminate fungi growth.

The resistant flies are evolved from batches placed in two-gallon jars having their insides well coated with DDT and diazinon. Only the ones still alive after twenty-four hours of exposure to these killers are collected for the egg-laying cages.

Thousands of cockroaches are bred here for lab use — principally the American, German, and Oriental. They are kept prisoner in large metal drums, made escape-proof by standing them in oil and providing them with an inside collar filled wth talcum. Occasionally one or two roaches more agile than the average do escape. A couple did while I was in their room and Dr. Gasser met the situation in an unscientific manner—he quickly stepped on them. He told me that a pair of small ones once got into a Geigy telephone outlet and managed, by procreating and feeding their offspring on wire insulation, to put out of commission one whole section of telephones.

In one of the rooms I was exposed to what appeared to be a copulatory rally of Asiatic migratory locusts, and in another watched the changing of the lettuce on which cotton army worms feed (they get a new salad each day so that no specimens will be lost by virus diseases). This is one of the most devilish pests of our Deep South, Egypt, Turkey, and Australia.

"At one time," explained Dr. Gasser, "the moths that lay the eggs wouldn't respond to the honey and water on which they are fed, and I had to feed each one personally by hand."

He spoke in German to the insectarium assistant, a young lady, who then opened one of the containers, brought forth a moth, and with some fluttering difficulty turned it over to Dr. Gasser. It tried to escape and in the ensuing confusion his glasses fell into one of the salads.

"It has been so long," he apologized, "since I have done it. Too much a paper man now and not enough an entomologist."

The moth fluttered in his hand. The fingers no longer had the agility of youth; the gold wedding band fit tightly. Finally, the entomologist prevailed over paper man and with a needle Dr. Gasser was able deftly to curl out the moth's extremely tiny nostrum to show me how each one of the nervous creatures had to be hand-fed every day until they became accustomed to their honey and water diet.

In the next room were walrus-like gastropods, big fat slimy tan slugs called *Arion*. Groups of coddling moths were busy laying eggs on ripe apples. One room was devoted to beanstalks on which were being cultivated millions of spider mites; in another were tanks containing water snails (*Planorbis guadelupensis*), the vector of bilharziosis, a dread disease of Africa that reduces the activity of humans in rice-planting areas. Colorado potato beetles were being deceived into year-round activity by an artificial elimination of winter (by light and controlled humidity), their time of diapause (overwintering).

My hands began to get a little itchy after viewing in succession: breeding stocks of the granary weevil, the bean weevil, the *Rhodniuswanzen* bug of Brazil (transmitter of Chagas disease), the *Sandzecken* of Africa, a repulsive-looking bloodsucking soft tick that works on natives sleeping on dirt floors of huts and gives them the reluctant fever. I was shown the mealy bug clustered in snowy-white masses on stems of potato plants, and also stable flies, the only Geigy ectoparasite boarders that are not fed on natural living blood; they get canned blood. Another curiosity of the insectaria is the *Aedes aegypti*, the yellow-fever-vector mosquito. Millions of its eggs are dried on wads of cotton, quick-frozen, and stored for future use. When heated, the eggs come alive and look like very active fine sand.

Dr. Gasser next took me to visit one of the scientific workrooms where resistance of flies to a pesticide was being tested, using perhaps the oldest known method — confinement of the insects to glass petri dishes containing a coating of the compound under study in an acetone solution or other solvent. Several dozen of these dishes, each containing a carefully measured varying amount of the active substance, were set out. Each held from fifteen to twenty flies. To determine the lethal effect of the compound, some groups were being subjected to continuous contact with it; others were being given what is termed "fractionated contact" — exposure for only short periods of time, proportionately reduced as the flies were changed from one dish to another. Flies and other test insects are exposed to pesticide gases in much the same way.

After a pesticide has proven satisfactory in the laboratories it is released for field trials on experimental farms near Basel, in the Rhone valley, or in northern Italy. For first trials a Geigy insecticide generally remains in Europe; for further testing it may be sent to one of the "daughter" company's six experimental farms in the United States or to farms of Geigy's "daughter" companies in France, Germany, or Mexico. If it is decided to go ahead with the new pesticide, a pilot plant must be outfitted to produce it in quantity — another costly step. Packaging is devised and sales, publicity, and farmer-education campaigns are set in motion.

But one of the biggest hurdles is still to be crossed. The product must have government approval before it can be sold in America, one of the world's richest marketplaces for agricultural pesticides. The annual gross retail pesticide business here amounts to about $265 million — or about 8.5 percent of gross agricultural chemical sales.

Both federal and state government agencies have regulatory and enforcement powers over the pesticide industry, its products, and the crops that are treated. No pesticide can be marketed in our country in interstate commerce until the United States Department of Agriculture has granted it registration. A pesticide is presumed guilty until proven innocent. The two big questions asked by the USDA regarding a pesticide are: is it safe to use, and will it do what it promises? The testing of a pesticide's chronic and sublethal effects is an essential requirement when such a substance is introduced. It must be known whether man, domestic animals, and wild game are likely to be affected directly by ingesting the pesticide at this concentration. It must also be determined that the concentration of the pesticide is such that it will control the pest adequately.

By law, tests to determine residues in pesticides must be measured in fractions of parts per million, called in the trade ppm. Louis A. McLean, secretary of a large American chemical corporation, once illustrated the analytical procedures by saying that if a standard jigger of vermouth were added to gin filling an eight-thousand-gallon railway tank car not only would a very dry martini be produced but the relationship of vermouth to the gin would be 1.46 ppm. On lettuce the permitted DDT residue is 7 ppm. That means that on three tons of lettuce one ounce of DDT residue would greatly exceed the permitted amount. To certify residues, three-generation reproduction studies on rats are now required for all new compounds on which tolerances are being established for the first time and for all compounds having fixed tolerances but for which revised ones are being requested.

The Pesticides Regulation Division of our government carries a staff of sixty-five highly qualified specialists whose skills are every bit as sophisticated as those of the men who have produced the pesticide. The new product is given a thorough going-over. If it meets all requirements a registration is bestowed on it. If, however, the compound leaves a residue and if food is involved in its use USDA delays registration until a residue tolerance has been established by the Food and Drug Administration (FDA). The USDA regulatory staff evaluates and approves or disapproves uses that bring pesticides into intimate contact with people in household applications — such as mothproofing, lawn and garden care, control of home pests, etc.

In order to have a tolerance set by FDA, the manufacturer must file a petition with that agency. The USDA then certifies to FDA that the product under consideration is useful and offers an opinion on whether the petitioner's proposed tolerance reasonably reflects the residues to be expected from its use according to directions. Present law requires that the petitioner present FDA with experimental evidence on toxicity to establish what tolerance, if any, will be safe, and to show that the tolerance can be met under practical conditions of the pesticide's use, and also to provide practical methods of analysis for its enforcement. A lot of paper work is involved and much elapsed time. Patience is a prime requisite.

Tolerances are based on extensive use data and toxicological testing in animals and frequently by metabolic studies in man. The margin of safety is wide, usually being set at one one-hundredth or less of the amount of the compound that produces *minimal* physiological effect in the most sensitive of at least two species of animals for a lifetime, or from two- to four-year periods. By this hundred-to-one factor the assumption is made that a human may be ten times as sensitive to the pesticide as the healthy test animals, and that children and aged or sick people may in turn be ten times as sensitive as normal persons.

The firm of Geigy has been through the regulatory approval mill so many times that it is taken for granted that things will be difficult before a product can be marketed. Undaunted, Geigy turns out one original formulation after another. One of the most important of its creations is an organic phosphate all-purpose insecticide called diazinon that perhaps is the firm's greatest discovery since DDT. A wide range of diazinon products are used by farmers on a large scale and by home gardeners against every sort of crawling pest. In the United States this pesticide is marketed as diazinon 50W (a 50 percent wettable powder) and diazinon AG500 (a four-pounds-per gallon emulsifiable solution). Growers of fruit and nut crops use diazinon against twelve kinds of aphids, nine mites, twelve scales, and twenty-two other destructive insects. With granular diazinon farmers go after corn borers, rootworms, potato wireworms, cutworms, mole crickets, and onion, root, and seedcorn maggots. Cotton growers use this insecticide against cotton leaf perforators, lygus bugs, aphids, leafhoppers, spider mites, cotton leafworms, and salt marsh caterpillars. Tobacco growers use it for the control of all kinds of soil insects, including wireworms, and for attacks on foliage insects. Diazinon protects thirty-six different vegetables and seventeen field crops from marauding insects. It can be used against lice and ticks in sheep, and is effective for control of turf insects (in lawns, golf courses, parks, and other grass areas). It works well against the insects that disfigure ornamental plants, and can be used to kill flies and other household insect pests, such as ants, brown dog ticks, carpet beetles, cockroaches, pantry pests, scorpions, silverfish, spiders, and grasshoppers. Diazinon mixed with methoxychlor is sold as alfa-tox for specific control of one of the most destructive insect pests of farming, the alfalfa weevil.

Geigy diazinon is used extensively in cattle and sheep countries to control and eliminate ticks — those bloodthirsty ectoparasites that cause $60 million worth of damage annually in South America alone, where there are a quarter of a million cattle — most in Brazil (41,660) and Argentina (31,250). The control of ticks is very important to the leather industry, as hides with holes in them cannot be fabricated profitably for use as upholstery materials or wearing apparel. In Australia, eighteen thousand ranchers care for 170 million sheep and there diazinon spray and dips are considered a godsend.

In the autumn of 1939 Dr. Paul Müller succeeded in producing a significant group of compounds by combining chloral with hydrocarbons and phenols. He began by synthesizing diphenyl-trichloroethane. Further research on the group eventually, by the combination of chloral and chlorobenzene, yielded 4,4-dichloro-diphenyltrichloroethane, the substance we know today as DDT (utilizing the initials of its three main parts). Then it was simply known as Experiment No. G. 1750, and later called gesarol. Laboratory tests and subsequent field trials using the new compound against flies, aphids, mosquitoes, and the Colorado beetle proved it to be remarkably effective, and the upshot was an application on May 8, 1941, to the Swiss Federal Research Stations at Wädenswil and Oerlikon for an official test, which resulted in approval of DDT as an insecticide. The rest is history.

"The new pesticide had come along as a just-right star in the proper constellation at exactly the right time in history," said Dr. Robert Zinkernagel, who is in charge of the section of pesticides called *Materialschutz*, protection of material. (I thought of what Beatrix Miller, British editor of *Vogue*, has said of Twiggy, that phenomenally popular fashion model with the angelic face and pipestem legs: "She's exactly the right look at the right time.")

"There is a book by Stefan Zweig," continued Dr. Zinkernagel, "*Sternstunden der Menschheit* — a rough translation would be 'turning points of civilization' — that is about just this idea of something or someone being just right at just the right time in history to turn its tide somewhat. Zweig writes, for instance, of Napoleon being at Waterloo at the wrong time for him, but just right for historic change. DDT came at precisely the right time to change the history of pesticides. Ten years earlier it would have been nothing; ten years later, not so much either. It came when it was needed most."

The advent of DDT was at a time when the Allies at war sorely needed such an insecticide to replace pyrethrum (made from chrysanthemums) and derris, the two known protectors against malaria and typhus. Their sources, in Japan and Kenya, South Africa, had been cut off by the war. Everyone concerned with DDT realized its tremendous importance to military medicine and hygiene. Accordingly, the diplomatic representatives in Bern of various belligerent powers were informed of the company's discovery and at the same time samples of it were sent through regular channels to Geigy organizations outside Switzerland with instructions to approach the governments of the nations in which those plants were situated. In January of 1943 a few pounds of high-purity DDT were produced at the Geigy Fine Chemical Laboratories at Trafford Park, England, and in April that year the first batch was made in a pilot plant in that country, with first bulk production following in November. In the meantime, pilot plant production of DDT was begun in America at the Cincinnati Chemical Works, a Geigy affiliate at Norwood, Ohio, in May 1943. Thus DDT reached the warring world and began battling its militant diseases. Supplies were ready in time to combat a rapidly spreading typhus epidemic in Naples, Italy, during the British occupation of the southern part of that nation in 1944. During the month of January, 1,300,000 Neapolitans were dusted with DDT at two delousing stations (72,000 on the peak day). In just one week cases of typhus fell sharply from 305 to 155. Later this wonder pesticide proved itself as a foe of the pests of war in Burma, the South Pacific arenas, and at Dakar, Africa, where it put down an outbreak of bubonic plague.

"But the way we use DDT today," I was told by Dr. Payot, "is a vast improvement over what it was like then. Then it was like a medieval cannon blast. It now is used with more sophistication — but all these refinements had to be learned."

The big difference between DDT and the stomach poisons then in use was that it killed insects by contact when they crawled over the stuff. Compared to the highly toxic pesticides then on the market, such as nicotine, the arsenicals, and dinitro cresols it truly was revolutionary. Very small amounts were effective against flies; it was not vito-toxic (harmful to plants); and it was relatively easy to manufacture. The process is not complicated. This compound can be formulated without difficulty into powders giving suspension in water, as well as into nonstaining and colorless dusts. The raw materials are readily and cheaply available.

In Dr. Payot's scholastic lecture to me as a class of one, I'd found out that DDT is an aromatic chlorinated hydrocarbon — and with the finest piece of chalk and the largest, cleanest blackboard I wouldn't attempt to diagram its complicated structure for you. Chemically, DDT is very stable with low water solubility. Therefore it is very persistent as a pesticide and slow-acting, a quality sometimes not desired by the public, who favor swift killers that have short residual action — just strong enough to kill the insects and then be degraded by light, humidity, and other weather factors. However, DDT is widely used by professional growers in tremendous quantities.

The Geigy patents on DDT have run out and of course other firms have moved in with their own formulations. Even when it was brand-new others were hot on the trail of DDT. Following the war competitors moved in quickly with DDT imitations, such as BHC (benzynehexachloride) made in both France and England, and several chlorinated hydrocarbon compounds made by American firms. But the true DDT continued to dominate the fields of agricultural insect pest control, hygiene, and public health.

After World War II the United States Armed Forces dumped huge quantities of DDT into the sea with deleterious effect on marine life. Rather than store the stuff for years, with almost certain deterioration, it was thought best to get rid of the surplus DDT and what cheaper way than to dump it into the ocean? Costs nothing but a little manpower and a few of the taxpayers' battlewagons for transport.

That sort of irresponsible action and a few other horrendous mistakes made in misusing DDT got the insecticide a bad press for a while, but there is no denying that DDT has a record of usefulness probably unequaled by any other substance synthesized by man. It has prevented at least twenty million deaths and a hundred times that many illnesses during the twenty-eight years of its existence. It still is the choice for malaria control (against the *Anopheles* mosquito) by the World Health Organization, which has used a billion pounds of DDT in the benighted areas of the world to combat vectors of persistent diseases. It was the first chemical ever to be used in ton lots. To date, more than a quarter of a billion native homes have been sprayed with DDT. Its long-lasting residue is a great advantage in long-term spraying programs in areas where malaria is prevalent and where spraying every month would be too expensive.

A spectacular success such as DDT doesn't come along every day of the week, or every year for that matter, but the challenges of pesticide production are never ending. Something new is always being tried. Certain scientists search for pesticides that will be more specific — that is, ones that will kill a selected insect and no others. Isolane is one of the specific pesticides now on the market. It was developed by Geigy back in the fifties. It works well against aphids in a low concentration — six grams of active ingredient in a hundred liters of water — and is popular in Switzerland, Italy, Holland, and Belgium, but has not yet been used in America, Great Britain, South America, Africa, or Asia. In Italy, Isolane has been successfully used on peaches. United States government regulations make the distribution of a specific insecticide difficult because of its usually high toxicity; handlers must be careful in using it. Too, in most cases the market for a specific is too small to warrant large-scale production.

The biggest drawback to biological control of insect pests as far as the consumer is concerned is that it just takes too long to become effective. While waiting for biological control to take over, no one wants to suffer through a long period of eating wormy or scarred fruit and insect-damaged vegetables. Even the most violent critic of chemical pesticides will be the first to call for an exterminator when there are fleas in the bedroom or cockroaches skittering out of the woodwork. Chemical pesticides are cheap, adaptable to many uses, and quick-acting.

Chemical pesticide people are mostly concerned that politicians are making capital of the renewed interest in biological control that was engendered by the publication in 1962 of the world-famous antipesticide book *Silent Spring* by Rachel Carson. The idea of getting rid of insect pests without poisons by letting them knock each other off or by letting nature take its course is an appealing one to present to constituents — and contented constituents mean votes at election time. Therefore a great deal of money in the form of government grants and aids is being shoveled out to people who have become ardent advocates of the nonchemical approach to the agricultural pest problem. Today, the big cabbage is going for biological control experiments. Everyone is trying to get into the act — and into Uncle Sam's pocket. Miss Carson, had she lived, no doubt would have been surprised by this mercenary turn as one result of her vigilante crusade.

Even though she has gone to Elysian fields (which are unsprayed, I trust), she still is not regarded by the pesticide industry as Rebecca of Sunnybrook Farm or the fairy godmother with golden wand. Her book cut the pesticide industry to the quick — she didn't play fairly, according to those she lit into. In the Compactus file of Geigy's Literaturstelle Schädlingsbekämpfung there are eight fat folders of clippings from the world press relating to Silent Spring. In going through them, I got some idea of the international furor the book kicked up — the opinions mostly were con, there were few pros in what I read.

Miss Carson was criticized mainly because she presented one side of a very important subject, and failed to tell of the part that pesticide chemicals play in the production of food and protection of public health. It also was claimed that she encouraged readers to draw conclusions that are unwarranted in the light of scientific facts. No one questioned her statement that above definite dose limits certain pesticides are poisonous to humans and will cause death if then ingested. But, according to her critics, Miss Carson consistently ignored the fact that the effects of a chemical are proportional to the dose, and also that even for the most toxic chemicals known no detectable toxic effects occur below a certain dose level. Strong objections were raised over the scientifically indefensible fallacy presented in Silent Spring that any substance which in any quantity is toxic must per se be a poison. By such definition, almost everything in everyday use would be a poison — water, salt, sugar, amino acids, minerals, vitamins, and so forth.

The use by man of any chemical substance whether as a food,

drug, cosmetic, pesticide or any other purpose is a potential hazard. But the majority of them, including pesticides, have a non-toxic dose for humans as well as a toxic one. In A.D. 1530, Paracelsus said, "*Dosis sola facit venenum* (The dose makes the poison)." If the use of a chemical were prohibited until all possible noninjurious effects could be eliminated, man would be denied the use of every chemical substance ever developed.

Parathion is one of the more deadly poisons. It destroys an enzyme needed by the body to allow muscles to relax. It also causes overstimulation of the heart and the gastrointestinal tract. The primary cause of death is a form of strangulation caused by constriction of the muscles related to breathing. Recently in Tijuana, Mexico, seventeen schoolchildren died from ingesting parathion that had accidentally become mixed in sugar. Only last November, 1967, in the town of Chiquinquira, Colombia, South America, seventy-seven persons, only four of them over seventeen years of age, died in one day from eating bread baked from flour that had become contaminated due to breakage of a pint bottle of parathion; at least 130 other persons were hospitalized. The government donated coffins to the stricken community; the church waived all funeral fees; and soldiers dug the graves. Men spoke in whispers, women wept, the gold, red and blue flag of Colombia was ribboned in black and flown at half-staff. No funeral music was played and the slow tolling of a church bell was so soft that the lowing of cattle could be heard over it. Antidotes called protopam and atropine were dispatched from the United States. These are antidotes used by the United States Army against nerve gas. Also last fall, in Florida, an orange picker and his wife were accused of poisoning their seven children by dosing their lunch with parathion.

Dr. Frederick J. Stare, chairman of the Department of Nutrition, Harvard School of Public Health, has said: "As a physician and student of nutrition for the last twenty-five years, let me state categorically that I do not know, nor have I ever heard, of one single case of ill health in man shown to be due to adding approved chemicals to foods. And I say *additional* chemicals because I wish to emphasize that all foods are chemicals. You and I, too, are chemicals — so much water, protein, fat, carbohydrates, vitamins and minerals."

At the American Medical Association Congress on Environmental Health Problems, Raymond L. White of the AMA's Division of Environmental Medicine and Medical Services, said: "There are uncertainties in the use of pesticides, but the overt hazards are no greater today than a decade ago and are probably far outweighed by the advantages of food production and the potential control of some twenty-seven diseases which affect mankind."

The major weakness of *Silent Spring* seemed to be in its suggestions by innuendo of prospects of distress and disaster far beyond probability. Everyone recognizes that human life encounters dangers and hazards in some degree every day, but critics of her book felt that perhaps Miss Carson went a bit overboard with her alarums. The opening movement of her anti-insecticide symphony is a masterpiece of apprehension capable of not only shaking to their roots flowery garden club members but of throwing a good scare into hairy-chested men.

One of the most on-target answers to Miss Carson's indictment of the chemical pesticide industry as irresponsible blackguards concerned only with making profits came from a gentleman named D. Boocock, public relations officer of the Industrial Pest Control Association of London, England, who wrote a parody of that scarey opening to *Silent Spring*, in which its author conjured up a hypothetical "town in the heart of America where all life seemed to be in harmony with its surroundings" that has been blighted by "a white powder" that "fell from the sky like snow."

In Miss Carson's fearful account, cattle and sheep sickened, hens could not hatch their eggs, strange illnesses appeared among the people, birds sang no more, fish in streams died, the roadsides were lined with browned vegetation, and little children were stricken at play and died within a few hours. Orson Welles in his tender prime, when he played bogeyman on the radio, couldn't have done a better job of frightening the populace.

In Mr. Boocock's imaginary town there is the same strange blight, the same evil spell settled on the community. Fields of grain

are full of weeds, in the orchards and on hillsides scab and coddling
moths have made the apple crop inedible and unsalable. Livestock
is listless and debilitated. Cattle suffer from tick-borne fevers; grubs
torture their bodies. The grain is alive with weevils and beetles.
Flour mill machinery is clogged with webbing spun by moths; spider beetles scurry in dark places. The townsfolk are hungry and at
night their sleep is disturbed by fleas, lice, and bedbugs. Flies and
cockroaches have multiplied tremendously and carry germs of en-
teric diseases from filth to food. Mr. Boocock's closing paragraph
says: "No witchcraft or no enemy action had brought these pests
and plagues to this stricken community. The people had done it
themselves. They had banned the use of pesticides because they
had read a highly coloured account of their disadvantages and had
forgotten the tremendous benefits they confer. They had mistaken
the exaggerated and prejudiced piece of special pleading for the
whole truth. They had read *Silent Spring* and taken it too much to
heart."

Many statements of *Silent Spring* were considered to be rash.
"We are in little better position than the guests of the Borgias,"
Miss Carson stated. Also: ". . . pollution of the ground water is
pollution of water everywhere." And again: "Each insecticide is
used for the simple reason that it is a deadly poison. It therefore
poisons all life with which it comes in contact."

Her well-intentioned utterings raised the hackles of scientists,
physicians, and other technically informed people. Said one such,
"It's a little as if Charlotte Brontë discovered radium."

The *Chemical Engineering News* headed its review: "Silence,
Miss Carson." The reviewer was Dr. William J. Darby, professor
and chairman of the Department of Biochemistry and director of
the Division of Nutrition at Vanderbilt University School of Medicine. Dr. Darby was upset by Miss Carson's phraseology relating to
pesticides "staggering in number" with a "power to kill" and "incredible potential for harm," representing a "train of disaster" resulting in a "chemical death rain" and being used with "little or no
advance investigation of their effect on soil, water, wildlife, and
man himself." He referred to these and other such reiterated allu-

sions to pesticides as sinister chemicals able to extinguish plant life, wildlife, aquatic life, and man life—producers of cancer, leukemia, sterility and cellular mutations—as "high-pitched sequences of anxieties . . . likely to be perused uncritically, to be regarded by the layman as authoritative and to arouse in him manifestations of anxieties and psychoneuroses. . . . The obvious effect on the reader will be to aggravate unjustifiably his own neurotic anxiety."

That aspect of the book was largely ignored, but by its shrill predictions of doom, Miss Carson's work whipped up enough hypertension among the populace to greatly accelerate nervous disorders, heart ailments, and faulty digestion — even to cause malnutrition, as a result of avoidance of certain foods due to fear that they might be poisoned. Dr. Darby's conclusion was that the responsible scientist should read *Silent Spring* "to understand the ignorance of those writing on the subject and the educational task which lies ahead."

Miss Carson's contention that pesticides are about to do us all in indeed cannot be supported by fact. On the authority of Dr. Wayland J. Hayes, chief of the Toxicology Center of the U.S. Public Health Service, Atlanta, Georgia, the number of accidental deaths from ingestion of pesticides annually in the United States ranges from 110 to 120. Figures of the National Office of Vital Statistics indicate that an average of 10 percent of deaths each year from solid and liquid poisons are attributed to pesticides. More people are damaged by farm tools and mechanical equipment, drugs, household chemicals (such as detergents, bleaches and soaps), solvents, and miscellaneous poisons than by pesticides. Twice as many deaths are caused by aspirin (it accounts for one-third of the poisoning deaths of small children) and one half as many by wasp stings.

Pesticides can enter the body by ingestion, absorption through skin contact, or by inhalation. Among vertebrates, fish are generally more sensitive to pesticide chemicals than are birds, and they more so than mammals. It is true that DDT can be stored in the fatty tissues of warm-blooded animals. Also, it is a fact that two different organo-phosphorous compounds may "potentiate" each other in a cooperative action called synergism, the joint performance of two agents which results in an effect greater than the sum of the individual effects. That is, a minute dose of either chemical may be harmless, but bringing the two together may cause a subtle interaction with lethal effect. The chances of this happening in a normally healthy human being are very rare, but if during an illness the body calls on its body-fat reserves, then accumulations of DDT might have some toxic effect. It is true, however, that not one person has been known to die of DDT poisoning. Human beings seem able to take aboard quite large amounts of DDT without apparent harm.

Scientists of the Food and Drug Administration and Public Health Service, working at the USDA laboratory at Orlando, Florida, administered a dose of five hundred milligrams of DDT (the equivalent of 17.5 thousandths of an ounce) to a man with no ill effect on him.

Dr. Wayland J. Hayes once fed to fifty-one convicts for one year DDT in a quantity that was two hundred times the normal amount found in the average daily meals (which is one three-hundredth of a gram; there are 28.35 grams to an ounce) and found that the men's health remained the same as that of the control group who were fed no DDT. When a certain level of residue accumulation in the body fat was reached the DDT was excreted almost as fast as it was ingested. Dr. Hayes has said in favor of pesticides: "During the years of investigation it has been impossible to confirm the allegation that insecticides, when properly used, are the causes of any diseases either of men or animals. When misused, however, they may produce poisoning."

If we want to get finicky about it, drinking hard liquor and eating candy and pastries likely cause more damage to human innards than any miniscule intake of pesticides. There are roughly five million alcoholics within our borders, losing $422 million in wages and costing industry $2 billion annually. Nobody seriously considers shuttering the bars or liquor stores. And who would ban the pastry baker and chocolates maker? Certainly no one in Switzerland, where the making of those confections is a fine art.

Between 1949 and 1955, of accidental deaths in the United States due to insecticides, 84 percent were induced by materials in common use prior to the advent of synthetic pesticide chemicals. Only 16 percent were due to the newer chlorinated hydrocarbon and organic phosphates combined. Arsenicals, the oldest of the so-called natural insecticides, caused 299 of 518 such deaths, compared with only seventy-nine charged to all insecticides introduced since 1946. From rodenticides in common use for many years there were 218 deaths.

The real hazards of using pesticides are irresponsibility, ignorance, delusion, skepticism, and carelessness in storage — especially in relation to children. Of 152 deaths due to pesticides in the United States in 1956, ninety-four or 62 percent of the total involved children under the age of ten; seventy-eight of them were under four. (Most of these deaths occur in the Southwest in ranch country; ranch hands pilfer small quantities of pesticides from the ranches on which they work, bring the poison liquid home in milk or soda-pop bottles, and the kids mistakenly take it for something potable.) Storage of pesticides in kitchen cupboards, pantries, and other readily accessible places is responsible for much food-poisoning illness and death. Many pesticide afflictions and fatalities are caused by overexposure to the chemicals, or by divergence from (or ignoring of) label directions in handling them. Accidents and deaths from pesticides involve mental reaction and human judgment and cannot be blamed entirely on toxicological factors. Public education is needed, not further legislation and regulation.

Most of the scientists who howled about the inaccuracies and biased viewpoint of Silent Spring admitted that the book rendered a service inasmuch as it obliquely aroused an apathetic, unscientific public to two of the world's most serious problems — the providing of enough food for an exploding population and the protection of man from the scourge of epidemic diseases.

It is high time that not only the general public but statesmen realize that the primary problem of the human race is agricultural — people must be fed adequately. It is hard to make love on an empty belly, and without love and sexuality all life ends. Most holders of high office have never known hunger; few have ever had the satisfaction of earth beneath their fingernails or between their toes.

Every day food must be provided for the number of people that is approximately one-sixth of the total number of humans that have ever lived on this planet from the time Adam arose fresh out of the ooze, met Eve, flexed his naked muscles, and discovered that his dependency was tiltable. Despite surpluses of food, more than half the men, women, and children in the world today go to bed hungry nearly every night. The world supply of food is so short, according to Dr. Georg Borgstrom, of the Department of Food Science of Michigan State University, that if all of it, including surplus stores, were distributed in equal shares to each person on the globe we all would be malnourished. Dr. Borgstrom further contends that if the entire world population was fed on the United States level all available food would be enough to satisfy less than half the human race.

What will happen when world population reaches the six-billion mark predicted for the year 2000? According to United Nations forecasts, the Far East will have the most people, 3,639 million. Latin America will contain 592 million; Africa, 421 million; the Near East, 27 million; Oceania, 29 million — while here in North America will be a mere 312 million. If the rest of the world isn't adequately fed no doubt it will try to gobble us up. So, consider — is it better to kill insects now or people later?

Today our advanced technology — television, radio, airmail, travel by jet, a plethora of publications — is making the empty-bellied of the world aware that millions of people do not go to bed hungry. If some of these deprived have become too ground down or are too isolated to know what's going on, there certainly are leaders among them who are alert to the globe's new beat and ready to pass the word along. The food shortage definitely should be international political problem number one. Lack of food is a basic factor in revolution. Every revolutionary knows that. In those areas of the world where chemical technology is not much used in agriculture, disease, famine, and unrest are common. Thus far, man has managed to stave off starvation, plague, and social-political upheaval in many parts of the world through the use of agricultural chemicals to promote the growing of more food.

Aldous Huxley, in a 1963 Ford Foundation paper, said: "By shifting our attention from the now completely irrelevant and anachronistic politics of nationalism and military power to the problems of the human species . . . we shall be . . . reducing the threat of sudden destruction by scientific war and at the same time reducing the threat of more gradual biological disaster."

In the castigation of pesticides the subject of ecological balance of nature frequently comes up. It is well to remember that man upset the balance of nature thousands of years ago when he invented weapons to use against animals, birds, and his peers. As living organisms we can never *return* to a primitive balance of nature, but can hope, in our present mechanized, automated, and accelerated life — so strongly oriented to artificial stimulation — to arrive at some new balance through harmonious extensions of ourselves within the framework of the existing laws of nature.

In this regard an interesting statement was made by George C. Decker, head of Economic Entomology at the State of Illinois Agricultural Experimental Station: "Nature recognizes no such categories as pests, beneficial forms, wildlife, domesticated species or inalienable rights of man. In nature every living organism is engaged in a relentless competition with every other organism upon which its interest impinges. Man is part of that environment but has the unique attribute, intellect, that enables him to dominate by using tools capable of changing physical and economical environments to suit his needs and whims. He selects certain plants and animals most desired by him. Those detrimental he calls pests to be suppressed or eliminated."

The general public is interested in rose sprays or weed killers and in getting rid of annoying household insects, but the farmer thinks mainly of his crops and how much money pesticides will save him. It is on croplands that spray insecticides are mostly used (15 percent of the nation's cropland undergoes pesticidal applications). Residential shade trees also are subjected to sprays, yet only 0.28 percent of 640 million acres of United States forest land has been treated by sprays, according to the Entomological Society of America.

Despite widespread insecticide use, USDA statistics indicate that insect pests account for annual crop losses in this country of more than $4 billion, animal losses of nearly $900 million, and destruction of eight billion feet of saw timber. If chemical pesticides were withdrawn from use — as was seriously advocated by the most fanatic of Miss Carson's followers — modern agriculture could not exist. The yields per acre, per man hour, and the quality of the product would all suffer materially. Uncontrolled nature generally is hostile to man's interests.

Insect pests cause wastage, inferior quality, and loss of productivity in food crops. Roughly one-half of the total of 686,000 species of scientifically classified insects in the world are phytophagus (they feed off plants); twenty-five thousand species are pests of crops. In the United States there are about three thousand species that eat plant life, and the same number of plant disease agents. Before chemical pesticide controls of any sort, nearly a century ago, the ravages of chinch bugs, grasshoppers, army worms, potato beetles, and other hungry mobs of insects literally forced many farmers to sell out or abandon their lands in the Midwest. There in 1867 began the first large-scale applications of chemical pesticides with the use of Paris green.

Field tests and conscientious studies indicate that no commercial crops of apples, peaches, cherries, sweet corn, grapes, strawberries, cranberries, raspberries, potatoes, tomatoes, carrots, kale, mustard, collard greens, spinach, or most other food plants could be grown practically and economically on a large scale without chemical pesticides and/or herbicides. Without them, the potato crop, for instance, is subject to attacks by the Colorado beetle or by late blight, the same that caused the notorious potato famine of 1845 and drove thousands of Irish from their native land to become bricklayers or policemen in America. (That was the only time in history when Europeans were reduced to eating insects as food.)

According to a fact book, *Agricultural Chemicals for Productivity*, of the Association of British Manufacturers of Agricultural Chemicals, pesticides have done wonders for British farmers and fruit growers. By data drawn from independent and official sources, this book indicates that tremendous crop improvements were made by the use of DDT. Cereal bunt, once infecting 33 percent of the crop, has become practically nonexistent, and smut now affects less than 1 percent, raising yields to as much as 8 percent — the equivalent of almost a million tons of grain. DDT sprays reduced by 50 percent attack by pea moth caterpillars. Without treatment the annual pea crop loss had been the yield from four thousand acres or five thousand tons, worth about £300,000. This report contends that, without spraying, losses in orchards from coddling moth, sawfly, and tortix moth amount to the equivalent yield from 33,400 acres.

Pesticides are important forest protectors. Termites alone destroy more wood annually than forest fires, and in combination with other insects cause from seven to ten times the damage wrought by destructive flames. Thousands of lodge pole pines can be laid low by bark beetles if not treated by pesticides. Great areas of forest — as much as an eight-hundred-acre-square tract — have been restored by pesticide after having been completely denuded by tent caterpillars.

The boll weevil, enemy of cotton crops, has done an incredible amount of damage in our South. Under ideal conditions one female weevil and her offspring will produce two million weevils from spring to fall. Even under chemical pesticide attack, weevils destroy over three million bales of cotton yearly, and since invading this country they have cost our economy at least $5 billion. Despite controls, weevils steal from each of us about ten dollars annually. Studies made by the USDA over periods of thirty-four and twenty years showed that without insecticide treatment cotton yields were reduced 25.5 percent and 41.8 percent respectively.

Another great destroyer of agricultural products is the cabbage aphid. Under normal conditions in New York state the average female is capable of having forty-one offspring. There are sixteen generations between the end of March and the beginning of October. That makes 1,560 sextillion from only one female. Each weighs about one milligram, so if all those descendants of one aphid in one season lived, they would outweigh the world's entire human population.

Without treatment by pesticides apples will be damaged up to 80 percent by the coddling moth and apple scab, and there will be damage to the trees by wood borers, scale insects, and other pests.

With no pesticide care, the yield of staple fiber, cereal, and other forage crops would be expected to drop by as much as 25 percent.

In the world today 20 percent of all foodstuffs is lost between sowing and harvesting due to weeds, fungi, and insects, and 10 percent of all food harvested is lost during its transportation and storage due to the attack of rodents, insects, and fungi. Chemical pesticides are needed to keep losses at those levels, and can be used to reduce them even further. Practically every authority who has studied the subject has concluded that if the world is to have an adequate food supply the use of pesticides must continue.

In the United States it takes only 7 percent of the workers to feed the rest of us. The percentage in the rest of the world is slightly over half. Our advantage is due largely to our farmers' intelligent usage of chemical pesticides. They are agricultural tools as important to the farm worker as his tractor, plow, and harrow. Like other tools of our civilization, pesticides are open to misuse and abuse, which can bring harm to humans, crops, animal, bird, and fish life, and contribute to pollution of the environment.

There have been several outstanding cases of horrible misuse of DDT, for instance. One of the most publicized was the killing of nearly all of the robins on the Michigan State University campus by indiscriminate extra-heavy spraying there with DDT of several thousand elm trees. The chemical accumulated in the soil over several years with the result that earthworms ingested it and in turn poisoned robins that ate the worms. In *Silent Spring*, Rachel Carson produced many examples of injudicious tragic use of pesticides on fish, citing one instance of Coho salmon from the waters of Vancouver Island, Canada, being blinded by pesticides. She also claimed that eagles were becoming sterile from eating fish that had been poisoned by pesticides, and wrote of the killing of game fish by pesticides that got into the Miramichi River on the coast of New Brunswick. *Silent Spring*, however, did not report the dramatic development of a pesticide to control the lamprey in the Great Lakes and so aid commercial fishermen there. Lake trout fishing is an important part of the economy of the Great Lakes region and a few years ago an eel-like lamprey began spreading out through the Welland Canal from its original home in Lake Ontario to Lake Superior, Lake Michigan, and Lake Huron. (A lamprey attaches its suction cup mouth to a fish and feeds on it.) Because of increase of the lampreys, financial damage to Great Lakes commercial fishermen was tremendous; by 1960 whitefish and lake trout had all but disappeared. Scientists, after experimenting with six thousand different chemicals, finally came up with some that would kill the lamprey without harming other fish and useful organisms of the lakes. It is believed that by use of these chemicals lampreys can be brought under control by 1970, and the fish industry of the Great Lakes is being restored.

Unless an American family has had a son or close relative in the Armed Forces in the war against Japan in the Pacific, in Korea, or now in Vietnam, it hardly knows the names much less the symptoms of the infectious diseases able to be transmitted by mosquitoes, lice, fleas, ticks, and other insects.

So, despite all the hue and cry over the evils of pesticides, they seem to be benefiting mankind considerably. It is likely that their use will continue and become more widespread. Without them even our annual summertime treks to the seashore would be much less attractive. Mosquito sprays in beach areas are taken for granted in Florida, and in France and Italy, in preparation for the annual invasion of money-spreading tourists, belts of fifteen kilometers in depth along the resort coasts are sprayed against mosquito larvae. In France alone last year one hundred tons of Geigy Sumathion were used.

Only one piece of legislation resulted from all the government hearings and recommendations on pesticides brought about by the fuss over *Silent Spring*. That was the 1964 Ribicoff Amendment to the Federal Insecticide, Fungicide and Rodenticide Act. The amendment did away with a provision of the law that called for compulsory registration of a pesticide "under protest" should a petitioner demand it in writing following refusal by the U.S. Department of Agriculture of a regular registration. The amendment also made mandatory the use of federal registration numbers on labels so that the user of a pesticide will know that he is using a federally registered product. The implementation of all other recommendations was accomplished within the setup of previously existing law. So it seems we were not as unprotected by our government agencies as *Silent Spring* led us to believe.

One major lesson learned by the public from the battle of Rachel Carson vs. the scientific community was that users of pesticides should read the labels. By so doing, and by conforming to the printed directions exactly as stated, consumers of pesticides will avoid the grief that has attended the flagrant misuse of pesticides in the past. It is not true that if a little insecticide is desirable, a lot is better. All chemicals should be treated as potentially dangerous if used without proper knowledge and caution. If the label says to wear protective clothing, goggles, gloves, or a respirator, do so, but avoid using that particular chemical around the home unless you've had experience in its use. Don't spray or dust on a windy day; don't smoke while distributing an insecticide in that manner. Be sure to wash your hands and face well after working with an insecticide and change to clean clothing (also wash the work clothes immediately). Dispose of empty pesticide containers so that they pose no hazard to humans, animals, or valuable plant life. If symptoms of illness occur during or shortly after working with an insecticide, get to a doctor or hospital as soon as possible. And it cannot be stated too strongly or too often, always be sure to *read your label*. It's a good rule to remember in any situation.

When my wife and I were visiting Peru, South America, some years ago (when of our present five children we had only two and a baby born there) we stayed for several months in the volcanic mountain city of Arequipa at the Quinta of that famous matriarch of the Andes, Tia Bates, beloved by the Indians (she'd been godmother to hundreds of their babies) and hostess at this residence hostelry to such luminary travelers as Noel Coward, General John Pershing, Gertrude Lawrence, Cardinal Spellman, and everybody else of importance who'd come to these parts. Tia Bates then was in her nineties, a charming but testy individual who viewed the passing parade with jaundiced eye and brooked no sass from anyone. She held the annoying world at bay with large regular slugs of pisco, the potent colorless hard liquor of the Andes, and on some days her dotage and the pisco would take over and then she'd confuse me with a husband who'd deserted her in favor of an Indian woman and had (Tia imagined in her befuddled state) now returned to the Quinta with his squaw (my Berta) and their three children (ours). "What am I to do, sonny?" Tia Bates would ask of me in mild panic. "They're down there living in the garden cottage, and I've got to get them out." Fortunately for us, reason usually returned in time to stay our eviction.

Tia loathed tourists, although she made a fair living by catering to them at her Quinta Bates. It was a tea-stop must on all the tours that were sent out from Lima. Tia was considered an Arequipa attraction on a par with Mount Misti, the city's most active volcano. She had to be pushed into acting as hostess for these tea parties, but with valiant effort and in her cup more pisco than tea, she was able to face these regular gatherings of nervous schoolteachers and rich widows. Tia despised them. Usually I was pressed into service by Tia to lend moral support at the *soirées*, and I well remember her merciless treatment of tourists who were confused over their train, airplane, or hotel reservations. She'd lean across the teacups and pastries (always alive with black flies), sometimes devilishly messing up a visitor's carefully coiffured head, and say scathingly, in syllables as measured as the beat of a metronome, "My dear, have you *read your ticket?*"

I never forget that question. Whenever I get into a tight spot, I just sit back and ask myself, "Sonny, have you *read your ticket?*" It's a good question for all of us. We need to know which way we're heading and who we are.

Have you read your ticket? And your label?

ACKNOWLEDGMENTS

This kind of book requires much cooperation from a great many people.

I appreciate especially the contribution of Mr. Frank Zachary of *Holiday* magazine, who gave the firm shove that sent me stumbling headlong into the pest arena. Heartfelt thanks are due those who in so many ways helped in the creation of this work, although it is possible to mention only the names of the ones to whom I am most indebted:

Berta, my wife, for her critical comment on the manuscript, and for her helpful suggestions as it was being written;

Toby Ballantine for his beautiful illustrations;

Miss Charlotte Russell for the cool unerring aim of her rhymes that complement the text so well;

Mr. Harry Sions for an astute and sensitive job of editing;

Mr. Bill Wright and Mr. Arnold Ehrlich, both former editors at *Holiday* magazine, for early enthusiasm for this project;

Miss Elinor Langer, of *Science* magazine, for making available to me her extensive research material on chemical-biological warfare;

Mr. Murry Raphael, director of the Pest Control Bureau, City of New York, for his untiring efforts in my behalf in relation to the rodent problem of that metropolis;

Dr. Ralph Heal and Dr. Philip Spear, of the National Pest Control Association, for allowing me free access to that organization's research facilities from which much valuable entomological, biological, and technical information was gained;

Mr. Edward Gottlieb for introducing me to the American affiliate of J. R. Geigy, S.A., of Switzerland;

Mr. John Hood and Mr. Nick B. DeManczuk, of that organization, for enabling me to visit Geigy headquarters in Basel, there to write the chapter on pesticide formulation;

Dr. Hans Gysin, head of the Geigy pesticide research in Basel; his deputy and assistant head Dr. Enrico Knüsli; and the following distinguished associates: Dr. Rudolf Gasser; Dr. Pierre H. Payot; Dr. Edgar Peheim; Dr. Robert Zinkernagel; Dr. Bruno E. Moeckli; Dr. Victor Fluck; Dr. Erich Kunz; and Herr Max Spindler, for their extraordinary efforts to make clear to me the workings of modern pesticide making;

Dr. William N. Sullivan, of the Entomology Research Division of the USDA, for his painstaking clarification of cockroach research;

Mr. John Fales, entomologist, for a personal introduction to his large international assemblage of cockroaches;

Dr. Samson R. Dutky, research biologist of the USDA, for much valuable scientific information concerning the cockroach biosatellite program;

Dr. Vincent G. Dethier, professor of zoology and psychology at the University of Pennsylvania, for revealing to me the intricacies of a fly's brain;

Mr. Dale Shaw, my friend and writing peer, for an intriguing slant on the ant;

Mr. Loring Dowst, Mrs. Jean Gleason, and Mr. Ken Platnick for choice research regarding the pigeon;

Mr. Edward C. Stearns, regional representative of Bruce Terminex Co., Inc., for his help in the area of termites;

Mr. Walter Blank, head of upstate New York's largest extermination service, for an insight into that fascinating business;

Mr. I. F. Stone for guidance in gathering material for the chapter about pests of war;

Mr. Hudson Hoagland, executive director of the Worcester Foundation for Experimental Biology, for the same sort of assistance;

Mr. Lawrence Scott, co-chairman of A Quaker Action Group, for his encouragement in my pursuit of truth in regard to the participation of insects in warfare;

Miss Barbara Deming, Miss Eleanor Hakim, Mr. Bram Luckum, and Mr. Erle Yahn for assistance in unmasking the pests of war;

Miss Carol Brightman and Mr. John McDermott, of *Viet Report, An Emergency News Bulletin on Southeast Asian Affairs*, for putting me in touch with fellow believers in peace;

Mrs. Meredith Mackley for being a conscientious humanist;

Congressman Robert W. Kastenmeyer, of Wisconsin, for taking time to discuss with me our nation's involvement in biological warfare;

Dr. Riley Housewright, scientific director at Fort Detrick, for his kindness in granting me an interview;

Lieutenant Colonel Charles W. Burtyk, Jr., of the United States Army, for his pertinent suggestions;

Harper & Row Publishers, Inc., for permission to quote from Mark Twain;

Mr. Nat Hentoff and his publisher, The Viking Press, for permission to quote from *Our Children Are Dying*;

Mr. Norman Eddy, director of Metro North Citizens' Committee and a member of the Mission Society of New York, for invaluable assistance in compiling information for the chapter on rats;

Mrs. Addie Lewis, Mr. Edwin Suarez, Mrs. Mildred Ryan, and Mrs. Pura Rodriguez, doughty dwellers in East Harlem, for being most cooperative in detailing the problems of slum tenants;

Mr. George Naiman and Mr. Israel Brod for enlightening me about the problems of slum landlords;

Mr. Dan Jones for rare data on plague.

Material was garnered from various periodicals, all mentioned by name in the text. The chapters on the cockroach, the ant, and the pigeon appeared in abbreviated form in *Holiday* magazine. A condensation of the chapter on the rat appeared in the United Nations Association magazine *Vista*.

And again, my sincere thanks to you all.

Bill Ballantine

NEW CITY, NEW YORK